THE CELL

Volume III

THE CELL

Biochemistry, Physiology, Morphology

THE CELL

Biochemistry, Physiology, Morphology

Edited by

JEAN BRACHET

Faculté des Sciences, Université libre de Bruxelles
Bruxelles, Belgique

ALFRED E. MIRSKY

The Rockefeller Institute
New York, New York

VOLUME III

MEIOSIS AND MITOSIS

1961

ACADEMIC PRESS, New York and London

ACADEMIC PRESS INC.
111 FIFTH AVENUE
NEW YORK 3, N. Y.

United Kingdom Edition
Published by
ACADEMIC PRESS INC. (LONDON) LTD.
17 OLD QUEEN STREET, LONDON SW 1

Library of Congress Catalog Card Number 59-7677

PRINTED IN THE UNITED STATES OF AMERICA

LIST OF CONTRIBUTORS

DANIEL MAZIA, *Department of Zoology, University of California, Berkeley, California*

M. M. RHOADES, *Department of Botany, Indiana University, Bloomington, Indiana*

PREFACE TO VOLUME III

The chapters on meiosis and mitosis, the only chapters in this volume, were originally intended for Volume II. They form a volume by themselves because Dr. Mazia wrote a Magnum Opus rather than a chapter. Needless to say, we had no desire to cut such a fine treatise on mitosis.

J. Brachet
A. E. Mirsky

CONTENTS

THE CELL: *Biochemistry, Physiology, Morphology*

C O M P L E T E   I N   5   V O L U M E S

VOLUME V: SPECIALIZED CELLS, PART 2

CONTENTS

CHAPTER 1

Meiosis

By M. M. RHOADES

I. INTRODUCTION

The essential characteristics of meiosis, namely pairing, crossing over, and reduction in chromosome number have long been understood in a gross cytological sense. The behavior and maneuvering of the chromosomes in meiosis occur at no other time in the life cycle. Special forces not present in somatic mitosis may be involved in these unique happenings as well as a modification of the time of inception of changes within the nucleus relative to those external to it. It must be admitted that our comprehension of basic meiotic processes is little if any greater than it was twenty years ago. Solution of these recondite problems will come only when more is understood of the physical and chemical nature

1

of cellular processes. A promising start has been made in this direction, but only the first steps have been taken and much remains to be done.

This is not the most propitious time to discuss meiosis. The basic assumptions of long held and widely accepted hypotheses are made highly suspect, and may indeed be proved untenable, by recent cyto-chemical studies on the time of chromosome reduplication. There is at the present no theory of meiosis that is wholly compatible with our knowledge of chromosome structure and cellular mechanics. Neverthe-less, a review of meiosis, incomplete though it is, may be of value if it does nothing more than point out the more glaring inconsistencies found in the voluminous literature.

The importance of meiosis in the life history of sexually reproducing forms has long been recognized. Consisting superficially of two cell divi-sions with only one reduplication of the chromosomes, it is the mech-anism by which the diploid number of chromosomes produced by fer-tilization is halved so that the gametes or sexual cells possess the haploid number. Fertilization and meiosis are compensating events; a failure of one or the other causes a breakdown in the orderly system of sexual re-production.

The invention of meiosis has led to evolutionary consequences of the first order of magnitude. Independent assortment of the members of dif-ferent pairs of chromosomes results in genotypic diversity since gametes are produced with random combinations of nonhomologous chromosomes from the two parental gametes. Additional genotypic diversity among the sexual cells arises from crossing over or recombination of segments be-tween the two homologous chromosomes of each bivalent. This ceaseless shuffling and recombination of chromosomes and chromosomal segments afford the organism a mechanism by which myriad constellations of genes are formed. Those best adapted to the environment will survive, the others perish. Thus recombination makes it possible for the organism to exploit its potential genic plasticity. The importance of crossing over is evidenced by its universal occurrence in sexually reproducing species. In most species crossing over occurs in both males and females, but cases are known where crossing over is confined to one sex. In species with haploid males and diploid females, genetic exchange is found only in females, while in species with diploid males and females, such as *Dro-sophila* and *Sciara*, crossing over occurs only in the homogametic sex. In no extant form is it missing in both sexes. It may be concluded that cross-ing over has a high adaptive value in the economy of the species.

Meiosis occurs at various times in different organisms. According to Wilson's (1937) classification, the gametic or terminal type of meiosis is characteristic of animals. The products of the two meiotic divisions are transformed into sperm and egg cells without undergoing further mitoses. In the zygotic or initial type, fertilization is followed immediately by meiosis and the zygote is the only diploid cell in the life cycle. Zygotic meiosis is the rule in lower plants. The sporic or indeterminate type of meiosis is found in higher plants and in some thallophytes but is unknown in animals inasmuch as they have no alternation of diploid and haploid generations. Meiosis takes place in the diploid sporophyte at some point intermediate between the zygote and the formation of gametes. Here the products of the two meiotic divisions are not gametes but haploid mega- and microspores, which undergo a number of somatic mitoses as they develop into female and male gametophytes, respectively. The sexual cells or gametes arise by differentiation of certain cells of the gametophytes.

At varying stages during development of organisms with gametic or sporic meiosis a group or groups of cells are set aside which are destined to undergo meiosis. These are the oögonial and spermatogonial cells in animals and the sporogenous or archesporial cells in plants. These gonial and sporogenous cells increase in number by ordinary somatic mitoses up to a specific time when somatic mitosis comes to an abrupt end. The stage is now set for the transition from mitosis to meiosis. The cells that are ready to enter meiosis are known as primary oöcytes and primary spermatocytes in animals and as pollen (microspore) mother cells and megaspore mother cells in the anthers and ovaries of plants. Any cell undergoing meiosis may be called a meiocyte.

The factors responsible for the transition from somatic mitosis to meiosis remain almost wholly unknown. Experimental modifications of meiosis and attempts to induce it have not led to particularly instructive results. Much of what is conjectured of the essential differences between the two types of division rests on inferences based on cytological observations. The informative studies by Tobias (1956) and Leblond and Clermont (1952) on the premeiotic mitoses in rodents, revealing that the last gonial divisions are intermediate between somatic mitosis and meiosis, need to be complemented by cytochemical data. It is lamentable that no adequate study has been made of the last premeiotic mitoses using both cytological and cytochemical techniques. The dearth of basic information, however, has proved no hindrance to the flowering of speculative hypotheses and magnificent generalizations.

The first meiotic prophase is not only of greater duration than that of a somatic prophase, but is also characterized by a marked increase in nuclear volume and hydration. Beasley (1938) found in both plants and animals that the volume of meiotic prophase nuclei was approximately three to four times that of mitotic prophase nuclei. The longer duration of meiotic prophase and the increase in size presumably reflect a unique physiological condition or change in the cytoplasm; this shift in cell metabolism outside the nucleus has been held to be responsible for the earlier initiation of prophase and formation of the spindle relative to the reproduction of the chromosomes (Darlington 1937, 1957).

The basic assumptions of Darlington's precocity theory of meiosis are that the leptotene chromosomes are not divided into chromatids and that homologous chromosomes pair because of this singleness. Normally double as in somatic prophase, the undivided chromosomes satisfy the mitotic affinity for doubleness by pairing. A number of cytologists (Mc-Clung, 1927a; Nebel and Ruttle, 1936; Stebbins, 1935; Atwood, 1937) believe that the chromosomes of the last premeiotic anaphase and telophase are visibly double; hence the chromosomes of leptonema each consist of two chromatids. Proponents of the precocity theory have dismissed or ignored these contrary cytological observations on the grounds that they were based on poorly fixed material, that the minute structures dealt with were mistakenly interpreted, and that the ultimate premeiotic division is not easy to identify accurately. Since cytological evidence for the singleness of leptotene chromosomes was also available, most cytogeneticists were willing to accept the precocity theory until definitely disproved. It has been said that cytogeneticists naively and uncritically adopted the precocity theory in spite of conflicting evidence. This criticism is no doubt justified, but Darlington's theory offers, as Sturtevant (1951) states, "a beautifully simple and satisfying scheme" which superficially, at least, accounts for chromosomal behavior and satisfies genetic theory. A further deterrent to abandoning the precocity theory was that no satisfactory substitute was offered. It is easy therefore to understand the wide acceptance of the precocity theory.

Recent cytochemical studies on the time of deoxyribonucleic acid (DNA) synthesis and chromosomal reduplication raise serious doubts as to the validity of the precocity theory as it was originally promulgated. Cytological observations on the doubleness or singleness of leptotene chromosomes might be questioned because of the subjective nature of interpretations of fine cytological detail, but this criticism can be leveled less readily against the cytochemical data. Since DNA is localized in the nucleus and specifically in the chromosomes, it is generally accepted that doubling of DNA is indicative of chromosomal reduplication; thus the time when synthesis of DNA occurs delimits the stage in cell division when the chromosomes become effectively double. Boivin and the Vendrelys (1948) and Mirsky and Ris (1949) found that the amount of DNA not only was relatively constant at a given stage in diploid somatic cells, but was twice that in the nuclei of haploid gametic cells. Subsequent work by Swift (1950a, b), Alfert (1950), and Pollister et al. (1951) disclosed that the amount of DNA at prophase in the somatic nuclei of a variety of organisms was double the amount found at telophase. Howard and Pelc (1952) found in the bean *Vicia faba* that incorporation of P^{32} into DNA occurred during interkinesis. A similar conclusion as to the time of DNA doubling was reached by Walker and Yates (1952). Autoradiographic and cytophotometric studies by Taylor and McMaster (1954) and Moses and Taylor (1955) revealed that incorporation of P^{32} into DNA took place concomitantly with an increase in the amount of DNA. This was true not only in somatic divisions, but more significantly at premeiotic interphase or early leptonema. Swift (1950a) reported that synthesis of DNA was completed by leptonema in the spermatocytes of the mouse and (1950b) during leptonema in *Tradescantia* sporocytes. According to Taylor (1953), incorporation of P^{32} into DNA occurred before leptonema in *Lilium* but not until early leptonema in *Tradescantia*. That doubling of DNA indicates chromosomal duplication is suggested by the findings of Alfert (1955) and Bloch and Godman (1955) that DNA and basic protein increase take place at the same time. Ansley (1957) also reported that doubling of DNA and of histone are coincident events. A correlation has been found between the kind of X-ray-induced breaks and the time of DNA doubling (Thoday, 1954; Mitra, 1956; Taylor, 1957). Prior to DNA synthesis, breakage is of the chromosome type whereas chromatid type aberrations are found after the DNA has doubled. Not only was this correlation found for ordinary somatic cells, but also in the last premeiotic interphase before microsporogenesis in *Lilium* (Mitra, 1956).

The experiments cited above suggest that doubling of DNA and chromosomal duplication take place before zygonema and therefore the chromosomes pair at a time when each consists of two chromatids, a fact which, if not irreconcilable with the precocity theory, necessitates its modification. It should be noted, however, that the time of DNA doubling varies in different forms and in different tissues (cf. Brachet, 1957). Furthermore, Ansley (1954, 1957) found that doubling of both DNA and histone occurred during zygonema—a time which fits the requirements of the precocity theory—and Sparrow et al. (1952) reported that an increase in DNA occurred between pachynema and diplonema in *Trillium* microsporocytes. These differences need to be resolved, but the evidence for chromosomal duplication prior to pairing at zygonema or pachynema is so convincing that any theory of meiosis based on a contrary assumption is highly questionable.

Although the precocity theory has been criticized as being nothing more than a restatement of meiotic events and in conflict with the evidence that pairing occurs after reduplication of the chromosomes, Darlington (1955) remains unshaken in his conviction of its essential correctness. He visualizes the leptotene chromosome as a column of nucleotides which has an unsaturated pairing face.[1] Each chromosome with its column of nucleotides acts as a structural unit and pairing occurs between unsaturated homologs. The columns of nucleotides are assumed to have both a pairing and a reproductive or splitting face. The two act similarly in that one attracts the components of similar columns (pairing of homologs) and the other similar particles from the substrate (reduplication). The single columns presumed to exist in early meiotic prophase have their pairing faces saturated by synapsis. Reduplication occurs after pairing, upsetting the equilibrium of the coiled pairs of columns and triggering the mechanical changes leading to breakage and new unions of broken ends (crossing over). Goldschmidt (1955) also suggests that the preleptotene or postleptotene chromosome contains single rather than the customary double chains of DNA. This would presumably lead to synapsis of the two homologous chromosomes, each with single DNA chains, and crossing over could occur as each DNA chain produced its complementary partner. There is no experimental evidence that the leptotene chromosomes have single-stranded DNA molecules as Darlington and Goldschmidt postulate. Although efforts have been made to interpret cytological observations on the assumption that the Watson-Crick model of DNA structure (Watson and Crick, 1953) is essentially correct, the difference in level of structural complexity between the DNA molecule and the chromosome has been largely ignored. A further complication is that the chromosome may not have all its DNA in a single double helix chain but may be many-stranded. For example, Ris (1957) believes that the leptotene chromosome consists of a number of 200-A. thick microfibrils each with a core of DNA and these in turn have a dual structure.

In contrast to the conception that meiotic prophase is precocious is the view held by Sax and Sax (1935), Stebbins (1935), Matsuura and Haga (1940), and others that meiosis is associated with a retardation in cellular metabolism. It is argued that the lengthened prophase permits

---

[1] The suggestion that chromosomes possess a pairing face was made by Cooper in 1938.

the uncoiling of the residual spirals of the preceding telophase; the complete despiralization of the chromonemata facilitates point-by-point pairing at zygonema. The position has been taken by some that pairing would take place in somatic prophase if the chromonemata became sufficiently uncoiled. It is known, however, that the chromosomes of *Neurospora* are greatly contracted when they pair (McClintock, 1945), and Oehlkers and Eberle (1957) found in *Bellevalia* that though the chromosomes of early leptonema were completely devoid of coils they developed numerous spirals by late leptonema. It can only be concluded that while despiralization may favor chromosome pairing it is not the primary agent for its induction. Huskins (1933) suggested that meiotic prophase was not really precocious, holding that it was the inhibition of chromosomal reduplication in the last premeiotic division which led to pairing. It should be recognized that both the Darlington and Huskins hypotheses assume an undivided condition of the meiotic chromosomes prior to synapsis, an assumption that is in conflict with many observations.

The importance of the physiological state of the nucleus for meiosis is revealed in the studies of Gustafsson (1938, 1939), Gentscheff and Gustafsson (1940), Stebbins (1941), and many others on the meiotic abnormalities found in apomictic plants where meiosis ranges from an essentially normal type to a typical mitotic division. The shift of meiosis to mitosis varied not only in degree but in manner of accomplishment in both megasporocytes and microsporocytes. The diverse modifications observed need not be given here, but cells with normal meiosis (pairing and bivalent formation) were found only when the initiation and duration of prophase and the relative development of both sporocytes and tapetal cells were the same as in sexual forms with normal meiosis. Stebbins points out that the failure of normal meiosis to occur in apomicts was invariably correlated with a short duration of prophase and a failure to undergo the rapid growth characteristic of early meiotic prophase in normal meiocytes; the time at which division began could be either early or late with respect to the developmental stage of the surrounding tissue. The relationship between abnormal tapetal development and atypical meiotic behavior suggests that the tapetum either elaborates or transmits substances necessary for the induction of meiosis in sporogenous cells. Any disturbance in the functioning of the tapetum could modify the meiotic processes. The Sertoli cells of the seminiferous tubules of animals may possess a meiosis-controlling function comparable to that of the tapetal cells of the plant anther. Gustafsson's observation that somatic cells in apomictic *Alchemilla* entered meiosis after degeneration of the true megaspore mother cell indicates that altered physiological conditions can induce meiosis. In these somatic cells making the transition from mitosis to meiosis the prophase growth was similar to that of normal meiocytes, but nothing is known about the factor or factors causing the extended prophasic growth.

Gregory (1940), working with excised anthers in culture solutions, concluded that meiosis was dependent upon substances produced by the vegetative parts of the plant. More recently, Sparrow and co-workers (1955) found that anthers of *Trillium* excised at several meiotic stages and grown in culture media supplemented with a variety of growth factors were able to complete meiosis and reach the mitotic microspore division. Only 22% of the anthers excised at pachynema and placed on the optimum medium were able to develop to the microspore mitosis, but 67% of the anthers removed at diplonema and similarly cultured underwent meiotic and postmeiotic development. Vasil (1957) reported that *Allium* anthers excised as early as leptonema passed through both meiotic divisions to produce quartets of microspores when grown on a basic medium containing either or both kinetin or gibberellic acid. These experiments and those of Taylor (1949, 1950), Linskens (1955, 1956), and others offer a promising approach to a better understanding of the biochemical and physiological factors controlling meiosis. However, the limitation of these studies should be recognized. What has been demonstrated is that once meiosis is initiated it can be sustained to completion if certain stimuli are present in the media, but they tell us nothing about what induced meiosis in the first place. An important advance in experimental plant cytology would be achieved if excised anthers with sporogenous or premeiotic cells could be successfully cultured and meiosis induced by the addition of specific chemical compounds.

The gonial cells of explanted mammalian gonads either fail to enter meiosis or meiosis is arrested, indicating that completion of meiosis is dependent upon stimuli external to the testis (Martinovitch, 1939). Combined cultivation with pituitary explants overcame the meiotic inhibition and mature sperm were formed (Gaillard, in Martinovitch, 1939). Other extratesticular factors such as body temperature, sex-hormonal balance, diurnal periodicity, etc., provide stimuli that regulate spermatogenesis (cf. Tobias, 1956). Although these studies are full of promise, it is evident that we are still far from the goal of understanding what brings about the transition from mitosis to meiosis.

Meiosis is a highly integrated system in which various events such as pairing, chiasma formation, spiralization, spindle formation, disjunction, cytokinesis, etc., are timed and coordinated with respect to one another so that meiosis usually runs a normal course. Upsets or accidents in timing or the omission of certain steps occur, however, which disrupt the regular sequence of events and lead to an aberrant meiosis. Accidents in meiosis, either of timing or of abnormal development, sporadically happen in normal strains and the frequency of meiotic irregularities can be markedly increased by environmental changes such as temperature shock. Oehlkers (1937) found that varying cultural conditions affected the frequency of chiasma formation and suggested that meiosis is controlled by the entire physiology of the plant. Of unquestionable significance is the fact that both mitosis and meiosis are under genotypic control. In many organisms mutant genes have been found which affect specific steps of the meiotic divisions. Among these are genes influencing pairing, chiasma number and localization, spiralization, spindle formation, disjunction at either the first or second meiotic divisions, and even the onset of meiosis. Further evidence of genic control of meiosis is found in the aberrant meiosis of sterile hybrids where abnormalities occur that cannot be ascribed to structural differences in the chromosomes (cf. Dobzhansky, 1941). These cases have been the subject of a number of brilliant investigations and a great deal of valuable information has been obtained. However informative they have been in describing the modifications of meiosis, these studies have failed to reveal the underlying factors. It is doubtful if a morphological description of these meiotic changes will lead to a real understanding of the causal factors; this awaits an analysis in physicochemical terms.

In an attempt to correlate synapsis with cytochemical changes in the chromosomes, Ansley (1957) compared the histone:DNA ratio in cells of *Loxa flavicolis* having a normal meiosis with that in the harlequin lobe of the testis in which pairing is absent. In both the normal and harlequin lobes the amount of DNA found in the spermatogonia is doubled during zygonema of the primary spermatocytes. In the normal cells, doubling of histones occurs simultaneously and a 1:1 ratio of histone:DNA is maintained throughout the course of meiosis. In asynaptic cells the histone:DNA ratio is 1:1 at interphase and early prophase, but at zygonema a ratio of 3:2 was found. Thus, the increase in histone was believed in some way to be responsible for the failure of pairing.

Earlier (1954) studies by Ansley on the microtestis of the centipede *Scutigera forceps*, where the chromosomes appear as univalents, disclosed a similar deviation in the histone:DNA ratio. However, the meiotic prophase of the microtestis of *Scutigera* is unlike that in the harlequin lobe of the *Loxa* testis. In the former there is no trace of leptonema, zygonema, pachynema, diplonema, and diakinesis, whereas in the latter the inhibition is not complete since a simulation of these stages occurs although the chromosomes remain unpaired. In *Scutigera* doubling of both DNA and histone occurs prematurely in the earliest stages of the primary spermatocytes and the amount of histone increases to give a 3:2 histone:DNA ratio at a stage comparable to zygonema. Ansley (1957) suggests that precocious synchronous increase of both histone and DNA inhibits one phase of meiosis and that asynchronous increase affects a different part. The precocious synchronous increase may be correlated with the inhibition of prophase as in *Scutigera* whereas the asynchronous increase may result in the failure of chiasma formation as in *Loxa*.

Cleveland (1959) reported that the sexual cycle in the symbiotic flagellates of the wood-feeding roach *Cryptocercus punctulatus* normally occurs only during the molting periods of their insect host. Molting is controlled by the hormone ecdysone, which is produced by the pro-thoracic glands under the stimulus of the neurosecretory cells of the insect brain. The hormone ecdysone is not present, or is in low titer, in intermolt periods and in the adult roach but is abundant at the time of ecdysis of the nymphs. Flagellates in the hind-gut of adult roaches repro-duce solely asexually, but upon the injection of ecdysone into the host the sexual cycle was induced in nearly all individuals. Since in the diploid species meiosis is the first stage in sexual reproduction, it follows that the change from a mitotic division to meiosis was brought about by ecdysone. Cleveland is uncertain whether ecdysone has a direct or in-direct effect, but we have here a good example of the induction of the sexual reproductive cycle by a specific chemical compound.

In studies of maize plants homozygous for a recessive gene (ameiotic) in which the potential meiocytes undergo a mitotic rather than a meiotic division, Sinha (1960) found that ameiotic plants had a higher concentra-tion of nucleic acid precursors as well as a difference in the composition of the precursor pool. There was an apparent difference in the amount of low molecular weight ribonucleic acid (RNA) in ameiotic and normal plants and the RNA:DNA ratio was higher in ameiotic than in normal sibs. Sinha suggests that the RNA:DNA ratio determines whether a mitotic or meiotic division will ensue—a higher RNA:DNA ratio resulting in mitosis and a lower one in meiosis. In support of this conclusion is the finding by Sisken (1959) that in *Tradescantia* root tips the synthesis of RNA was completed in interphase before DNA synthesis whereas in the pollen mother cells (PMC) of *Tradescantia* synthesis of RNA took place at the time of and following DNA formation (Moses and Taylor, 1955). Taylor (1958, 1959a) also found that the time of RNA and DNA syn-thesis differed in meiocytes and in somatically dividing cells. RNA con-tinued to be synthesized in meiocytes after DNA duplication while in somatic cells there was no increase in RNA after DNA synthesis. In ameiotic plants there is a disturbance of nucleic acid metabolism, but it is not clear which of the observed differences is responsible for the failure of meiosis.

Although these studies admittedly are no more than a beginning in the analysis of the changes in nuclear chemistry occurring in the meiotic divisions, these and further cytochemical investigations offer promise of eventually accounting in chemical terms for such phenomena as the transition from a somatic mitosis to a meiotic mitosis, the nature of synapsis, etc.

II. MEIOTIC BEHAVIOR OF CHROMOSOMES

The evolution of meiosis is remarkable for its conservatism. Two systems, however, can be recognized which, though producing the same end result, differ sufficiently in the comportment of the chromosomes to justify distinguishing between them. One has chromosomes with localized centromeres and the other with nonlocalized centromeres, and it is this modification in centromeric structure that is responsible for their meiotic differences.

Localized centromeres are found in the great majority of plants and animals. These all have, with the exception of some of the Diptera, essentially the same kind of meiosis, which may be termed the standard type. Among the Vertebrata, according to White (1948), not a single case is known where meiosis deviates from the standard type. In contrast with this uniformity is the frequency of anomalous types of meiosis found in organisms with nonlocalized centromeres. A standard, or primitive, type exists, but certain insects have meiotic mechanisms with bizarre and fantastic features. It was not realized until 1935 (Schrader) that the centromere could be other than a discrete organelle of the chromosome. However, in the following years it became evident that all studied members of the Hemiptera have nonlocalized centromeres. They have also been reported in the Arachnida and the Lepidoptera, but how widespread they are in these groups is uncertain. Among plants, the genus *Luzula* of the Juncaceae unquestionably has nonlocalized centromeres, and they may occur in the Cyperaceae but the small size of the chromosomes makes a decision difficult. Future investigations will doubtless disclose that many more organisms have nonlocalized centromeres, but they will constitute a minority group. It is regrettable that little or nothing is known of the genetics of any species with nonlocalized centromeres.

Let us first consider the various stages of standard meiosis in forms with localized centromeres. Only the broad outlines of meiosis will be presented at this time; a more thorough discussion of important and controversial issues is reserved for other sections. A schematic diagram of the behavior of a single pair of chromosomes is shown in Fig. 1.

In describing the first meiotic prophase it is customary and useful to designate the different stages as leptonema, zygonema, pachynema, diplonema, and diakinesis, but it should be recognized that the transition of these sequential stages from one to another is a gradual and continuous process. Each of the stages when fully developed is clearly distinguishable, but intermediate periods may offer some difficulty in classifying. For example, it is a matter of choice in differentiating between a late diplotene and an early diakinetic stage.

Mitosis in premeiotic cells has not been extensively studied, but in maize it appears that the prophase chromosomes are more extended than in ordinary somatic cells. It is as if in these cells, eventually to become meiocytes, the chromosomes gradually attain the degree of uncoiling they possess at leptonema. According to Oksala (1944) the spermatogonial mitoses of the dragonfly progressively became more meiotic in character insofar as the time of spindle formation relative to the contraction of the chromosomes was concerned. Tobias (1956) found in the last two premeiotic mitoses before spermatogenesis in the gerbil that the telophase chromosomes of the penultimate division went directly into prophase of the ultimate gonial division. Both in the duration of the prophase stage and in length of metaphase chromosomes the premeiotic mitoses were intermediate between the early spermatogonial divisions and the first meiotic division. It has been generally observed that the contraction of metaphase chromosomes of the gonial divisions exceeds that found in typical somatic mitoses and approaches that of first metaphase chromosomes.

The interphase before meiotic prophase finds the chromosomes as thin extended threads (chromonemata) with the relic coils from the preceding telophase. That the arrangement of the chromosomes within the nucleus is not random is evident from the fact that at leptonema the centric regions of the chromosomes lie together in one part of the nucleus (the so-called Rabl orientation); this position reflects their movement to the spindle pole at the preceding anaphase and also indicates that the chromosomes undergo little movement during interphase.

A. Preleptonema and Leptonema

The onset of meiotic prophase is marked by an increase in nuclear volume followed by gradual modifications in nuclear structure. The first steps in the transition from premeiotic interphase to meiotic prophase

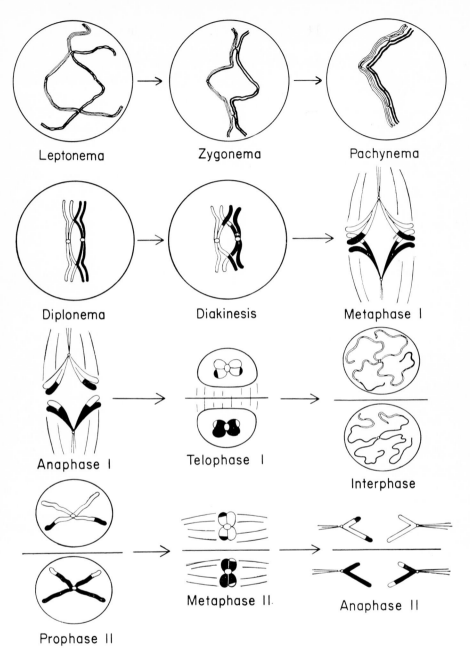

Leptonema → Zygonema → Pachynema

Diplonema → Diakinesis → Metaphase I

Anaphase I → Telophase I → Interphase

→ Prophase II → Metaphase II → Anaphase II

Prophase II

Fig. 1. Schematic diagram of meiotic behavior of a bivalent chromosome with localized centromeres. The leptotene and zygotene chromosomes are drawn as consisting of two chromatids although this is controversial. A further questionable representation is that of an exchange at leptonema, but there is substantial evidence of chromosomal duplication prior to zygonema. If recombination takes place at the time of DNA replication, it is difficult to avoid the conclusion that it occurs before zygonema and may occur in interphase.

occur in the preleptotene stage. As the chromosomes become more condensed and chromatic, they appear as coiled threads which resemble those found in the early prophase of a somatic mitosis. This has been called the "premeiotic spiral prophase" stage by Nebel and Ruttle (1936); it constitutes the first meiotic stage and has been observed by a number of workers including Newton (1926) in *Tulipa,* Shinke (1934) in *Sagittaria,* Nebel and Ruttle (1936) in *Tradescantia* and *Trillium,* and Hiraoka (1941) in *Trillium, Psilotum, Frittilaria,* and *Vicia.* The preleptotene spiral is lost as the chromsomes unravel to form the greatly extended and uncoiled threads found at early leptonema. In Darlington's (1947) photographs of preleptonema in *Frittilaria* there is no spiral prophase stage but localized accumulations of DNA are present which resemble prochromosomes or chromocenters. Presumably the spiral prophase stage in plants is comparable to the prochromosome stage in animals (Wilson, 1937). The spiral prophase stage has been observed in a number of organisms and it may be of widespread occurrence.

The unpaired chromosomes at early leptonema are at their maximum extension (Figs. 2 and 9). In *Bellevalia* they are at first wholly devoid of spirals (Fig. 2), but by late leptonema (Fig. 3) the chromonema of uniform diameter is thrown into a large number of coils of small size (Oehlkers and Eberle, 1957). That the chromomeres characteristically found in leptotene and pachytene chromosomes are the consequence of differences in the tightness of the coils along the chromonemata is clearly evident in *Bellevalia.* Ris (1945) long maintained that chromomeres were merely regions of the chromonema which were more tightly coiled than the lesser coiled interchromomeric regions, and recent investigations have substantiated his conclusion. Although the larger "chromomeres" are constant in size, position, and number, this is not true for the smaller. The doubleness of the leptotene chromosomes observed in a number of organisms (Huskins, 1937; Geitler, 1938; Nebel, 1939; Oehlkers and Eberle, 1957; and others), together with cytochemical evidence that DNA and histone synthesis occurs before zygonema, strongly suggests that the chromosomes come into synaptic association in a divided condition. In many animals, especially those with definite centers, the free ends of the leptotene chromosomes are attracted to the side of the nucleus nearest the centrosome, with the body of the chromosome extending in a loop into the interior of the nucleus. Known as the bouquet stage, this polarization of the free ends, which may persist into pachynema (Fig. 8), is believed to facilitate synapsis of the distal ends, since they lie grouped together. In plant meiocytes the chromosomes may be clumped in a dense tangle of threads to one side of the nucleus in what is called the

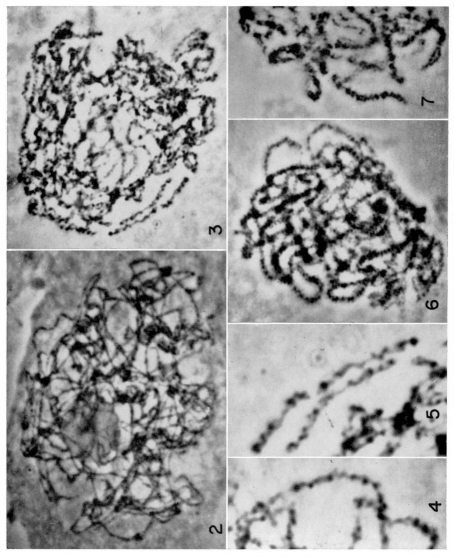

Figs. 2–7. Leptonema and zygonema in *Bellevalia*. From Oehlkers and Eberle (1957).

Fig. 2. Early leptonema showing the great extension of the chromosomes and the absence of a spiral structure.

Figs. 3, 4, and 5. Later leptonema. The spiral structure of the unpaired chromosomes is clearly evident.

Figs. 6 and 7. Late zygonema with pairing nearly completed. At the right in Fig. 6, unpaired strands are evident.

synizetic knot. Synizesis occurs at leptonema in *Lilium* but at zygonema in maize. Although it has been claimed that its appearance depends on the fixing solution and that it is a fixation artifact, it has also been suggested that it is comparable to the bouquet stage of animals. A second bouquet stage occurs in the mantids (Hughes-Schrader, 1943) at pachy-

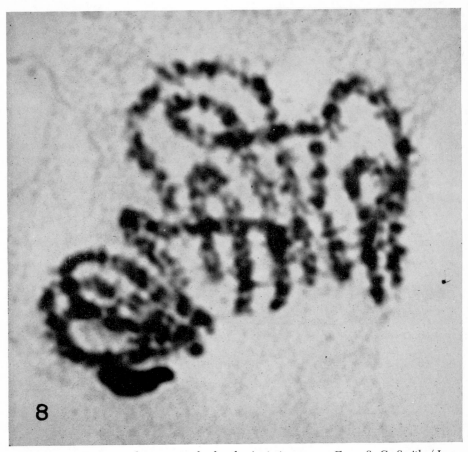

FIG. 8. Pachytene bouquet in the beetle *Agriotis mancus*. From S. G. Smith (*J. Heredity* **47**, 2-10, 1956).

nema after the first bouquet has disappeared. Schrader (1953) emphasizes that bouquet formation indicates an interaction between chromosome ends (telomeres) and the centrosome bringing about a chromosome movement wholly independent of the spindle.

The nucleolus found at the beginning of the first meiotic prophase of maize microsporocytes is a relatively small spherical structure which gradually increases in size during leptonema, doubles both its volume and RNA content at some point between leptonema and zygonema, and reaches its maximum size at mid-pachynema. The increase in nucleolar volume is related to the synthesis of RNA and proteins. Lin (1955) has shown that incorporation of proteins into the nucleolus lags behind RNA synthesis and, in fact, is controlled by the RNA. Usually only one nucleolus is present at leptonema to which is attached at different positions the two nucleolar organizers.

B. Zygonema

The end of leptonema finds the chromonemata shorter in length and wider in diameter as a result of a gradual increase in diameter of the earlier-formed spirals. Pairing, which, by cytological observations, first takes place during zygonema,[2] is therefore not between completely stretched chromosomes as was once believed. The nuclear complement in diploids consists of pairs of homologous chromosomes, one homolog of each pair being contributed by the egg and the other by the sperm. With the exception of the Diptera, where somatic pairing occurs at anaphase of the last premeiotic division, the two members of each pair of chromosomes are not closely oriented in the nucleus at leptonema and may in some instances lie separated by distances of several microns. However, the spatial distribution of leptotene chromosomes is difficult to ascertain cytologically and little is known of the relative position of the homologous chromosomes. Smith (1942) following Wilson's (1912) earlier suggestion, believes that "in the premeiotic telophase there is an active mutual selection of maternal and paternal homologues during their movements toward the poles." There is scant evidence supporting a premeiotic regrouping of like homologs in forms (with terminal or sporic meiosis) other than the Diptera, and it is obviously impossible in lower plants with zygotic meiosis. It is, of course, evident that such a disposition of chromosomes would make it easier for homologs to find one another as they pair. If the homologs are intimately associated prior to leptonema, it is possible that crossing over could take place before the beginning of meiosis. The precise time of crossing over has never been determined, and until it has, this possibility should not be rejected.

Disregarding for the moment the nature of the attraction between similar chromosomes, which will be considered in detail later, it is clear that homologous chromosomes are brought into apposition at one or several places and, after the initial contact is effected, that pairing con-

---

[2] See page 46, where the concept of effective pairing of minute regions at interphase or leptonema is discussed.

tinues in a zipperlike fashion along the chromosome. Darlington (1935, 1940) believes that the time available for pairing may be insufficient to allow pairing along the entire length of the chromosome. If initial contact is near the centric region (procentric), pairing may fail in distal regions, and conversely if synapsis starts at the distal ends and progresses proximally then segments adjacent to the centromere may be unpaired if the time in which pairing takes place is restricted. With random points of initial pairing there will be no localization of unpaired segments. However, in many forms pairing is complete at pachynema and there is no effective time limit. Zygonema is often a difficult stage to study cytologically; in maize, for example, zygonema finds the chromosomes lying in a tangled mass to one side of the nucleus. In other forms the cytological picture is less confusing; in *Bellevalia* the homologs appear to be loosely paired at first, but this is followed by a more intimate apposition as the gyres of the two chromosomes become paranemically disposed.

In basic diploids the homologous chromosomes have only one choice of a pairing partner, but in polyploids this restriction is no longer imposed. It is noteworthy that in triploid and tetraploid plants pairing is always two-by-two at any one region although there are frequent changes of pairing partners. Contrasted with this restriction on meiotic synapsis is the pairing found in the polytene chromosomes of the salivary glands of triploid *Drosophila* where the forces bringing about pairing are not saturated by a two-by-two association. In trisomic and triploid forms the three homologs may be jointly synapsed throughout their entire lengths. Schultz and Hungerford (1953 and unpublished) made a detailed study of the pairing pattern of salivary gland chromosomes in diploid, triploid, and aneuploid individuals as well as in structurally heterozygous forms. Even though salivary pairing may not be representative of that in the meiocytes of *Drosophila,* their data afford some interesting conclusions. Failure of terminal pairing was infrequent, suggesting that the free ends experience little difficulty in synapsis. Asynaptic regions adjacent to the chromocenter were more frequently found. Intercalary unpaired regions were generally small, indicating that synapsis begun at both the chromocenter and distal ends generally proceeded to completion.

C. Pachynema

When zygotene pairing ceases the nucleus is at pachynema. A stage of long duration, it has been called a "stable stage" since pairing has been completed (Swanson, 1957). The number of pairs is half the diploid number of chromosomes. The paired homologs, consisting of four chromatids and known as tetrads or bivalents, become both shorter and thicker by a progressive increase in the diameter of their coils. The length of the pachytene chromosomes of *Bellevalia* is one-fourth to one-sixth that of leptonema, and a comparable reduction in length is found in maize (Figs. 9 and 10). The two closely apposed homologs are, in some forms at least, relationally twisted around one another. This relational coiling has been held to play an essential role in crossing over (see page 44).

It cannot be too strongly emphasized that the chromatid is the unit of crossing over and of segregation. If each chromatid is polynemic, the macromolecular subunits act as a single entity in crossing over and segregation. The time of division of a meiotic chromosome into chromatids remains a controversial matter despite recent cytochemical evidence indicating that it occurs before zygonema. It has been argued that doubling of the chemical components does not necessarily mean division into two functionally independent chromatids and that this could conceivably occur later. Some of the current hypotheses on the cause of pairing and on the mechanism of crossing over are based on the tenet that division into chromatids takes place at zygonema or pachynema. If the basic assumption is incorrect, then these hypotheses become invalidated. A more thorough discussion of this point is given elsewhere in this chapter.

Linear differentiation in chromosome morphology is best observed at pachynema. It is the meiotic stage which has been widely exploited in cytogenetic studies. Adjacent to the differentially staining centric region are often found deeply staining segments designated as heterochromatin. More distal regions with a lighter staining, finer chromomeric structure are called euchromatic. In favorable material each pair of chromosomes can be recognized at pachynema by relative total length, position of centromere, distinctive patterns of chromomeres, and the presence of large heterochromatic bodies (knobs) which occupy specific positions in the chromosomes.

D. Diplonema

During pachynema the intimately paired chromosomes exhibit no tendency to fall apart, and it is not until diplonema (Fig. 11) that a repulsion (due to a so-called body repulsion presumably of an electrostatic nature) is first evident. So strong is this force that the members of each pair would in many organisms become completely dissociated to form univalents were it not for the presence of one or more chiasmata which bind them together. That a repulsion also exists between homologous centromeres has been claimed because of the greater attenuation of the centric loops observed in some organisms, but the existence of centric

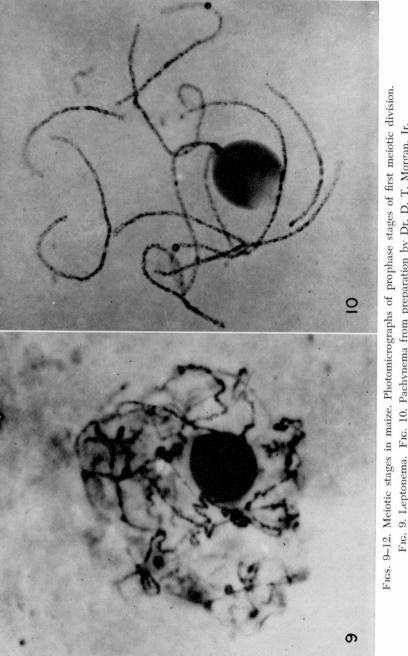

FIGS. 9–12. Meiotic stages in maize. Photomicrographs of prophase stages of first meiotic division. FIG. 9. Leptonema. FIG. 10. Pachynema from preparation by Dr. D. T. Morgan, Jr.

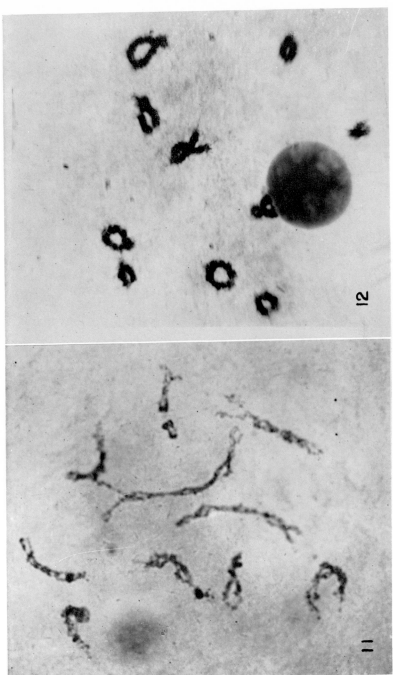

FIG. 11. Diplonema stained with aceto-orcein; nucleolus not visible. FIG. 12. Diakinesis.

repulsion at diplonema has been questioned and in maize the homologous centromeres are often found associated until late diplonema. As the chromosomes separate, they open out to form the loops and nodes characteristic of diplonema. The chiasmata are at the nodal regions and, par-

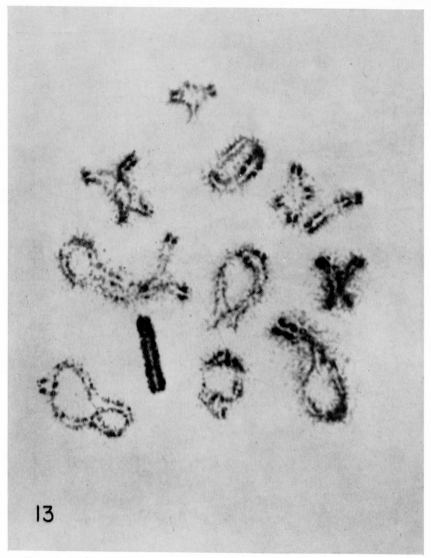

FIG. 13. Diakinesis in the grasshopper *Schistocerca gregaria* showing chiasmata. The unpaired (single) X chromosome is heteropycnotic. From J. H. Tjio and A. Levan (*Annales de la Estacion Experimental de Aula Dei* **3**(2), 225-228, 1954).

ticularly in some animal meiocytes as those of the grasshopper (Fig. 13), are seen to consist of a change of partners between two pairs of chromatids to produce an X-shaped figure. Only two of the four chromatids are involved in the exchange. Although exceptions are known, there is good evidence in a few organisms that the cytologically observed chiasmata correspond to points where genetic crossing over has taken place.

The position and number of chiasmata determine the configuration of a bivalent at diplonema and later stages (Fig. 13). Bivalents with one nonterminal chiasma appear as a cross and those with one terminal chiasma are rod-shaped. Pairs with a terminal chiasma in each arm are ring-shaped and so on. That successive loops in bivalents having more than two chiasmata are at right angles to one another is attributed to torsion in the system of paired homologs. The maximum number of chiasmata is found at diplonema. In some organisms there is no decrease in chiasma frequency as meiosis proceeds to metaphase I, but in others, notably those with small chromosomes, chiasma frequency may be less at later stages of meiotic prophase. This reduction is caused by the movement of interstitial or proximal chiasmata along the arms of paired chromosomes from their place of origin to more distal positions. According to Darlington's "electrostatic theory of terminalization" there are two kinds of repelling forces operating at diplonema. One is a generalized, less effective electronegative charge concentrated on the surface of the chromosome throughout its length, and the second is a special charge localized at the centromere. The generalized charge tends to force the chromosomes apart while the stronger centromere repulsion causes distal movement of the chiasmata to the ends. Swanson (1942, 1957) questions the reality of the forces postulated by Darlington in terminalization and suggests that, if it occurs, it is effected by despiralization of the chromosomes. The number of coils is greatest at leptonema and becomes smaller as prophase advances by an increase in gyre diameter. Swanson's despiralization hypothesis assumes that the change from a condition of many small coils to one of fewer and larger gyres develops mechanical tension which, if strong enough, will force the chiasmata to slide along the chromosomes. Experimentally it has been found that contracted chromosomes with fewer coils have more terminal chiasmata than do bivalents with many coils. Östergren (1943) offers a somewhat different explanation of terminalization based on the idea that movement of chiasmata dissipates the tension established by the chiasmata themselves.

In those organisms where association of homologs until anaphase I depends upon the presence of chiasmata, every pair must have at least one chiasma. Longer chromosomes usually have more chiasmata than do shorter ones, but there is no direct proportionality between chromosome length and chiasma frequency. Chiasmata may be localized near the centromere as in *Allium fistulosum, Fritillaria meleagris,* and *Mecostethus* or near the distal ends as in *Philocleon,* or they may occur more or less randomly as is the general rule. Localization of chiasmata, in some cases known to reflect the kind of pairing at zygonema, has been shown to be under genic control.

Genetic data from *Drosophila,* maize, and other well-studied forms show that one crossover will suppress the occurrence of others in short adjacent segments if they lie in the same arm of the chromosome but no inhibition (interference) is found if the regions are on opposite sides of the centromere. Chiasma interference of a similar nature has also been reported (Haldane, 1931). There are, however, exceptional cases where chiasma interference extends across the centromere and pairs of metacentric chromosomes possess only one chiasma. First reported by Pätau (1941) and Callan and Montalenti (1947) in *Culex,* it has been observed in a number of organisms (cf. Oksala, 1952). Especially instructive would be a detailed comparison of genetically determined interference with cytologically measured chiasma interference in the same species, but this is yet to be done.

In spermatogenesis and more often in oögenesis of some animals, diplonema is a difficult stage to study because the chromosomes appear to revert to an interphase state becoming diffuse in appearance and poorly characterized. The diffuse stage is, however, merely an interruption in the course of meiosis apparently caused by unusual metabolic conditions such as extended growth of the cytoplasm and in no wise is an essential feature.

E. Diakinesis

As meiosis advances from diplonema to diakinesis (Fig. 12) the chromosomes become shorter by a closer approximation of the gyres, and at late diakinesis, when the last remnant of the nucleolus customarily disappears, the chromosomes are contracted, deep-staining bodies. During diplonema and diakinesis the decrease in size of the nucleolus coincides with a rapid increase in the basophilia of the chromosomes. Since the increasing stainability of the chromosomes at late meiotic prophase occurs as the nucleolus gradually diminishes in size, it has been suggested that nucleolar material is incorporated into the chromosomes (McClintock, 1934), but this has been questioned.

The chromosomes in earlier stages of meiosis appear to be more or less randomly distributed throughout the nucleus, but during diakinesis the bivalents migrate to the periphery of the nucleus, where they lie in close juxtaposition to the nuclear membrane and widely separated from one another. This peripheral movement is found in organisms with and without well-defined centers. In general, there is neither attraction nor repulsion between centers and chromosomes at diakinesis. However, in *Brachystethus* and *Mecistorhinus* the diakinetic autosomes assume a position midway between the two centers as if a repelling force were present (Schrader, 1946a, b) and in *Anisolabis* the bivalents become segregated into two groups at opposite ends of the nucleus where the centrioles lie (Schrader, 1941). It may be significant that these are organisms with nonlocalized centromeres. At late diakinesis, concomitant with the breakdown of the nuclear membrane and formation of the spindle, there occurs in a few forms, notably the mantid (White, 1941; Hughes-Schrader, 1943), a remarkable separation of the two homologous centric regions which leads to a marked attenuation of the chromosomes. Known as the premetaphase stretch, this behavior is believed to denote an attraction between centromere and center. The bivalents re-contract before moving onto the spindle at metaphase. Limited in its occurrence to relatively few organisms, the premetaphase stretch must be considered exceptional.

If there is no terminalization of chiasmata, the shape of bivalents at diakinesis is not significantly different from that at diplonema, but with terminalization there is a corresponding modification in bivalent appearance. With the dissolution of the nuclear membrane the diakinetic stage is ended and the compact bivalents will next move onto the spindle at metaphase.

F. Metaphase I

After the nuclear membrane has disappeared, a bipolar spindle is formed onto which the bivalents move and become oriented. The time between disintegration of the nuclear membrane and establishment of the bivalents on the spindle has been called prometaphase. At full metaphase (Fig. 14) the two homologous centromeres of each tetrad or bivalent lie in the longitudinal axis of the spindle on opposite sides of the equatorial plate (co-orientation). When equilibrium is reached, the two centric regions are equidistant from the spindle plate. The distance from centromere to the equatorial plate is determined by the position of the proximal chiasmata. Polar views of metaphase I disclose only the distribution of the bivalents on the spindle plate and reveal neither the number of chiasmata nor the shapes of the bivalents. These can be seen clearly in side or lateral views of the spindle. The number and position

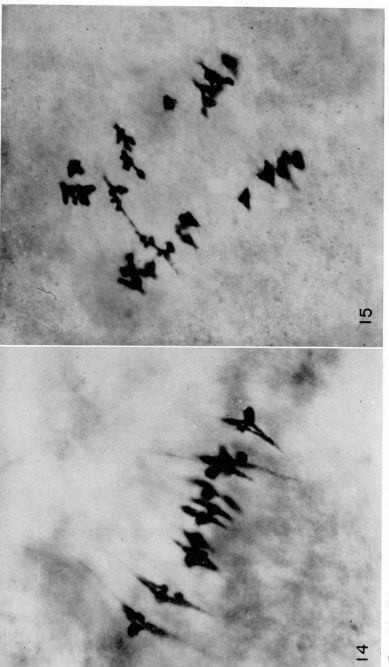

FIGS. 14–17. Meiosis in maize (continued). FIG. 14. Metaphase I showing co-orientation of bivalents. FIG. 15. Anaphase I with two disjoining dyads connected by a persistent chiasma.

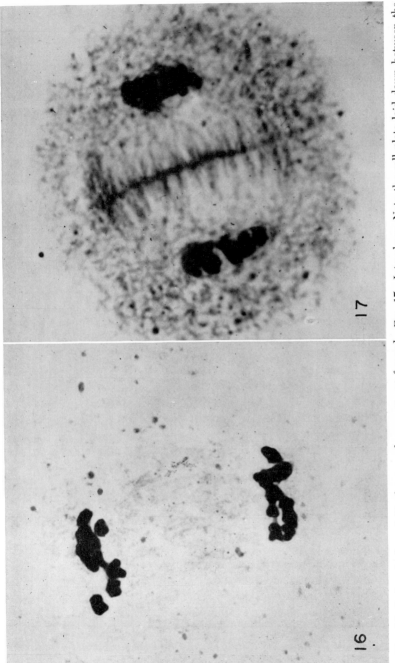

Fig. 16. Early telophase I. Nuclear membrane not yet formed. Fig. 17. Interphase. Note the cell plate laid down between the two interphasic nuclei.

of the chiasmata together with relative arm lengths determine the shape and appearance of the metaphase I bivalent.

Connecting the centric regions to the nearest pole are the half-spindle or chromosomal fibers for whose production the centromere is essential. The centric region is the only part of the chromosome attached to the spindle. Uncertain though the exact method is by which the chromosomal fibers effect poleward movement at anaphase, it is clear that they are responsible for orderly anaphase migration. Although the centric region of each homolog is probably structurally double (Lima-de-Faria, 1953), it is functionally single since homologous centric regions are oriented and pass to opposite poles.

G. Anaphase I

Separation of each tetrad into two dyad chromosomes takes place at anaphase I as the two co-oriented centric regions begin moving to opposite poles. As the centric regions move poleward the chiasmata slip to and finally off the free ends, thus disengaging the paired homologs. Two disjoining dyads connected by a persistent chiasma are shown in Fig. 15, where the other dyads have become wholly separate. A dyad consists of two chromatids, each made up of two arms; therefore it appears at anaphase I as a double V if the chromosome is metacentric or a double J if it is acrocentric. A telocentric chromosome would form a single V-shaped dyad. The four arms of a dyad do not lie closely appressed during anaphase I but diverge as if they were mutually repelling one another.

The two chromatids of a dyad are conjoined at or near the centric region. Although each homolog consists of two chromatids, the centric region is functionally single since anaphase I is reductional for the centromere region. However, Lima-de-Faria (1953, 1957) believes the centric region is double, with each chromatid having its own centromere, and that the undivided condition of the chromatin adjacent to the centromere binds together the two sister chromatids. Irrespective of the way it is achieved, there is good evidence that the centric region undergoes a reductional segregation at anaphase I. Direct cytological evidence that this is so was first provided by McClintock (1933), who studied the anaphase I separation of a heteromorphic pair of chromosomes in maize. One chromosome was telocentric, consisting only of the short arm, while the other was normal, having both a short and a long arm. If anaphase I were equational for the centric region, each dyad would have two short arms and one long arm. If reductional segregation occurred, one dyad would consist of two short arms and the other of two short and two long arms. Only the latter type of anaphase figure was observed. Matsuura

(1957), working with heteromorphic pairs in *Trillium*, reported a high and varying frequency of equational centric separations at anaphase I, but his data can be accounted for by chiasmata in the deficient arm.

Reduction of chromosome number is held to occur in the first meiotic division since the number of dyad chromosomes at each pole is one-half the diploid number of chromosomes. It is true that each dyad has two chromatids, but they remain conjoined until anaphase II and the criterion for reduction is the number of independent chromosomal bodies at each pole.

Every bivalent is composed of two chromatids of maternal and two of paternal origin. The orientation of the different tetrads on the metaphase spindle must be random since an independent assortment of the chromosomes of different pairs is demanded by genetic theory and indeed has been shown to occur cytologically (Carothers, 1921).

H. *Telophase I and Interphase*

Once the dyads reach the spindle poles they form at each pole a telophasic nucleus with a nuclear membrane and then go into a short interphase before passing into the second meiotic division (Figs. 16 and 17). This is the common sequence, but in *Trillium* and the Odonata the telophase and interphase are omitted and the anaphase group of dyads enters the second division with little or no change in chromosome length or in coiling. In maize the dyads at early telophase are more contracted than at the preceding anaphase; the four arms of each dyad are spherical masses of chromatin (Fig. 16). As telophase advances, the nuclear membrane is formed and the chromosomes elongate, presumably by a loosening of the coils, and gradually assume the diffuseness characteristic of interphase chromosomes. Interphase is of too short duration, however, to permit the chromosomes to become as extended as in a typical metabolic nucleus or to allow formation of a single large nucleolus. No reduplication of the chromosomes occurs between the first and second meiotic divisions, and the dyads of anaphase reappear unchanged in prophase II. In maize and in many plants a cell plate is formed between the two telophasic nuclei, dividing the mother cell into two daughter cells (bipartitioning), but in others cytokinesis is deferred until the end of both meiotic divisions (quadripartitioning).

I. *Prophase II*

Compared with the first meiotic division, the second is unspectacular with no unusual phenomena. It superficially resembles an ordinary somatic division. At early prophase II the two chromatids of each dyad look like X's since they are conjoined by a common centric region and the four arms are widely separated. There is no relational coiling. The X-shaped dyads are several times longer than at telophase I, but the chromonemata are not completely uncoiled. The dual nature of prophase II chromosomes is exceptionally clear in Figs. 18 and 19. The centric region varies in stainability; in maize it is so lightly stained with carmine that it appears as a constriction while in *Agapanthus* a fine chromomeric structure is evident. The proximal segments of the two short arms of each dyad appear to be united, as do the proximal regions of the two long arms. The chromatid arms become progressively shorter and stain more deeply in later prophase stages, and the compact dyads of late prophase II or metaphase II resemble those of telophase I (Figs. 16 and 20). The genetic constitution of the two chromatids of each dyad depends upon the kind and number of crossovers which took place in the first meiotic prophase. If no crossing over occurred the dyad would consist of two identical sister chromatids of either paternal or maternal origin, but with crossing over each chromatid could possess segments derived from both parental chromosomes. The only regions invariably composed of segments from sister chromatids are those immediately adjacent to the centromere and proximal to the first chiasmata.

J. *Metaphase II and Anaphase II*

Prior to metaphase II the nuclear membrane disappears and the spindle develops upon which the dyads become oriented with their centric regions lying on the equatorial plate (auto-orientation). The centromere of each dyad now becomes functionally double; chromosomal fibers arise from the centromeres and the two chromatids move to opposite poles during anaphase II (Fig. 21). The term "monad" has been used to designate an anaphase II chromatid since "dyad" refers to the chromosomal condition present from anaphase I to metaphase II and "tetrad" to the bivalent of the first meiotic prophase and metaphase. The course of events in the distribution of chromatids during meiosis in maize may be summarized as follows. Ten bivalents or tetrads (40 chromatids) are present at metaphase I. During anaphase I, 10 dyads (20 chromatids) pass to each pole. The two daughter cells or nuclei have 10 dyads at metaphase II which are equationally separated in anaphase, with 10 monads (10 chromatids) going to each of the 4 haploid nuclei formed at the end of the 2 meiotic divisions. Meiosis has run its course and both reduction in chromosome number and recombination have been achieved.

III. Anomalous Meiotic Behavior in Organisms with Localized Centromeres

Although the majority of organisms with localized centromeres have a uniform or standard type of meiosis, variations do exist. In many cases they may be relatively unimportant modifications such as a diffuse diplonema, others are more radical departures from normal, and some are so profoundly different that they are inexplicable in terms of the laws governing chromosome behavior in standard meiosis. Anomalous kinds of meiosis occur chiefly in the insects; this is particularly true of the Diptera, where a wide diversity is found. In the suborder Nematocera there is a standard meiosis in some families with chiasmata in both oögenesis and spermatogenesis as in the midges and mosquitoes, while highly aberrant types of meiosis are encountered in the Sciaridae and Cecidomyidae. Oögenesis is normal in *Drosophila*, but there is no crossing over in the males. This may be true for all members of the suborder Brachycera (White, 1954). In general, meiosis in the males has undergone the greatest modifications, with oögenesis remaining unchanged. Meiosis is known to be under genic control and there is no reason to doubt that the various anomalous types arose from mutations, but the time and order of their occurrence in the evolutionary history of the species can only be conjectured. It is also difficult to understand why some insects came to have complex kinds of meiosis when the same end result could be attained by much simpler mechanisms.

It should be emphasized that for every major modification of meiosis there is some compensatory change or else the reproductive process would break down. In those forms where chiasmata are necessary for the orderly orientation of the bivalents on the spindle, unpaired chromosomes usually behave irregularly and frequently fail to be included in the telophase nuclei. However, in organisms such as the grasshoppers, where the males are XO and the single X chromosome is unpaired at metaphase I, some mechanism other than that controlling disjunction of the paired autosomes ensures its orderly though precocious passage to one pole in anaphase I. An equational division of the X-dyad occurs in the second division, so two of the four spermatids have an X and two are no-X. Even in tetraploid spermatocytes the two X chromosomes are unpaired at metaphase, possibly because their heteropycnosis inhibits chiasma formation, and each is reductionally segregated in anaphase I in the same fashion as that of the single X in diploid meiocytes. Another example of a compensating mechanism is found in spermatogenesis of the haploid hymenopterous males where all chromosomes are unpaired.

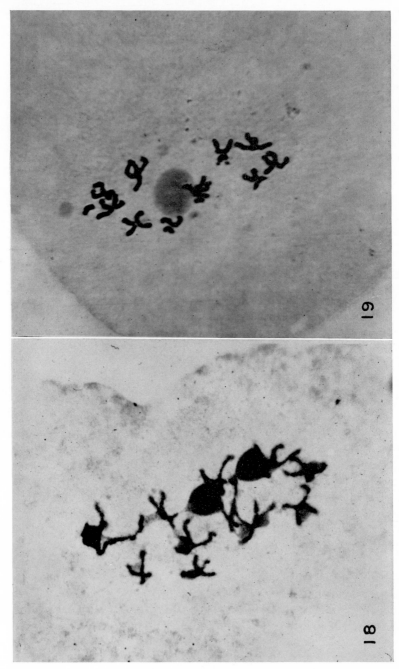

FIGS. 18–21. Meiosis in maize (continued). FIG. 18. Early prophase II showing X-shaped dyads and dispersed matrical material. FIG. 19. Later prophase II in which dyads have contracted.

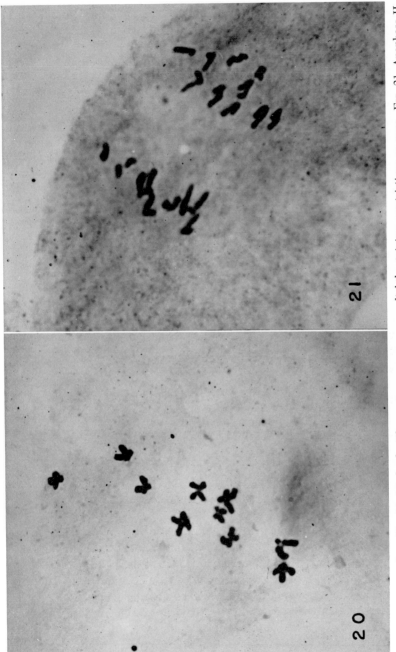

Fig. 20. Metaphase II with 10 dyads. The centromeres appear as lightly staining constrictions or gaps. Fig. 21. Anaphase II. Ten chromatids (monads) are passing to each pole. The localized centric regions lead the way to the poles.

A spindle is formed at metaphase I, but there is no anaphase and all the chromosomes are included in one nucleus, which undergoes an equational division at anaphase II. That this behavior is genetically determined and is not the consequence of the haploid condition is evident from the studies of Torvik-Greb (1935), who found that the meiotic behavior in the exceptional diploid males of *Habrobracon* was identical to that in haploids. Another example of compensating mechanisms is found in apomictic forms where the diploid eggs resulting from aberrant meiosis are able to divide without the usual stimulus of fertilization.

Spermatogenesis in *Drosophila* is anomalous in that there is no crossing over. The paired condition of the autosomes and of the X-Y bivalent is due not to chiasmata, but to an attraction force which may be that responsible for the somatic pairing found in the Diptera. Cooper (1941) reported that the autosomal pairs in *Melophagus*, another dipteran, were held together by an attraction between the short arms of the acrocentric chromosomes; the major portions of the chromosomes were not in contact and no chiasmata were present. The X and Y chromosomes never pair yet pass to opposite poles at anaphase I. An interesting variation in the male *Drosophila* meiosis is the genetically determined "sex-ratio" condition present in some strains of *Drosophila pseudoobscura* and several other species. Males with the "sex-ratio" condition produce a high percentage of daughters in matings with normal females instead of the expected 1:1 sex ratio. During spermatogenesis the X and Y chromosomes remain unpaired, the X dividing equationally at each division. In the two meiotic divisions the four chromatids are distributed among the four spermatids, so nearly every sperm receives an X chromosome. The Y chromosome usually degenerates (Sturtevant and Dobzhansky, 1936). Novitski (1947) reported that the "sex-ratio" condition in *Drosophila affinis* producing nearly all female progeny was modified by a recessive autosomal mutation. Males homozygous for this recessive mutation and carrying "sex-ratio" had progenies with many more males than females, but the cytological basis was not investigated.

The orientation of the two chromosomes of a bivalent with respect to the two spindle poles is ordinarily at random, as is the orientation of the different pairs with respect to one another. If this were not so, Mendel's laws would not hold. A number of cases, however, have been reported where nonrandom segregation occurs in that a particular chromosome preferentially passes to a specific pole. Since in oögenesis only one of the four haploid nuclei becomes the egg pronucleus while the other three pass into nonfunctional polar bodies and since in megasporogenesis usually only one of the four megaspores develops into the embryo sac, it follows that the chromosome preferentially segregated to the spindle pole from which the functional egg or megaspore nucleus was derived would be present in more than half of the offspring. Sandler and Novitski (1957) have given the name "meiotic drive" to the preferential inclusion of a specific chromosome in the gametes. The "sex-ratio" condition is an example of meiotic drive, as is the preferential segregation of abnormal chromosome 10 in maize found by Rhoades (1942), where neocentromere formation in heterozygous dyads may be responsible for preferential orientation on the spindle (Rhoades, 1952). It is interesting to note that simultaneous preferential segregation of two pairs of chromosomes does not affect their independent assortment. In both of these cases the aberrant behavior is controlled by genetic factors, but nonrandom disjunction resulting from structural dissimilarity of the two members of a pair has been reported in *Drosophila* by Novitski (1951), who found that the shorter member of a heteromorphic pair was included in the egg nucleus more often than the longer chromosome. The cytological mechanism bringing this about has not been elucidated.

The fungus gnat *Sciara* has evolved a type of spermatogenesis which seems incredibly complex (Metz, 1938). Although the chromosomal complement of the germ line is the same in males and females, there are great differences between spermatogenesis and oögenesis. Oögenesis with pairing, crossing over, and random segregation is normal, but in spermatogenesis these unusual features are found: (1) no pairing (hence no crossing over) of homologous chromosomes; (2) instead of a bipolar spindle, a unipolar one is formed at metaphase I; (3) only the chromosomes derived from the maternal parent move to the acuminate pole; the paternal chromosomes, although connected to the pole by chromosomal fibers, appear to pass in the opposite direction to form a nucleus which degenerates; (4) the secondary spermatocyte with only maternal chromosomes undergoes an essentially normal second meiotic division except that both chromatids of the X-chromosome dyad pass precociously to the same pole. The nucleus with two X chromosomes is transformed into a spermatid and the other degenerates. Consequently only one functional sperm instead of the customary four is produced by each spermatocyte. White (1948) does not overemphasize the complexity of the situation when he writes: "The meiosis of the male Sciaridae is so unique in character that it is hard to imagine how it could have arisen in the course of evolution or how it really 'works' at the present time."

No less complicated is meiosis in the gall midges, which are fairly closely related to *Sciara*. Much of what is known comes from the work of White (cf. 1954). In both *Sciara* and the gall midges there are certain

chromosomes which are eliminated from the somatic cells but are retained in the germ track. However, some species of *Sciara* have no]
(limited) chromosomes, and in those which possess them the number
ranges from one to three, while the number of limited (E) chromosomes
in the gall midges is much higher although varying in different species.
In spermatogenesis there is no pairing in the first meiotic prophase; the
spindle at metaphase I is bipolar with one acuminate and one broad
pole. A haploid set of the S chromosomes passes to the acuminate pole
while the broad pole receives a similar set of S chromosomes and all of
the E chromosomes. The two secondary spermatocytes are of unequal
size, and it is the smaller one with a single set of S chromosomes which
completes the second division to form two spermatids.

The study of oögenesis is more difficult technically and the precise
details are uncertain, but it is evident that the functional egg nucleus
possesses a haploid set of S chromosomes and all of the E chromosomes,
so the fertilized egg has a full complement of both S and E chromosomes.
Since pairs of S chromosomes are found at metaphase I, it is assumed
that crossing over occurs between the two sets of S chromosomes; there
is no pairing among the E chromosomes. The behavior of the unpaired
E chromosomes in the first and second divisions needs further study, but
they are included at the pole from which the functional egg nucleus develops while the polar body has a single set of S chromosomes.

IV. The Nature of the Synaptic Force

Muller (1947) emphasized the parallelism between gene duplication,
where nonspecific components of the medium are selected and combined
into a form corresponding to the parental gene, and the phenomenon of
synapsis, where individual genes on homologous chromosomes are attracted and become associated in two's—i.e., the same basic forces or
principles may be acting in both gene synthesis and synapsis. If this be
true, then recently gained knowledge on chromosome structure and
duplication may be helpful in arriving at some consistent theory of pairing and crossing over.

If at the onset of the first meiotic prophase the homologous chromosomes are randomly distributed throughout the nucleus, there must exist
some mechanism by which homologous segments are brought together.
The nature of this long-range force, which is seemingly effective over
distances of several microns, has long concerned those interested in
cellular behavior. An answer has been sought in terms of known physical
phenomena but no satisfactory solution has been attained since none is
subject to experimental test. Nevertheless several interesting suggestions

have been offered which have the merit, at least, of calling attention to one of the least understood attributes of chromosomes.

The physical phenomenon whereby an alternately contracting and expanding body immersed in a liquid attracts another pulsating body is known as the Guyot-Bjerknes effect. If the vibrational frequencies of two molecular bodies or systems are in phase—i.e., when one contracts so does the other—they are attracted toward one another, whereas they are repelled if out of phase. Systems with different vibrational frequencies are neither repelled nor attracted. As early as 1907, Lamb had invoked this phenomenon to account for the apparent force emanating from the centrosome. Muller (1941) suggested that the long-range attractive forces bringing homologous regions together might be due to their possessing similar vibrational frequencies. This idea was developed in greater detail by Fabergé (1942). He suggested that each pairing unit along the chromosome, not necessarily a single gene, has a characteristic frequency of vibration which attracts similarly pulsating regions in the homologous chromosome so that the two like chromosomes move toward one another.

Friedrich-Freksa's (1940) hypothesis that dipole moments bring about pairing of homologous chromosomes several microns distant at leptonema rests, as do all extant physical explanations, on unproved assumptions. However, the assumption that nucleic acid is not found continuously along the chromosome but is located transversely at certain places on a protein backbone is not inconsistent with the concept of chromosome structure currently held by some investigators (cf. Taylor, 1957). Serra's (1955) criticism of this hypothesis because it permits an attractive force between nonhomologous chromosomes although to a lesser degree than between homologous ones does not appear to be justified. Indeed, his criticism concerns one of the pertinent points of this hypothesis. That nonhomologous chromosomes or segments may pair has been unequivocally demonstrated in maize, and any hypothesis that accounts for this nonspecific pairing is thereby rendered more acceptable.

Serra (1947) advanced what is termed a structural hypothesis since it is based on the assumption that the leptotene chromosomes possess numerous flexible loops or fibrils extending laterally several microns from the chromosome. Each of these loops is assumed to be different from the others, and when two similar loops or lateral protrusions on homologous chromosomes chance to meet it leads to intimate pairing. No long-range forces are necessary on this hypothesis, but it rests on a tenuous factual basis. It is true that the lamp-brush chromosomes have laterally protruding loops but these are exceptional chromosomes that are not typical of the great majority of leptotene chromosomes.

Lindegren and Bridges (1938) proposed an agglutination hypothesis to account for the chromomere-to-chromomere pairing found at pachynema. Each chromomere was considered to act as an antigen forming a specific antibody on its surface. Adsorption would occur when two allelic chromomeres happen to come in contact. The chromomeres on each side of the already agglutinated chromomeres would then fuse and a zipper-like pairing throughout the length of the chromosomes would follow. This hypothesis has no long-range force that operates to bring distantly situated homologs together.

Delbrück (1941) believes that long-range forces cannot be involved in pairing for two reasons: (1) the two homologs must be in equivalent states; therefore their like electric charges would lead to repulsion; (2) the forces must be specific for the chemical constitution of each chromomere and it has not been found possible to devise a model for specific attractive forces operating over a distance of several microns. According to Delbrück, pairing results from short-distance chemical interactions which come into play after contact between the two homologs has been initiated, possibly by movement due to thermal agitation or to some intrinsic property of the chromosomes. Pairing is conceived as the intimate association of self-reproducing entities within the chromosomes coupled with the chemical reduction of each pair of peptide bonds, so that between each pair a resonance bond is formed. A change in redox would then reverse this situation and permit the separation of the two homologs and the synapsis of new chromatids by the addition of new material and further oxidation. In Delbrück's hypothesis no role is given to nucleic acid. If DNA is the primary genic material, any theory of pairing which ignores it may be suspect of offering at best only a partial solution of the causal mechanisms. Pairing is assumed to occur between phage chromosomes, and these are believed to consist only of DNA. Delbrück's hypothesis also assumes that pairing occurs before duplication; this is consistent with Pritchard's (1960) hypothesis of the effective pairing of small segments during interphase. On this concept the intimate pairing observed at pachynema serves to ensure the orderly segregation of chromosomes at anaphase I.

Although some investigators question the existence of long-range forces on the grounds that no known physical phenomena are adequate to account for forces of the required magnitude, there is good cytological evidence that they do exist and are instrumental in bringing widely separated chromosomes together. Moreover, recent physical studies on intermolecular forces due to quantum-mechanical and thermal charge fluctuations suggest that the degree of specificity of the van der Waals-

London-Kirkwood forces may be sufficient to account for the attraction of like-for-like. Molecules in a liquid medium which have the same distribution of oscillator polarizabilities and oscillator orientations over the frequency spectrum are specifically attracted to one another (Jehle, 1957; Yos and co-workers, 1957a, b). Presumably each gene or pairing unit along the chromosome would have its characteristic fluctuation. Since van der Waals forces are additive, the attraction force of one chromosome for its homolog would be the sum of the forces produced by the individual genes. Larger structures would therefore have greater forces of attraction. According to Oster (1957), pairing occurs when attraction between homologous chromosomes due to additive van der Waals forces is greater than the ionic double-layer repulsion. Van der Waals forces would become operative between particles at a distance comparable with the size of the particles. He believes it is not necessary to assume special types of physical phenomena such as "tuned gene oscillators." Unfortunately little is known of the strength or magnitude of the intermolecular forces existing between the large nucleoprotein molecules of the chromosomes, and at the present time these speculations are largely of theoretical interest.

Cooper (1948) raises the question whether or not it is necessary to assume the existence of long-range forces. He suggests that chance contact between homologous chromosomes may occur if the prophase chromosomes are capable of movement, as has been observed in living choroidal cells of the chick and during cleavage of the *Pediculopsis* egg. Once two homologous regions have been brought together by random movement of the chromosomes, a progressive zipperlike pairing follows, leading to a complete chromomere-by-chromomere pairing throughout the entire length of the chromosomes. Pairing would also be facilitated if the two homologs underwent relational coiling. In some forms both relational coiling and a zipperlike pairing may be responsible for synapsis at zygonema, but relational coiling of the two homologs does not universally occur. Cooper points out that, if pairing subsequent to the first point of contact is due to relational coiling, this would account for the relative absence of interlocking of different homologs at pachynema and later stages. This, however, would not be the case if more than one point of contact was made simultaneously at different places along the chromosome. Interlocking should be frequently found on Pritchard's (1960) hypothesis of effective pairing of small segments. The exceptional occurrence of interlocked bivalents is not in support of this hypothesis.

Muller (1947) questions that the homologous loci of the leptotene chromosomes are brought into atomic distances of one another by fortuitous movements due to thermal agitation after which a zipperlike pairing proceeds along the chromosomes. The strongest argument against synapsis occurring in this manner is the observation by McClintock (1945) and Singleton (1953) in *Neurospora* that pairing of the homologs begins when they have reached a contracted state. The condensed homologs lie adjacent to, but not in physical contact with, one another. The intimate association characteristic of pachytene chromosomes usually begins at one or both ends and progresses along the chromosome until all segments are intimately paired. Concomitant with this close synapsis is the elongation, presumably by uncoiling of the chromonemata, which continues until the chromosomes are fully extended and resemble in both pairing and extension the pachytene chromosomes of other forms. If the coming together of the contracted chromosomes is due to some kind of long-range force, it follows that this force is operative at a time when the chromosomes are tightly coiled. Although unlikely, the possibility has not been excluded that their juxtaposition resulted from random movement of the chromosomes and no long-range force was involved.

Inasmuch as meiosis takes place immediately following syngamy in *Neurospora,* synapsis involved homologs previously separated in two haploid nuclei. The spatial arrangement in the two sets of seven chromosomes of the fusion nucleus is presumably free of any selective orientation of homologs. Olive (1949) working with the rust *Coleosporium* and El Ani (1956) with the ascomycete *Hypomyces* likewise found that pairing was initiated between relatively contracted chromosomes followed by elongation of the chromonemata. According to El Ani the distal heterochromatic regions of the highly condensed chromosomes aggregate in early meiotic prophase to form a "bouquet"; this would facilitate the initial pairing between the distal ends of homologous chromosomes since they would be lying in close proximity. Singleton reported a bouquet stage in the two prefusion haploid nuclei but was not certain that a similar configuration existed in the fusion nucleus. Olive observed that all chromosomes of the fusion nucleus became attached to the nucleolus in early prophase. This produces a type of polarization not essentially different from the bouquet produced by fusion of heterochromatin. It may be that in the fungi generally meiosis differs from that in higher forms in that synapsis first occurs between condensed chromosomes rather than between the elongated chromosomes of typical leptonema. However, two reports apparently are at variance with this conclusion. Wakayama (1930) reported in the Agaricaceae that the chromosomes appeared at leptonema as elongated threads which later paired, and

Wells (1956) believes that in *Sporormia* synapsis does not occur between condensed chromosomes, but the critical stage was difficult to observe.

The pairing force is, in general, highly specific and brings together homologous segments so that at pachynema the two like chromosomes are in intimate association with a chromomere-by-chromomere pairing. That the chromosome as a whole is not the unit of pairing is clearly evident from the synaptic relationships found in structural heterozygotes. For example, a translocated chromosome consists of segments from chromosome A and from chromosome B. The A portion of the translocated chromosome pairs with the homologous loci in the intact A chromosome and the B portion synapses with homologous regions in the whole B chromosome. In many organisms pairing apparently occurs only between homologous regions, but there is at least one notable exception to this generalization of the high specificity of synaptic affinity. McClintock (1933) believes that there is a powerful tendency for all parts of chromosomes to be associated in pairs regardless of homologies. This is a generalized and nonspecific attraction. Superimposed on this generalized attraction is the specific attraction between homologous segments. In structural homozygotes synapsis occurs with rare exceptions only between homologous segments, but in aneuploid and structurally heterozygous individuals the generalized pairing force is in itself sufficiently strong to bring about pairing of nonhomologous segments if homologous regions are absent or not in close proximity. Nonhomologous pairing is frequently encountered in monoploid sporocytes (Ernst, 1939; Levan, 1942; McClintock, 1933), where each chromosome is represented singly and has no homolog with which to pair; in aneuploid types such as primary trisomes, where at any one level only two of the three homologs come together leaving the third chromosome unpaired; and in translocation and inversion heterozygotes.

Since nonhomologously paired regions at pachynema usually fall apart at diplonema, it has been concluded that crossing over rarely occurs between nonhomologously paired segments. However, a number of cases of structurally modified chromosomes have arisen in strains where nonhomologous pairing was known to occur, and it is believed that illegitimate crossing over occasionally takes place.

There is some uncertainty whether or not nonhomologous pairing is a phenomenon of widespread occurrence. Unfortunately, the critical stage of pachynema in most plants and animals is usually so poor that it is impossible to tell whether synapsis invariably involves like segments. Recently Cooper and associates (1955) suggested that the high percentage of nondisjunction found in *Drosophila* heterozygous for inversions in two or more of the major chromosomes could be accounted for by nonhomologous pairing with an attendant failure of normal segregation. There is, however, no cytological basis for this suggestion.

Despite the unequivocal demonstration of nonhomologous pairing in maize, the pairing force is generally believed to be highly specific since at least in the salivary chromosomes it produces pairing of short homologous regions. White (1954) states the prevailing view when he writes: "We accordingly have to visualize, not merely a general attraction between homologous chromosomes but many thousands of different forces of attraction (presumably as many as there are pairs of genes)." Accordingly, each locus would produce a characteristic pairing force different from that of all other loci.

V. The Mechanism of Crossing Over

Before considering modern concepts of the process of recombination, let us first review earlier hypotheses which until recent years were in vogue. According to Belling's (1931) hypothesis of the mechanism of crossing over, pairing at zygonema takes place between undivided chromosomes which become relationally coiled. Duplication occurs first for the chromomeres and later for the threads or fibers that connect adjacent chromomeres. The nascent threads unite the newly formed adjacent chromomeres that lie closest together. Since at each half-twist or overlap of the coiled homologs the distance between adjacent non-sister chromomeres is less than that between sister chromomeres, the connecting threads would unite non-sister chromomeres and thus produce two crossover chromatids. The parental strands act as templates in forming partial replicas (chromomeres) which are later coupled to form new chromatids. If the partial replicas formed by one homolog are linked together, a noncrossover chromatid identical to the parent strand is produced. Crossover chromatids arise when partial replicas originating from different templates are joined together. If the production of crossovers were restricted to the newly formed chromatids, all the double crossovers would be of the two-strand type and, irrespective of the number of points of crossing over, the number of crossover chromosomes could not exceed 50%. Genetic data, however, show that three- and four-strand doubles occur with an apparent random frequency (no chromatid interference) and that the number of crossover chromosomes often exceeds 50% in multiple-point linkage experiments. Faced with these inescapable facts, Belling (1933) modified his hypothesis to conform to the requirements of genetic data by assuming that no distinction existed between parental and new chromomeres; the interconnecting threads could link parental with newly formed chromomeres. In effect, this is sister-strand crossing over. Schwartz's (1953, 1954) reports of sister-strand crossing over appear to strengthen Belling's modified hypothesis although the course of events need not be as Belling postulated. However, the concept of the leptotene chromosome as a string of chromomeres with interconnecting fibrils needs to be revised. Ris (1945), Oehlkers and Eberle (1957), and others have shown that chromomeres are regions where the chromonemata are tightly coiled. The distinction between chromomeres and interchromomeric threads is more apparent than real.

The doubling of DNA and of basic proteins at leptonema or earlier, the production of chromatid breaks following X-irradiation of nuclei at premeiotic interphase, and the longitudinal split observed at leptonema all suggest that reproduction of the chromosomes has occurred before zygonema. If established beyond peradventure, they would appear to justify Taylor's (1957) statement that Belling's hypothesis is no longer tenable. However, Schultz and Redfield (1951) question if the doubling of DNA before pairing is in conflict with Belling's scheme. According to Belling, chromosome reproduction consists of two steps: first, the duplication of chromomeres and second, the formation of the connecting threads. They argue that the doubling of DNA could represent only chromomere duplication and that thread formation could occur later, as Belling reported. DNA doubling and chromosomal replication, in their opinion, cannot be equated. Furthermore, the belief that the division state of a chromosome can be accurately determined by the production of chromatid versus chromosome breaks following X-irradiation has been challenged. Swanson (1957) writes "radiations are not sufficiently delicate to permit the determination of the multiplicity of chromosome structure. . . . The question of when the chromosome is longitudinally duplicated cannot, therefore, be answered through radiation experiments with any degree of certainty."

It has been suggested that cytological observations by a number of competent investigators of the longitudinal doubleness of leptotene chromosomes should be reconsidered in the light of recent reports that the chromosomes may always be multistranded. The apparent doubleness could reflect a regrouping of the strands. Despite criticisms of the validity of the observations indicating that chromosomal reduplication has occurred before pachynema, the evidence is substantial enough to cast grave doubt on Belling's assumption that crossing over takes place at this stage.

Occupying an integral place in Darlington's (1937) precocity theory of meiosis is his conception of the mechanism of crossing over. The following sequence of events is postulated. The first meiotic prophase begins before the chromosomes have reduplicated; it is precocious. Homologous chromosomes, because they are single, are attracted by one another and pairing results. Each chromosome possesses an internal molecular coiling arising from an asymmetrical molecular pattern (long-chain molecules of nucleoprotein). The paired, but undivided, chromosomes coil relationally around one another so that the torsion of their internal coiling is in equilibrium with the opposite torsion of their relational coiling (i.e., the direction of the relational coiling is opposite to that of the internal coiling). Division into chromatids now takes place which upsets this equilibrium and subjects the chromatids to torsion. A break in one chromatid is followed by a break in a second (non-sister) chromatid at exactly the same point. The broken ends move apart and rotate so fusion can occur, giving rise to crossover chromatids. Darlington's torsion hypothesis has been criticized on various grounds (Sax, 1936); an argument against its validity is the evidence that the chromosomes have reduplicated before zygotene pairing.

White's (1942, 1951) "frontier" hypothesis assumes that chiasmata most frequently arise at or near the junction of heterochromatic and euchromatic regions. Splitting of these regions is asynchronous, the euchromatic segments becoming double before the heterochromatic. A repulsion force causes the euchromatic regions to fall apart while the heterochromatic regions are held together. It is postulated that a localized strain develops at the junction of the two kinds of chromatin and that the tension thus produced will lead to breakage followed by crossing over. As Swanson (1957) has indicated, this is a variation of Darlington's torsion hypothesis and is subject to the same criticisms.

Any explanation of the mechanism of crossing over must take into account the following facts derived from genetic studies:

(1) Exactly reciprocal products are usually formed.

(2) At any one exchange only two of the four chromatids are involved. The chromatid, whether multi- or single-stranded, is the functional unit in crossing over. In those fungi with eight-spored asci the two sister spores of each spore pair are identical. Therefore, the four chromatids segregated into four nuclei as a consequence of the two meiotic divisions are genetically pure.

(3) All four chromatids of a tetrad may be recombinant strands if more than one exchange occurs. In those bivalents with two points of exchange, two-, three-, and four-strand doubles are found. Although contrary data have been reported by Lindegren and Lindegren (1942), it is probable that the chromatids involved in one exchange do not influence

in any way those taking part in a second exchange—i.e., there is no chromatid interference. Whether or not the three kinds of doubles occur in random proportions is less important than the fact that all three classes are produced.

(4) High negative interference has been reported in minute segments of *Aspergillus* and *Neurospora*. It may be questioned, however, if this is a universal phenomenon. Indeed, de Serres (1958) found both positive and negative interference in *Neurospora*. Studying recombination within a small segment including the ad_3 locus, he reported positive interference when *ad* alleles of different origin were involved and negative interference when alleles derived from the same strain were crossed. de Serres suggests that the positive interference found in combinations of alleles of dissimilar origin is caused by structural heterozygosity which lowers the frequency of multiple exchanges. Negative interference should be intelligible, but it need not be an essential part of the process of recombination.

In addition to fulfilling the above desiderata an acceptable mechanism should be compatible with cytochemical determinations of the time of DNA and chromosomal duplication. It is generally assumed that recombination cannot be divorced from replication because it is difficult to conceive how mechanical breakage involving fully formed chromatids could give rise to exactly reciprocal crossovers. The evidence strongly suggests that chromosomal duplication occurs before the pairing observed cytologically at zygonema.

The Belling and Darlington hypotheses and all others postulating crossing over at zygonema or later appear to be no longer tenable, but no satisfactory alternative has been offered. Much of the difficulty stems from the fact that we seek to explain recombination between chromosomes when we know little of their structure. To some, the chromosome (or more precisely the chromatid) is multistranded. Others envisage it as possessing a single double helix of pure DNA with accessory material as protein, RNA, etc. It has also been proposed that the chromatid has a single double helix composed of different DNA molecules arranged linearly and connected by links of protein (Schwartz, 1955; Taylor, 1959b; Freese, 1958).

One of the essential features of Belling's hypothesis, a kind of copy-choice in which differential joining occurs following replication, has been incorporated into modern theories (Lederberg, 1955). The best evidence for copy-choice comes from experiments with phage. When bacteria are doubly infected with two strains of phage differing by two linked markers, there is very little correlation in the frequencies of the complementary crossover classes in the progeny from a single bacterium (Hershey, 1958). The mechanism producing recombinants in phage is thought to involve a differential replication along the two parental DNA molecules resulting in a single new crossover strand instead of two complementary products. Copy-choice by differential replication as in phage will not satisfactorily account for the two reciprocal recombinants formed at every point of exchange in classic crossing over. The suggestion has been made that there might be two ways by which recombination takes place in higher forms. It is by a kind of copy-choice for loci situated in the same DNA molecule, and for loci in different DNA molecules it occurs through breakage and reunion of the protein links joining the DNA molecules. The copy-choice mechanism would operate at the time of DNA doubling whereas that involving exchanges at the links might occur later. Tetrads with a 3:1 ratio of allelic markers (gene conversion) and nonreciprocal recombination, which are exceptionally found in *Aspergillus, Neurospora,* and yeast, could come by the asynchronous replication of the templates, with one of them forming an extra copy of a certain segment and both copies becoming incorporated into the two newly formed strands. Westergaard (1960) subscribes to the belief that nonreciprocal recombination arises from a mechanism different from that responsible for reciprocal recombination. The exceptional tetrads mentioned above are held to come from the infrequent functioning of a relic mechanism which has been largely discarded in higher forms. However, Pritchard (1960) and Pontecorvo (1958) maintain that the copy-choice mechanism accounts satisfactorily for both intra- and intercistron recombination.

A promising explanation of crossing over assumes that recombination takes place before zygotene pairing at the time of DNA replication. Pontecorvo and Pritchard, influenced by the discovery of localized negative interference and by the finding that DNA duplication occurs before zygonema, suggest that contact between homologous chromosomes, which is required on any hypothesis, occurs in interphase or in very early meiotic prophase at the time of DNA replication. Following this homologous contact, called effective pairing, recombination occurs by copy-choice—i.e., the newly formed strands may switch from one template to another. The extent of the regions undergoing effective pairing is believed to be small (estimated by Pritchard to be less than one map unit in length) and the number per chromosome low. If it is assumed that one exchange does not affect the probability of a second exchange, then the frequency of double exchanges in a specific, effectively paired segment would be the product of the frequency of each of the two events. In the great majority of cells this segment of the chromosome would not be effectively paired. The high negative interference found in minute segments is thought to be due to the large contribution made to the total gametic output by cells where no effective pairing took place. The phenomenon of classic chiasma interference is explicable if effective pairing of one segment reduces the probability of such pairing in an adjacent region.

Attempts have been made to explain recombination at a molecular level. Taylor's *et al.* (1957) studies of chromosomal replication indicate that the chromosome consists of two units, each of which forms a new strand. Upon the completion of the replication process both of the sister chromosomes consist of one old and one new unit—i.e., replication is semiconservative in mitosis. However, nothing is known of the mode of replication of the chromosomes at meiosis and it may be conservative rather than semiconservative. It is tempting to surmise that the two units of a chromosome correspond to the two chains of a double helix and that these separate at the time of replication and, acting as templates, form complementary strands as in DNA replication on the Watson-Crick model. It is an attractive hypothesis which affords certain predictions.

If the DNA of a chromosome is in a single double helix, if replication is semiconservative at meiosis as it is at mitosis, and if recombination takes place by a copy-choice mechanism between the newly formed polynucleotide chains of two paired homologous templates, chromatids will be formed with hybrid molecules. At the first postmeiotic division there will be segregation of the dissimilar subunits and sister nuclei of differing genetic constitution will result. However, spore pairs with dissimilar members have not been found in tetrad analysis of *Neurospora* and *Aspergillus*.

According to Pritchard (1960), members of spore pairs will be similar if it is further assumed that an exchange involving the newly formed strands is accompanied by an exchange between the two template strands. This could occur either by breakage and reunion within the DNA molecule or more likely by dissolution of the bonds between the DNA molecules and the protein links, followed by new attachments. Such a mechanism resembles the modified Belling hypothesis although the time at which the postulated events occur need not be at pachynema as Belling believed. A conservative mode of replication at meiosis will give rise to identical spores within a pair, but breakage and reunion of the parental templates are necessary to account for three- and four-strand double crossovers. Patently, at the present time our knowledge of chromosome structure and of the method of replication at meiosis is too limited to permit more than speculation concerning the nature of the recombination process at the molecular level in higher forms.

VI. The Relationship of Chiasmata to Crossing Over and Metaphase Pairing

Homologous chromosomes, which are intimately paired at pachynema, repel each other at diplonema and tend to fall apart. According to the chiasma hypothesis of metaphase pairing (Darlington, 1929a, b), only the presence of chiasmata prevents desynapsis and the formation of univalents, which would be irregularly assorted at anaphase. Chiasmata are therefore held to be necessary for orderly segregation at meiosis. Although chiasma formation is in many forms a sufficient condition for postdiplotene association, it is not always essential. Even in *Drosophila* females, where crossing over normally occurs and chiasmata might be supposed to be essential for orderly disjunction, Cooper (1945) found that the almost complete suppression of crossing over did not result in irregular assortment. In a number of insects (e.g., the mantid *Callimantis*) chiasmata are not formed between the two homologs yet they remain as pairs until anaphase I. The nature of the force or forces responsible for this specific attraction remains unknown although it has been conjectured that it involves an affinity between the end chromomeres (telomeres).

The relationship of chiasmata to genetic crossing over was a controversial issue in the 1930's, but today it is widely held that in most organisms a chiasma represents a genetic crossover. On the partial chiasma-type theory (Janssen, 1909, 1924; Darlington, 1932) each chiasma observed at diplonema has arisen from an antecedent crossover involving two non-sister chromatids. These could arise at or near pachynema as required by the Belling and Darlington theories of crossing over or at the time of effective pairing during interphase or in early prophase before zygonema, as suggested by Pritchard. Before any movement (terminalization) of the chiasmata toward the distal ends takes place, the two-by-two opening out to produce the loops between successive chiasmata is invariably, so it is argued, in the reductional plane. Any reduction in the number of chiasmata from diplonema to metaphase I is due to terminalization.

The classic hypothesis (McClung, 1927b; Sax, 1932) related the formation of chiasmata to a two-by-two opening out in alternate planes— i.e., on one side of a chiasma there is a reductional separation and on the other side an equational separation of the four chromatids. Genetic crossing over resulted when some chiasmata broke and new unions occurred to produce crossover chromatids. Chiasma formation thus preceded crossing over and was not a consequence of it; the converse is true on the partial chiasmatype theory. Reduction in the number of chiasmata during the meiotic prophase results from the dissolution of chiasmata by the occurrence of crossing over. It is the decrease in chiasma number which measures the amount of recombination. On the classic hypothesis there is no one-to-one relationship between chiasma number and the total amount of genetic recombination.

The neoclassic hypothesis (Matsuura, 1937, 1950; Haga, 1944, 1953), a variant of the two-plane or classic hypothesis (Sax, 1932), also assumes that chiasmata come from an alternate reductional and equational separation of the four chromatids. However, a decrease in chiasma number during meiotic prophase was believed not to occur. On the neoclassic hypothesis crossing over does not take place until anaphase I when the two relationally twisted chromatids of each arm are transformed into two parallelly coiled strands. Where non-sister chromatids were associated because of an earlier equational separation, a genetic crossover would arise at every half-twist of the relationally coiled chromatids. More crossovers would be produced than are realized in genetic experiments. Furthermore, it is known that crossing over takes place during or before meiotic prophase, and the kinds of diplotene configurations expected on the neoclassic hypothesis in inversion heterozygotes have not been found (Brown and Zohary, 1955).

Critical evidence for the partial chiasmatype theory comes from the work of Brown and Zohary (1955) on two heteromorphic pairs and a paracentric inversion in *Lilium*. In a plant heterozygous for a terminal deficiency including two-thirds of the short arm of chromosome A, the normal and deficient short arms had a single chiasma in 70% of the PMC at metaphase I. An equational separation of the short arm was found in 71% of the anaphase I cells—i.e., each of the two disjoining dyads had one chromatid with a normal short arm and one with a deficient short arm. A similar study was made with a second terminal deficiency involving about two-thirds of the long arm of chromosome I. Single chiasmata were found in the long arm in 90% of the PMC and an equational separation in 89% of the cells at anaphase I. The correspondence between chiasma frequency and equational separation at anaphase I is precisely that expected on the partial chiasmatype theory.

Further support for this theory is found in their studies on chiasma frequencies at diakinesis and anaphase I configurations in a plant heterozygous for a paracentric inversion. The regular occurrence at diakinesis of a chiasma in the proximal segment between centromere and inversion led to the expectation of a 1:1 ratio of dicentric bridges and loop chromatids at anaphase I. This expectation was closely approximated. Moreover, the open reversed chiasmata and the asymmetric configurations observed at diplonema and diakinesis are explicable only on the partial chiasmatype theory unless some rather improbable assumptions are made. The configurations expected on the neo-two-plane (classic) theory of Matsuura (1950) were never observed.

Every genetic crossover gives rise to a chiasma observable at diplonema on the partial chiasmatype theory. It follows that a 2:1 relationship between chiasma frequency and map distance should exist in a specific chromosome segment which can be recognized cytologically and is marked in genetic experiments. (The expected ratio of 2:1 rather than 1:1 stems from the fact that at a point of genetic exchange only two of the four chromatids are crossover strands.) If it were possible to determine chiasma frequency in a particular segment of the chromosome for which the crossover distance was known from genetic studies and if the frequency of chiasmata proved to be double the recombination percentage, such a parallel study would constitute unequivocal evidence for the partial chiasmatype theory. Just such an experiment was made in maize by Beadle (1932). Working with a heterozygous translocation involving chromosomes 8 and 9, he determined the frequency of late prophase configurations in which a chiasma apparently was present in an interstitial region for which estimates of the map distance were available. The interstitial segment lying in the long arm of chromosome 9 between the centromere and the translocation point was associated, by presumptive chiasmata, in 20% of the pollen mother cells. Burnham (1930 and unpublished) had found 12% recombination for this region. Since 10% of recombination would be expected if every chiasma were a point of genetic crossing over, the correspondence between observed and expected percentages was very good, and this experiment has been held to demonstrate beyond question the validity of the partial chiasmatype theory. Unfortunately, no recombination value for the interstitial region was obtained in those plants in which the chiasma frequency was cytologically determined. The great variability in crossover values found in different plants and in different strains argues against full acceptance of this correlation between chiasmata and crossing over. Moreover, a 2:1 relationship between chiasmata and map distance in interstitial segments would occur only if alternate and adjacent-1 segregations of the members of the ring of four are equally likely to occur. Burnham (1950) demonstrated that adjacent-2 segregations do not occur with interstitial crossovers, but there is no published evidence of the randomness of alternate and adjacent-1 segregations. If only alternate segregation took place the two crossover chromatids would not be recovered since they are included in inviable spores; adjacent-1 segregation places only crossover chromatids in the viable spores. It is uncertain, however, how serious these reservations are and even though this work does not constitute the "experimentum crucis," it provides support for the partial chiasmatype theory.

Additional evidence supporting the chiasmatype theory is found in the double interlocking of two bivalents (Mather, 1933; Beal, 1936; Upcott, 1936; Smith and Boothroyd, 1942), in meiotic configurations of trivalents and quadrivalents with intercalary chiasmata (Darlington, 1930), in the "figures-of-eight" resulting from chiasmata in interstitial segments of translocation heterozygotes (Sansome, 1933), in the relationship between chiasma frequency and equational separation in heteromorphic homologs (Huskins and Spier, 1934; Koller, 1938), and in associations of fragment chromosomes with normal homologs (Mather, 1935). The similar effects of environmental changes on chiasma frequency and recombination values found by Ernst (1938) and Oehlkers (1940) also point to the correctness of the chiasmatype hypothesis.

That chiasmata are points of genetic crossing over is a conclusion based upon the cumulative evidence from diverse studies; the wide applicability of the chiasmatype theory cannot be doubted, but it is true that in some forms chiasmata may have nothing to do with crossing over. Such is the situation in *Drosophila*, where Kaufmann (1934) and Cooper (1949) found the frequent occurrence of chiasmata in the somatically paired chromosomes of oögonial and spermatogonial cells and, more significantly (Cooper, 1949), in the primary spermatocytes where genetic crossing over does not occur. Cooper's observations constitute the strongest evidence against the partial chiasmatype theory of chiasma formation, but it should be remembered that, unlike most forms, the homologous chromosomes of *Drosophila* are closely associated in somatic cells. In somatic pairing the longitudinally split chromosomes pair intimately along their lengths, then open out and separate (Kaufmann, 1934). It may well be that this somatic pairing leads to the formation of chiasma-like configurations which are unrelated to crossing over. The chiasmatype theory apparently does not hold for *Drosophila*, but its general validity is well established. Sturtevant's (1951) dictum that it is no longer permissible to equate a cytologically observed chiasma with a genetic crossover should be restricted for the present, at least, to *Drosophila*. It ignores a number of studies, such as Brown and Zohary's work with heteromorphic bivalents, that show a one-to-one relationship between chiasmata and genetic crossovers. However, one can still agree with Kaufmann that, in the absence of parallel genetic evidence, caution should be exercised before concluding that the presence of chiasmata is proof that crossing over has occurred.

Steinitz-Sears and Sears (1953) studied chiasmata and crossing over in a bivalent composed of two dicentric chromosomes. Chiasmata between the two centric regions occurred in 28% of the PMC at metaphase I, but only 9% of the cells at anaphase I had the double dicentric bridges expected from a genetic exchange between the two centric regions—a result clearly not in accord with the chiasmatype theory. However, one of the two centromeres which each chromosome possessed was defective and the other was normal in its mitotic activity. Bridge formation at anaphase I depends upon the singleness of the defective centric region which effectively prevents terminalization of the intercalary chiasmata. Since the centric region of a meiotic chromosome is probably structurally double, as Lima-de-Faria (1949) and others maintain, the noncorrespondence between chiasma and bridge frequency may be simply due to the equational separation of the defective centric region at anaphase I. This would permit chiasma terminalization and no bridges would be produced. Steinitz-Sears and Sears recognize that the discrepancy observed in their experiments cannot be considered as critical evidence against the chiasmatype theory since other explanations are possible.

VII. Reductional versus Equational Disjunction

Considerable confusion exists over the use and meaning of the terms reductional division, equational division, equational segregation, reductional segregation, prereduction, and postreduction. Much of the difficulty stems from the fact that these terms do not always have the same connotation to cytologists and to geneticists. Perhaps the easiest way to indicate what these terms signify is by the following illustration. Let us consider a single pair of chromosomes with localized centromeres. One of the two homologs carries the recessive a and b alleles while the other has the dominant A and B alleles. The linear order is centromere-A-B. One chiasma is formed between the A and B loci. This represents a genetic crossover between two non-sister chromatids. At metaphase I this bivalent is co-oriented on the spindle with the centromere of one homolog lying above the equatorial plate and the other below. The two functionally single centromeres of the bivalent pass to opposite poles at anaphase. One dyad consists of the A B and the A b chromatids; the other has the a b and a B chromatids. The A locus would undergo a reductional segregation at anaphase I since two A-bearing chromatids go to one pole and two a-bearing chromatids to the opposite pole. Each of the two disjoining dyads possesses one B and one b allele, so this locus is equationally segregated. The second meiotic anaphase will be equational for the A locus and reductional for the B locus. Prereduction is synonymous with reductional segregation at anaphase I and post-reduction with equational segregation at anaphase I.

The term reductional division has commonly been taken to mean the division where the number of chromosomes is halved. In forms with localized centromeres where the two chromatids of each anaphase I dyad are associated by a common centric region, the first meiotic division is called the reductional division since the number of independent chromosomal units at each pole is half the somatic number. However, in forms with nonlocalized centromeres where the chromatids are wholly autonomous and independent structures, two completely separated chromatids move to each pole at anaphase I. Inasmuch as the chromatid of anaphase is considered to be a chromosome, each pole at telophase I has an unreduced number of chromosomes. It is true that a reassociation or secondary pairing occurs during interphase so that the two homologous chromatids are "paired" at metaphase II, but the actual reduction in chromosome number appears to take place at the second meiotic division in organisms with nonlocalized centromeres.

Hughes-Schrader (1955) states that from a cytological point of view the difference between a reductional and an equational separation depends upon the orientation on the spindle of the two chromosomes comprising the bivalent. If the two chromosomes, terminally attached at one end, orient independently (auto-orientation) at metaphase I then anaphase separation is said to be equational, while co-orientation leads to a reductional separation. The maternal or paternal origin of the two chromatids, or their parts, passing to each pole is ignored since the criterion is solely cytological. However, if the terminal association of the two homologs is due to a chiasma, and this is equivalent to a genetic crossover, it follows that part of each homolog will undergo a reductional and part an equational segregation at anaphase I.

With the possible exception of the Odonata (Oksala, 1952) and *Sphagnum* (Sorsa, 1956), forms with localized centromeres have their bivalent chromosomes co-oriented at metaphase I. There is some uncertainty in the Odonata as to the type of centromere present but in *Sphagnum*, according to Sorsa, the chromosomes have localized centromeres. At anaphase I the bivalents first co-orient in the usual manner but later become auto-oriented owing to a precocious centromere division, which gives a tetrad composed of four independent chromatids rather than the customary one of two dyads, each with a functionally undivided centromere. The precocious centromere division in *Sphagnum* is accompanied by, and perhaps reflects, a change in the spindle, which becomes quadripolar. The time of effective centromere division is thus held to determine whether anaphase I is reductional or equational or, to put it otherwise, whether the chromosomes at metaphase I are co-oriented or auto-oriented. In many forms with nonlocalized centromeres the first meiotic division is believed to be equational and the second reductional, but this is a cytological distinction that ignores the genic constitution of the chromatids going to the same pole. The co-orientation needed for reduction comes from the pairing of the two homologous chromatids at telophase I or interphase.

According to Östergren (1951) a difference in coiling of the localized centric regions in somatic and meiotic chromosomes is responsible for auto-orientation of the former and co-orientation of the latter. A somatic chromosome at metaphase consists of two chromatids, each with a kinetic spherule in the centric region. Although the centric region may be structurally double at metaphase, it is believed that the two kinetic faces (spindle spherules) are united either by an undivided portion of the centromere or are bound together in some way. It is noteworthy that the centric region of a somatic chromosome usually appears as a constriction dividing the chromosome into two arms, each with closely coiled chromonemata. Östergren has interpreted this to mean that the coiling found in the arms does not extend into the centric region. He suggests that the relatively uncoiled condition of the centric region permits the two kinetic faces to be directed toward opposite poles of the spindle. An attraction or pulling force of some kind acts between the two kinetic spherules, placed on opposite sides of the chromosome, and the spindle poles to bring the chromosome, or more precisely its centric region, to a position of equilibrium at metaphase midway between the two poles—i.e., the two centric faces become oriented axially on the spindle and are directed toward opposite poles. This is known as auto-orientation (Darlington, 1937).

In contrast to the uncoiled nature of the centromere of a somatic chromosome is that reported by Östergren for meiotic chromosomes. The lack of a centric constriction in chromosomes at first metaphase is interpreted by Östergren to mean that the centric region is spiralized in the same way as the rest of the chromonemata. It is argued that spiralization would bring the two centric regions of each homolog close together in the appressed coils of the two chromatids. Spatially restricted to one side of the chromosome, they would not be able to assume positions on opposite sides as they do in mitotic chromosomes and would jointly face one of the two poles. A similar condition would exist in the homologous chromosome of the bivalent. In effect, the two centric regions of each chromosome would be functionally single even though structurally double as observed by Lima-de-Faria (1953). Since the two centromeres of a bivalent are co-oriented on the spindle at metaphase I with the centromere of one homolog above the equatorial plate and that of the other below, there is apparently some interaction between centromere and pole or possibly a mutual repulsion between homologous centromeres of bivalents that leads to their orientation toward opposite poles rather than both facing the same pole.

Co-orientation of homologous centromeres unquestionably leads to their reductional separation at anaphase I. It is not clear, however, whether this is brought about because the centric region, or the proximal chromatin (Lima-de Faria), of each chromosome is undivided at this time and remains so until anaphase II, as many believe is true, or because the two centromeres of each homolog act as a unit, possibly by the spiralization mechanism of Östergren.

VIII. Meiotic Behavior in Forms with Nonlocalized Centromeres

Battaglia (cf. Battaglia and Boyes, 1955) believes there are three fundamental types of meiosis, which he calls eumeiosis, pseudomeiosis, and parameiosis. In eumeiosis all chromosomes are paired and behave similarly; either co-orientation (prereduction) or auto-orientation (post-reduction) may occur at metaphase I. Pseudomeiosis is characterized by the formation of univalents because of asynapsis or, if pairing occurred, because of the complete dissolution of all chiasmata. The univalents divide equationally at anaphase I. According to Battaglia, the univalents will be randomly (hence irregularly) segregated at the second meiotic division if chromosome reduplication does not take place during interphase, whereas the second division will be mitotic if reduplication has occurred. All intermediate conditions between eumeiosis and pseudomeiosis are called parameiosis. The sole criterion of classification is the degree of pairing between homologous chromosomes; no distinction is made on the basis of orientation on the spindle.

Although Battaglia's classification has some merit, it is felt that the differences in chromosome behavior in meiosis found between forms with co-orientation and those with auto-orientation are so striking that they should be regarded as having different meiotic systems. Furthermore, Battaglia's classification has no provision for those forms where univalents always occur at metaphase I yet a regular disjunction takes place at the second division even though the chromosomes have not reduplicated during interphase. It is undoubtedly significant that with one or two possible exceptions, which are discussed elsewhere, all forms with localized centromeres have co-oriented bivalents at metaphase I and auto-oriented dyads at metaphase II. On the other hand organisms with nonlocalized centromeres have in many cases, although not in all, auto-orientation at metaphase I and co-orientation at metaphase II—i.e., the meiotic sequence is inverted.

Presumably all Hemiptera have nonlocalized or diffuse centromeres, but the chromosomes of the suborder Heteroptera, according to White (1954, p. 301), "are rather ill-adapted for detailed analysis of their structure, and the status of centromeres in this group is far from certain." In the case of the Homoptera the existence of diffuse centromeres has been established beyond peradventure (Hughes-Schrader and Ris, 1941). The plant *Luzula*, a member of the Juncaceae, is also known to possess chromosomes with nonlocalized centromeres (Malheiros *et al.*, 1947).

Since auto-orientation at first metaphase is almost invariably restricted to those organisms with diffuse centromeres, it is logical to assume, as Castro (1950) has done, that there is an interdependence between the two phenomena. The thoroughly investigated cases in the sternorrhynchous Homoptera, including the coccids and the aphids, show auto-orientation at first metaphase (Hughes-Schrader, 1948). Presence of diffuse centromeres does not always lead to an inverted meiotic sequence, however. The chromosomes of the auchenorrhynchous Homoptera, which possess diffuse centromeres, are reported to co-orient at first metaphase, and a similar orientation is believed to occur for the autosomal pairs of most heteropteran species although the X is auto-oriented in spermatogenesis (cf. Helenius, 1952). On the other hand, the clear demonstration by Malheiros and co-workers (1947) that *Luzula purpurea* has both nonlocalized centromeres and auto-orientation of the bivalents at first metaphase greatly strengthens the concept that auto-orientation is dependent upon nonlocalized centromeres. Brown (1954) found no evidence that the bivalents of *Luzula campestris* divided equationally at metaphase I, but Hughes-Schrader (1955) inclines to the opinion that this is a case of concealed inversion of the meiotic sequence since in organisms with nonlocalized centromeres it is difficult to ascertain the kind of orientation when the chromosomes are so short and compact that their long axis cannot be recognized. If such an explanation holds for *Luzula campestris*, it may apply to other forms with nonlocalized centromeres where the bivalents were thought to be co-oriented.

The Schraders' intensive studies and those of Ris on the cytology of the Homoptera have revealed that chromosome behavior in these insects is basically unlike that in most forms and that they possess a different kind of chromosome organization. In the coccids and the aphids, the most thoroughly analyzed groups, occur such anomalies as the linear aggregation of all the chromosomes on the spindle, chromatid autonomy in spindle formation and disjunction, asynapsis, and modification of bivalent structure and orientation. The exceptional mitotic and meiotic behavior of the coccids and aphids, while not intelligible on the basis of concepts of chromosome behavior established from more orthodox forms, can be attributed directly or indirectly to their possessing chromosomes with diffuse or nonlocalized rather than localized centromeres (Hughes-Schrader, 1948). A chromosome with a diffuse centromere has no localized organelle which elaborates chromosomal fibers, but the entire body of the chromosome forms a sheet of chromosomal fibers on the poleward surface; these converge to the pole. Sister chromatids are not bound at any point by centric connections and a complete spatial separation is possible, which makes the chromatid, or in some coccids the half chromatid, an autonomous entity. A metaphase chromosome in which the half chromatids are resolvable consists of four parallel, coiled chromonemata separated throughout their length. At metaphase the body of the chromosome lies on the spindle plate at right angles to the polar axis with the split between its chromatids corresponding to the equatorial plate. The chromosomal fibers formed by the entire poleward surface of each chromatid pull the chromatids poleward with the long axis of the chromatids at right angles to that of the spindle—i.e., they move broad-side to the poles and do not have at anaphase the V- or J-shaped appearance of chromosomes with localized centromeres.

Although striking variations exist in meiosis of different coccid groups, there is fortunately in *Puto* a primitive or basic type that may be the archetype of the more complex systems. In both sexes of *Puto* bivalents are formed, but the chiasmata are completely terminalized by metaphase I and a bivalent consists of two chromosomes in tandem association. Each member of a pair is auto-oriented on the spindle as in a somatic metaphase. Anaphase I is equational for all noncrossover regions. The two chromatids going to each pole are independent bodies with no centromeric connections. During interphase the two homologous chromatids at each pole undergo a secondary pairing and these dyads become co-oriented on the metaphase II spindle. This secondary pairing in interphase is necessary for orderly segregation at anaphase II. The second division is reductional for noncrossover regions (Fig. 22). It will be recalled that in bivalents with localized centromeres anaphase I is reductional for noncrossover regions and anaphase II is equational for noncrossover segments; the inverse sequence is found in the coccids.

Spermatogenesis in the coccids is characterized by diversity. According to the excellent summary by Hughes-Schrader (1948), male meiosis falls into five categories. One is the primitive type previously described for *Puto*. A second type is that exemplified by *Matsucoccus*, which has a primitive meiosis except for the behavior of the compound X chromosome. In spermatogenesis the six unpaired X chromosomes form a ring or plate around the bivalent autosomes at metaphase I. The compound X chromosomes all move to one pole in anaphase I and the second division is equational for the X's. The behavior of the autosomes is the same as in *Puto*. A third type of male meiosis occurs in the iceryine coccids, which have haploid males. Of interest here is the intranuclear origin of the spindle. Only one meiotic division takes place, which is equational.

Considerably more complexity is found in male meiosis of the Llaveiini which is designated the Llaveiini type. In *Llaveia bouvari* the following unique specializations are found, according to Hughes-Schrader. The prophase nucleus becomes lobed or partitioned with each bivalent (or univalent, if there is asynapsis) becoming isolated in a separate vesicle. The spindle of metaphase I is compounded by the parallel alignment of the individual spindles formed by each chromosomal unit. In approximately 5 % of the meiocytes there is asynapsis of the shorter pair of autosomes. The two unpaired chromosomes, however, divide equationally in the first division; the two homologous chromatids at each pole become paired during interphase and then separate to opposite poles at anaphase II. Asynapsis in forms with localized centromeres almost invariably leads to irregular distribution, but it is compatible with orderly segregation in the coccids since, paired or unpaired, each chromosome divides equationally in the first division and the secondary pairing in interphase ensures a regular disjunction in anaphase II.

Fɪɢ. 22. Schematic diagrams comparing the meiotic behavior of a bivalent having localized centromeres with one having nonlocalized centromeres as in the coccid *Puto* and in *Luzula purpurea*. The chiasma in the localized type has become terminalized by metaphase I; this by no means occurs in all forms with localized centromeres but is the rule in forms with nonlocalized centromeres. Note that there is no difference between the basic coccid type and the *Luzula* type, but both differ markedly in behavior from the localized type. Sketch prepared by Tristão de Mello-Sampayo.

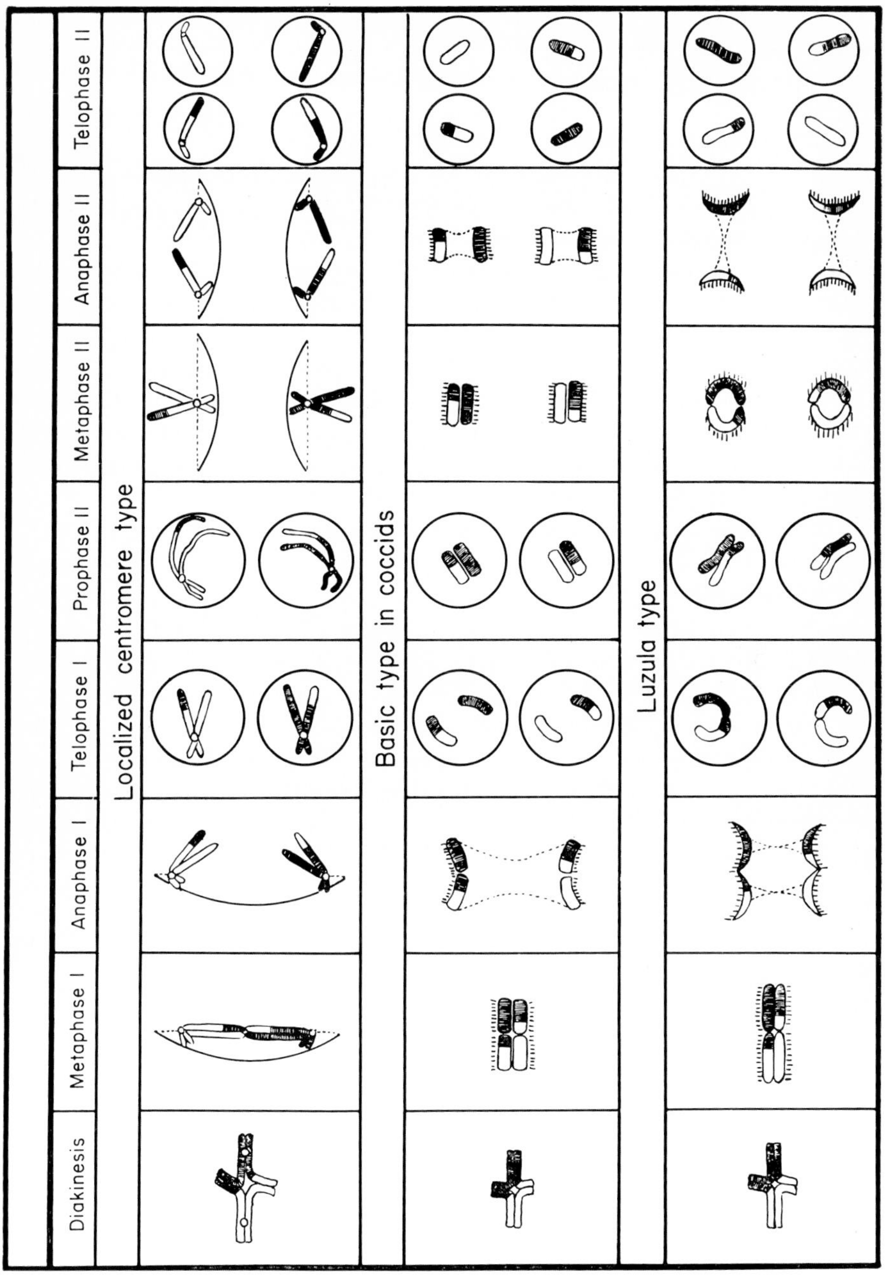
Diakinesis
Metaphase I
Anaphase I
Telophase I
Prophase II
Metaphase II
Anaphase II
Telophase II
Localized centromere type
Basic type in coccids
Luzula type

In *Llaveiella taenechina,* another llaveiine, a striking feature is the clear separation of each chromosome into its constituent half chromatids. Each member of a bivalent, with its terminal association of homologous chromosomes, is four-parted. In anaphase I the pairs of half chromatids may disjoin independently—i.e., the unit of anaphase disjunction is a half chromatid instead of a whole chromatid. In some meiocytes the two chromatids of the single X chromosome lie in separate vesicles. Each chromatid divides equationally at anaphase I, so two half chromatids are at each pole. These pair during interphase and as a reconstituted chromatid pass together to one pole at anaphase II. The chromatid is the unit of segregation even though it may be dissociated temporarily into half chromatids.

The meiotic conditions found by Schrader (1931) in *Protortonia primitiva* are the most specialized of the llaveiini. The *Protortonia* males have two pairs of autosomes and a single X chromosome. During the transition from gonial telophase to meiotic prophase all five chromosomes become dissociated into chromatids. The prophase nucleus has four vesicles: the largest contains four chromatids, probably from a pair of autosomes; two medium-sized vesicles have two chromatids each, representing one member of an autosomal pair; and the smaller vesicle contains two X chromatids. The chromatids within each vesicle reassociate to form chains of two or four (depending on the number of chromatids in the vesicle), which become aligned parallel to the long axis of the vesicle. Chromosomal fibers develop from the poleward face of each chromatid as the vesicle walls disappear. Anaphase disjunction is often asynchronous for the members of different chains and occurs without prior orientation on the spindle plate. The first division is equational and five chromatids go to each pole. Reassociation (secondary pairing) at interphase gives rise to chains of two and three chromatids which first become parallelly oriented and then compressed together so that by second metaphase a linear chain of five chromatids is formed which lies lengthwise from one end of the cell to the other. Two chromatids pass to one pole and three to the other in anaphase II. The ordering of the five chromatids in the linear aggregate must be such that an orderly segregation will occur—i.e., one chromatid from each of the two autosomes is at each pole while the X chromatid is randomly distributed to either pole. Although asynapsis is complete in *Protortonia* the equational nature of the first division and the secondary pairing during interphase result in orderly segregation and reduction.

The lecanoid type of male meiosis in the coccids is characterized by orderly segregation without either synapsis in the first division or secondary pairing during interphase. This is achieved as follows. Males have two haploid sets of chromosomes, which differ in their behavior and coiling cycle. One set remains in a permanently contracted state while the other set is composed of euchromatic chromosomes. Although the heteropycnotic and euchromatic sets approach metaphase I at a different tempo, they are indistinguishable by metaphase and all divide equationally at anaphase I. Each anaphase group has a set of chromatids from both the heteropycnotic and euchromatic chromosomes. In the second division the heteropycnotic set forms a half spindle to which these chromosomes move, thus separating them from the euchromatic set, which forms no spindle and undergoes no division. At telophase II there are four nuclei, two with heteropycnotic chromosomes and two with euchromatic chromosomes, each in the haploid number. Only the nuclei with haploid sets of euchromatic chromosomes give rise to spermatids.

Although oögenesis in the coccids is generally of the primitive type found in spermatogenesis of *Puto*, a few modifications have arisen. Some forms have an obligate diploid parthenogenesis. No pairing of chromosomes occurs in the single meiotic division, which is equational. The diploid egg pronucleus undergoes cleavage without fertilization and only female offspring are produced. In coccids with facultative diploid parthenogenesis, meiosis is of the usual coccid type and haploid egg and polar nuclei are formed. Fusion of the second polar body with the egg pronucleus occurs, and this "fertilized" diploid egg cell begins cleavage to form a female embryo. Sperm are believed to be capable of fertilizing the egg, but this infrequently ocurs as males are rarely found. Another type of parthenogenesis is that where a normal meiosis results in haploid eggs which, if fertilized by sperm, produce diploid females but develop into haploid males if unfertilized. A unique situation is found in the hermaphroditic individuals of *Icerya purchasi* which have a gonad (ovotestis) whose interior portion consists of haploid cells, due to a somatic reduction in number, and is male tissue. One equational division occurs in the spermatocytes to form two spermatids. Oögenesis in the enveloping diploid tissue of the gonad is normal. Self fertilization is the rule but unfertilized eggs can develop into haploid males. The above deviations from normal oögenesis are interesting, but compared with the spectacular happenings in coccid spermatogenesis they are a drab and lack-luster lot.

The report in 1947 by Malheiros and associates that *Luzula purpurea* ($2n = 6$) had nonlocalized centromeres made it evident that this kind of centromere organization was not confined to the Hemiptera. The meiotic comportment of the chromosomes of this plant is in no essential way different from the primitive type of meiosis found in the coccid *Puto*. The early prophase stages are somewhat difficult to study, but chiasmata are apparent at diplonema and diakinesis. These undergo terminalization, and by metaphase I the two chromosomes of each pair are associated only at their ends. The four independent chromatids com-

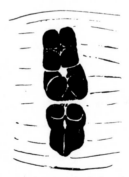

Fig. 23. Metaphase I showing orientation of the three bivalents in two microsporocytes of *Luzula purpurea*. See text for further discussion. From Malheiros *et al.* (1947).

prising each bivalent can be clearly seen. Metaphase I bivalents with one chiasma have the two homologs lying end to end connected by the single chiasma. At metaphase I these rod bivalents lie (Fig. 23) with their long axis at right angles to that of the spindle. A bivalent with two or more chiasmata has no free ends if the chiasmata terminalize in opposite directions. This bivalent would appear as a double ring with each ring comprised of two chromatids. At metaphase I the double ring lies flat on the spindle plate. The two chromatids of the lower ring pass to the nearest pole as do the two chromatids of the upper ring. Each chromatid forms its own sheet of chromosomal fibers. The two homologous chromatids passing to the same pole usually lie close together, but in some meiocytes they are well separated although connected by thin strands of matrical material. It is uncertain whether the two homologous chromatids in anaphase are wholly independent units as they are in coccids, or whether they are comparable to those in the aphid which are terminally connected by a "half chiasma" (Ris, 1942).

Since the bivalents are auto-oriented on the spindle the first division is equational from a cytological point of view. Genetically the situation is more complex. Lacking a localized centric region, which is reductionally separated at anaphase I and can be used as a point of reference, there is no one region that invariably undergoes reductional segregation. Chiasmata are present in prophase, and if chiasmata represent genetic crossing over, anaphase I will be reductional for some regions and equational for others depending upon the number and location of chiasmata and upon the prometaphase rearrangement of the four chromatids.

Since the ends of the chromatids lead in the poleward migration the chromatids characteristically assume the appearance of U's. During telophase the homologous chromatids become associated at both ends to form dyads. This association, which is maintained until anaphase II, is comparable to the secondary pairing in the aphids and coccids and in all cases leads to the same result—namely, co-orientation of the dyads at metaphase II followed by separation of the two chromatids at anaphase. It is noteworthy that the chromosomes of aphids, coccids, and *Luzula* have in common not only nonlocalized centromeres, but a low viscosity of the chromosomal matrix. This is evidenced by the interzonal connections between disjoining anaphase chromosomes observed in the Hemiptera and in *Luzula*, which are believed to represent the fluid matrical material, and by the deformation of the chromosome body during anaphase. Interzonal connections are less pronounced in *L. purpurea* than in other species of *Luzula*. The stickiness of the matrical material also accounts for the temporary adhesions between nonhomologous chromosomes. Castro *et al.* (1949) suggest that the fluid matrix allows the substance responsible for production of chromosomal fibers to leak out and become distributed along the entire length of the chromosome. A somewhat different explanation is that advanced by Brown (1954), who assigns centric activity to the matrix itself. Clearly, however, some intimate relationship exists between nonlocalized centric regions and matrical viscosity; the significance of this correlation is supported by the increased stickiness of chromosomes in forms with localized centromeres which exhibit neocentric activity. The existence of a matrix has been questioned by many cytologists, but its presence in chromosomes with nonlocalized centromeres cannot be gainsaid. In fact, Ris (1957), who found no evidence of matrical material in his studies on organisms with localized centromeres, assigned an important role to the matrix in his analysis of chromosome behavior in the aphid (Ris, 1942).

In his study of meiosis in *L. campestris* ($2n = 12$), Brown (1954) made certain observations that are at variance with those reported for *L. purpurea*. The meiotic stages in *L. campestris* are shown in Figs. 24–37. The early prophase stages of *L. campestris* are more amenable to cytological analysis than those of *L. purpurea*, but the smaller size of the chromosomes makes it more difficult to ascertain the kind of orientation at metaphase. The preleptotene stage consists of three phases. The nucleus of the primary microsporocyte at the beginning of meiosis has the appearance of a typical metabolic nucleus, but this is followed by a chromatic phase marked by a disproportionate enlargement of heterochromatic bodies; the nucleus as a whole stains more deeply (Fig. 24). The chromatic phase is succeeded by a clear phase in which the large heterochromatic bodies decrease in size and cannot be distinguished from the now numerous chromomerelike structures (Fig. 25). The clear phase passes directly into leptonema with its increased nuclear size and greatly extended chromosomes (Fig. 26). Zygonema is difficult to analyze since the chromosomes are clumped together adjacent to the nucleolus. At pachynema the synapsed threads clearly reveal the chromomeric pattern, which permits recognition of the different chromosomes; there is no evidence of structures that could be identified as centric regions (Fig. 27). Contraction of the chromonemata continues as the nucleus proceeds from pachynema to diplonema (Figs. 28 and 29), but the diplotene bivalents have a glazed appearance that obscures the quadripartite nature of the bivalent, and adherence between nonhomologous bivalents is of frequent occurrence. The diakinetic bivalents are similar to those found in organisms with localized centromeres (Fig. 30). The association of most or all of the bivalents into one group at late diakinesis is presumably due to a stickiness of their ends. Chiasmata, which can be clearly seen, are for the most part interstitially located; terminalization is completed during prometaphase. The nucleolus fragments into numerous small bodies during diakinesis, but these disappear by metaphase I.

Up to metaphase I there is nothing exceptional in the behavior of the chromosomes and the brief account given above could well apply to forms with localized centromeres. The first metaphase bivalents clearly show their quadripartite nature, but some are so compact as to appear

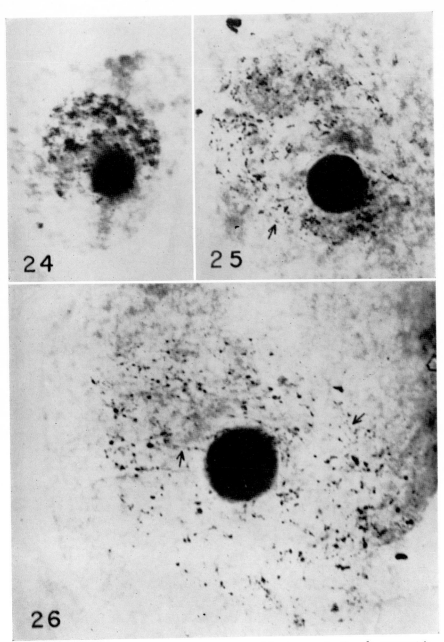

FIGS. 24–26. Phases of preleptotene stage and leptonema in *Luzula campestris*. The arrows in Figs. 25 and 26 indicate achromatic regions. From Brown (1954). FIG. 24. Chromatic phase of preleptotene stage. FIG. 25. Clear phase of preleptotene stage. FIG. 26. Leptonema.

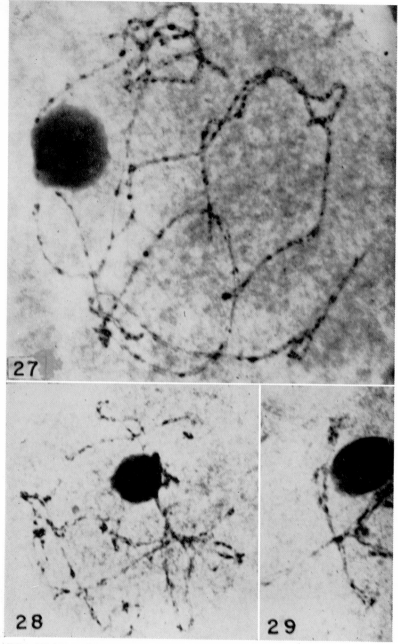

Figs. 27–29. Pachynema (Fig. 27) and diplonema (Figs. 28 and 29) in *Luzula campestris*. From Brown (1954).

as nearly spherical bodies (Fig. 32). Others have a rectangular appearance with a chromatid at each corner of the rectangle. The bivalents are arranged on the spindle at metaphase I with the open face of the rectangular-shaped tetrad at right angles to the spindle plate. The two chromatids located in the upper corners of the rectangle pass to one pole and the two in the lower corners pass to the other pole. The anaphase configurations in *L. campestris* are similar to those in *L. purpurea* except that the interzonal connections are more prominent and are not ruptured as quickly (Figs. 33–37). There is no significant difference in chromosome behavior in the remaining stages of meiosis in the two species. Brown, however, sees no evidence of auto-orientation at metaphase I in *L. campestris* and questions whether the species has an inverted meiotic sequence.

Granting that achiasmate meioses of the kind found in certain Homoptera have an equational first division and a reductional second division, Brown argues that in chiasmate meioses, where the centromere is nonlocalized, the presence of chiasmata rules out the possibility of an equational separation at anaphase I. With a potentially free assortment of the four chromatids at prometaphase in a bivalent with one chiasma only, one of the three possible two-by-two separations of the four chromatids at anaphase I would be equational. If crossing over has occurred, it is meaningless in a genetic sense to say that one division is equational and the other reductional, but the cytological distinction between an equational and reductional separation is real since it is based on the way the chromosomes are oriented on the spindle. Auto-orientation at metaphase I is found in *L. purpurea*, but Brown states that in *L. campestris* the chromosomes are perpendicular to the metaphase plate (co-oriented) at both meiotic divisions; he found no evidence of an inversion of the meiotic sequence.

That auto-orientation occurs in *L. purpurea* is apparent not only from the orientation of normal bivalents, but also from the anaphase I separation of translocation heterozygotes where chromatid rings-of-four passed to each pole (Castro and Noronha-Wagner, 1952; Castro et al., 1949) and from the anaphase separation of heteromorphic bivalents observed by LaCour (1952). Brown suggests that these observations can be simply explained on the assumption of a mutual repulsion of free chromatids. For example, at the time of chromatid rearrangement in a heteromorphic bivalent the two large chromatids would be more influenced by each other than by the smaller chromatids of the homolog and they would therefore be oriented on the spindle as a univalent. The two chromatids of the smaller chromosome would be oriented similarly

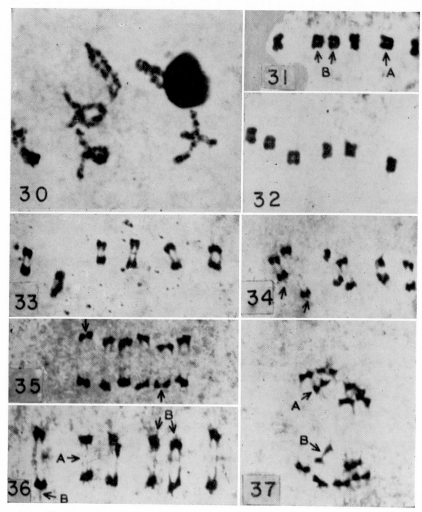

Figs. 30–37. Stages of meiosis in *Luzula campestris*. From Brown (1954).

Fig. 30. Diakinesis showing chiasmata in the six bivalents.

Fig. 31. Late prometaphase. Note the compact, nearly spherical appearance of the bivalents.

Fig. 32. Metaphase I showing quadripartite structure of the bivalents.

Figs. 33–37. Various stages of anaphase I. The arrows in Figs. 34 and 35 indicate matrical material. In Fig. 36, arrow A designates a tripartite interzonal and arrows B point toward polar matrical material. In Fig. 37, arrows A and B indicate matrix.

so the metaphase bivalent would apparently undergo an equational separation at anaphase I. It is difficult to understand on this scheme why half-translocation figures should occur in anaphase I or why tetravalents should give chromatid or half rings-of-four after anaphase I separation (Sampayo and co-workers, 1951). As Hughes-Schrader (1955) emphasizes, the small size of the chromosomes of L. campestris does not facilitate recognition of the long axis of the chromosomes at metaphase I, which is necessary in deciding the mode of orientation. Perhaps a final decision as to the kind of orientation in L. campestris should be kept in abeyance, but in L. purpurea, the aphids, and the coccids, the case for an inversion of the meiotic sequence seems clearly established.

The marked interzonal connections found in the tetraploid species ($2n = 12$) L. campestris and L. nemorosa, which are generally believed to be of matrical origin, are given quite a different interpretation by Noronha-Wagner and Castro (1952). Indeed their interpretation of the course of meiosis is at variance with that reported for other organisms although Piza (1953) maintains that a similar sequence of events is found in the Hemiptera. Each chromosome is believed to be an isochromosome with two identical halves. The metaphase I bivalent consists of two pairs of chromatids which are said to be oriented on the spindle parallel to its longitudinal axis and to each other. The two ends of each of the four chromatids move to opposite poles, producing bridgelike configurations similar to those coming from dicentric chromosomes with localized centromeres. The four chromatids rupture during anaphase at their midpoints, and the broken ends of the four hemichromatids at each pole fuse to form two isochromatids. The metaphase II dyads arise from an end-to-end association of the homologous isochromatids, and their orientation on the spindle is the same as that for the bivalents at metaphase I. In anaphase II the opposite ends of each chromatid pass to different poles. Again there is a rupturing of the stretched chromatids at their midpoints. The two hemichromatids at each telophase II pole undergo fusion of broken ends to reconstitute a single isochromatid. This ingenious and fanciful hypothesis, which was designated "mis-meiosis" by Battaglia (1955), is discredited by the fact that the chromomere patterns in the two halves of each of the pachytene chromosomes do not correspond (i.e., the pattern in one half is different from that in the other half of the same chromosome) and by the lack of pairing between the two halves of one chromosome.

Races of Luzula species in the campestris-multiflora complex have polyploid numbers of chromosomes. The increase in chromosome number is accompanied by no increase in chromatin mass nor by an increase in the total length of the chromosomal complement. This kind of ploidy seems to involve fragmentation (Malheiros and Gardé, 1947); it was designated endonuclear polyploidy by Nordenskiöld (cf. 1956) and agmatoploidy by Malheiros-Gardé and Gardé (1951). Schrader (1947) pointed out that the possession of a nonlocalized centromere could lead to a variation in chromosome number inasmuch as all fragments arising by breakage form chromosomal fibers and have a regular mitotic behavior. That variation in chromosome number due to fragmentation occurs in organisms with nonlocalized centromeres has been established.

Noronha-Wagner and Castro suggest that agmatoploidy (endonuclear polyploidy) arises when the broken ends of the homologous hemichromatids, produced by breakage of the stretched anaphase chromatids, do not fuse but heal, thus resulting in two chromosomal bodies where one existed before. A situation comparable to agmatoploidy in *Luzula* was reported by Schrader and Hughes-Schrader (1956) in the hemipteran genus *Thyanta* where *T. calceata* has double the number of chromosomes in the related diploid species. The chromosomes of *T. calceata* are smaller than those of the diploids, but the amount of DNA per nucleus in "tetraploid" *T. calceata* and in the diploid species is the same. Schrader and Hughes-Schrader reject the idea that doubling of chromosome number came from a transverse fragmentation and prefer to ascribe it to a longitudinal breakage or lengthwise division of the polynemic chromosome into two parts. Each of these, with one-half the usual number of basic strands, became separated and functioned as an independent chromosome with a reduced number of microfibrils. The halving of the degree of polynemy would explain the equivalence of DNA in the "tetraploid" and diploid forms.

The occurrence of the same unique cytological features in the plant *Luzula* and in the hemipteran insects is undoubtedly a consequence of their possessing the same type of centromere organization. The complex behavior of these organisms is of extraordinary interest, and it may be expected that further investigations will greatly enhance our understanding of chromosomal mechanics.

REFERENCES

Alfert, M. (1950). *J. Cellular Comp. Physiol.* **36**, 381-406.
Alfert, M. (1955). "Symposium on Fine Structure of Cells," Leiden, 1954. Interscience, New York.
Ansley, H. R. (1954). *Chromosoma* **6**, 656-695.
Ansley, H. R. (1957). *Chromosoma* **8**, 380-395.
Atwood, S. (1937). *La Cellule* **46**, 391-409.
Battaglia, E. (1955). *Bull. Torrey Botan. Club* **82**, 383-396.

Battaglia, E., and Boyes, J. W. (1955). *Caryologia* **8**, 87-134.

Beadle, G. W. (1932). *Genetics* **17**, 481-501.

Beal, J. M. (1936). *Botan. Gaz.* **97**, 678-680.

Beasley, J. O. (1938). *Botan. Gaz.* **99**, 865-871.

Belling, J. (1931). *Univ. Calif. (Berkeley) Publ. Botany* **16**, 153-170.

Belling, J. (1933). *Genetics* **18**, 388-413.

Bloch, D. P., and Godman, G. C. (1955). *J. Biophys. Biochem. Cytol.* **1**, 17-28.

Boivin, A., Vendrely, R., and Vendrely, C. (1948). *Compt. rend. acad. sci.* **226**, 1061.

Brachet, J. (1957). "Biochemical Cytology." Academic Press, New York.

Brown, S. W. (1954). *Univ. Calif. (Berkeley) Publ. Botany* **27**, 231-278.

Brown, S. W., and Zohary, D. (1955). *Genetics* **40**, 850-873.

Burnham, C. R. (1930). *Proc. Natl. Acad. Sci. U.S.* **16**, 269-277.

Burnham, C. R. (1950). *Genetics* **35**, 446-481.

Callan, H. G., and Montalenti, G. (1947). *J. Genet.* **48**, 119-134.

Carothers, E. E. (1921). *J. Morphol.* **35**, 2.

Castro, D. (1950). *Genet. iberica* **2**, 201-209.

Castro, D., and Noronha-Wagner, M. (1952). *Agronomia lusitana* **14**, 95-99.

Castro, D., Camara, A., and Malheiros, N. (1949). *Proc. Intern. Congr. Genet. 8th Congr., Stockholm* 548-550.

Cleveland, L. R. (1959). *Proc. Natl. Acad. Sci. U.S.* **45**, 747-753.

Cooper, K. W. (1938). *Proc. Natl. Acad. Sci. U.S.* **24**, 452-458.

Cooper, K. W. (1941). *Proc. Natl. Acad. Sci. U.S.* **27**, 109-114.

Cooper, K. W. (1945). *Genetics* **30**, 472-484.

Cooper, K. W. (1948). *J. Exptl. Zool.* **108**, 327-336.

Cooper, K. W. (1949). *J. Morphol.* **84**, 81-122.

Cooper, K. W., Zimmering, S., and Krivshenko, J. (1955). *Proc. Natl. Acad. Sci. U.S.* **41**, 911-914.

Darlington, C. D. (1929a). *J. Genet.* **21**, 17-56.

Darlington, C. D. (1929b). *J. Genet.* **21**, 207-286.

Darlington, C. D. (1930). *Proc. Roy. Soc.* **B107**, 50-59.

Darlington, C. D. (1932). "Recent Advances in Cytology," 1st ed. Blakiston's, Philadelphia, Pennsylvania.

Darlington, C. D. (1935). *Proc. Roy. Soc.* **B118**, 33-96.

Darlington, C. D. (1937). "Recent Advances in Cytology," 2nd ed. Blakiston's, Philadelphia, Pennsylvania.

Darlington, C. D. (1940). *Biol. Revs. Cambridge Phil. Soc.* **15**, 307-322.

Darlington, C. D. (1947). *Symposia Soc. Exptl. Biol.* **1**, 252-269.

Darlington, C. D. (1955). *Nature* **176**, 1139-1144.

Darlington, C. D. (1957). "Conference on Chromosomes," Lecture 7. W. E. J. Tjeenk Willink, Zwolle, The Netherlands.

Delbrück, M. (1941). *Cold Spring Harbor Symposia Quant. Biol.* **9**, 122-126.

de Serres, F. J. (1958). *Cold Spring Harbor Symposia Quant. Biol.* **23**, 111-118.

Dobzhansky, Th. (1941). "Genetics and the Origin of Species," 2nd ed. Columbia Univ. Press, New York.

El Ani, A. S. (1956). *Am. J. Botany* **43**, 769-777.

Ernst, H. (1938). *Z. Botan.* **33**, 241-294.

Ernst, H. (1939). *Z. Botan.* **35**, 161-190.

Fabergé, A. C. (1942). *J. Genet.* **43**, 121-144.

Freese, E. (1958). *Cold Spring Harbor Symposia Quant. Biol.* **23**, 13-18.

Friedrich-Freksa, H. (1940). *Naturwissenschaften* **28**, 376-379.
Geitler, L. (1938). "Chromosomenbau." Borntraeger, Berlin.
Gentscheff, G., and Gustafsson, Å. (1940). *Hereditas* **26**, 209-249.
Goldschmidt, R. B. (1955). "Theoretical Genetics." Univ. Calif. Press, Berkeley and Los Angeles, California.
Gregory, W. C. (1940). *Am. J. Botany* **27**, 687-691.
Gustafsson, Å. (1938). *Hereditas* **25**, 31-32.
Gustafsson, Å. (1939). *Hereditas* **25**, 289-322.
Haga, T. (1944). *J. Fac. Sci. Hokkaido Univ., Ser. V* **5**(3), 121-198.
Haga, T. (1953). *Cytologia (Tokyo)* **18**, 50-66.
Haldane, J. B. S. (1931). *Cytologia (Tokyo)* **3**, 54-65.
Helenius, O. (1952). *Hereditas* **38**, 420-424.
Hershey, A. D. (1958). *Cold Spring Harbor Symposia Quant. Biol.* **23**, 19-46.
Hiraoka, T. (1941). *Cytologia (Tokyo)* **11**, 473-482.
Howard, A., and Pelc, S. R. (1952). *Heredity* **6**, Suppl., 261-274.
Hughes-Schrader, S. (1943). *Biol. Bull.* **85**, 265-300.
Hughes-Schrader, S. (1948). *Advances in Genet.* **2**, 127-203.
Hughes-Schrader, S. (1955). *Chromosoma* **7**, 420-438.
Hughes-Schrader, S., and Ris, H. (1941). *J. Exptl. Zool.* **87**, 429-451.
Huskins, C. L. (1933). *Nature* **132**, 62-63.
Huskins, C. L. (1937). *Cytologia (Tokyo), Fujii Jubilee Vol.*, 1015-1022.
Huskins, C. L., and Spier, J. D. (1934). *Cytologia (Tokyo)* **5**, 269-277.
Janssen, F. A. (1909). *La Cellule* **25**, 387-411.
Janssen, F. A. (1924). *La Cellule* **34**, 135-359.
Jehle, H. (1957). *Proc. Natl. Acad. Sci. U.S.* **43**, 847-855.
Kaufmann, B. P. (1934). *J. Morphol.* **56**, 125-155.
Koller, P. C. (1938). *J. Genet.* **36**, 177-195.
La Cour, L. F. (1952). *Heredity* **6**, Suppl., 77-81.
Lamb, A. B. (1907). *J. Exptl. Zool.* **5**, 27-33.
Leblond, C. P., and Clermont, Y. (1952). *Am. J. Anat.* **90**, 167-215.
Lederberg, J. (1955). *J. Cellular Comp. Physiol.* **45**, Suppl. 2, 75-107.
Levan, A. (1942). *Hereditas* **28**, 177-211.
Lima-de-Faria, A. (1949). *Hereditas* **35**, 77-85.
Lima-de-Faria, A. (1953). *Chromosoma* **6**, 33-44.
Lima-de-Faria, A. (1957). *Proc. Intern. Genet. Symposia, Tokyo and Kyoto, 1956.*
Lin, M. (1955). *Chromosoma* **7**, 340-370.
Lindegren, C. C., and Bridges, C. B. (1938). *Science* **87**, 510-511.
Lindegren, C., and Lindegren, G. (1942). *Genetics* **27**, 1-24.
Linskens, H. F. (1955). *Fortschr. Botan.* **18**, 329-346.
Linskens, H. F. (1956). *Ber. deut. botan. Ges.* **69**, 353-360.
McClintock, B. (1933). *Z. Zellforsch. u. mikrskop. Anat. Abt. B.* **19**, 191-237.
McClintock, B. (1934). *Z. Zellforsch. u. mikrskop. Anat.* **21**, 294-328.
McClintock, B. (1945). *Am. J. Botany* **32**, 671-678.
McClung, C. E. (1927a). *J. Morphol. Physiol.* **43**, 181-265.
McClung, C. E. (1927b). *Quart. Rev. Biol.* **2**, 344-366.
Malheiros, N., and Gardé, A. (1947). *Agronomia lusitana* **9**, 75-79.
Malheiros, N., Castro, D., and Camara, A. (1947). *Agronomia lusitana* **9**, 51-71.
Malheiros-Gardé, N., and Gardé, A. (1951). *Genet. iberica* **3**, 155-176.
Martinovitch, P. N. (1939). *Arch. exptl. Zellforsch. Gewebezücht.* **22**, 74-76.

Mather, K. (1933). *Am. Naturalist* **67**, 476-479.

Mather, K. (1935). *Cytologia* (*Tokyo*) **6**, 354-380.

Matsuura, H. (1937). *Cytologia* (*Tokyo*) **8**, 142-177.

Matsuura, H. (1950). *Cytologia* **16**, 48-57.

Matsuura, H. (1957). *Proc. Intern. Genet. Symposia, Tokyo and Kyoto, 1956*, pp. 110-112.

Matsuura, H., and Haga, T. (1940). *Cytologia* (*Tokyo*) **10**, 382-389.

Metz, C. W. (1938). *Am. Naturalist* **72**, 485-519.

Mirsky, A. E., and Ris, H. (1949). *Nature* **163**, 666-667.

Mitra, S. (1956). *Genetics* **41**, 654.

Moses, M. J., and Taylor, J. H. (1955). *Exptl. Cell Research* **9**, 474-488.

Muller, H. J. (1941). *Cold Spring Harbor Symposia Quant. Biol.* **9**, 290-308.

Muller, H. J. (1947). *Proc. Roy. Soc.* **B134**, 1-37.

Nebel, B. R. (1939). *Botan. Rev.* **5**, 563-626.

Nebel, B. R., and Ruttle, M. L. (1936). *Am. J. Botany* **23**, 652-663.

Newton, W. C. F. (1926). *J. Linnean Soc. London Botany* **47**.

Nordenskiöld, H. (1956). *Hereditas* **42**, 7-73.

Noronha-Wagner, M., and Castro, D. (1952). *Sci. Genet.* (*Turin*) **4**, 154-161.

Novitski, E. (1947). *Genetics* **32**, 526-534.

Novitski, E. (1951). *Genetics* **36**, 267-280.

Oehlkers, F. (1937). *Biol. Zentr.* **57**, 126-149.

Oehlkers, F. (1940). *Biol. Zentr.* **60**, 337-348.

Oehlkers, F., and Eberle, P. (1957). *Chromosoma* **8**, 351-363.

Oksala, T. (1944). *Ann. Acad. Sci. Fennicae Ser. A IV*, **5**, 1-34.

Oksala, T. (1952). *Hereditas* **38**, 449-480.

Olive, L. S. (1949). *Am. J. Botany* **36**, 41-54.

Oster, G. (1957). *J. Cellular Comp. Physiol.* **49**, Suppl. **1**, 129-140.

Östergren, G. (1943). *Hereditas* **29**, 444-450.

Östergren, G. (1951). *Hereditas* **37**, 85-156.

Pätau, K. (1941). *Chromosoma* **2**, 36-63.

Piza, S. (1953). *Anais escola super. agr. Luiz de Queiroz* **3**, 90-97.

Pollister, A. W., Swift, H., and Alfert, M. (1951). *J. Cellular Comp. Physiol.* **38**, Suppl. **1**, 101-119.

Pontecorvo, G. (1958). "Trends in Genetic Analysis." Columbia Univ. Press, New York.

Pritchard, R. H. (1960). "Microbial Genetics." Cambridge Univ. Press, London and New York.

Rhoades, M. M. (1942). *Genetics* **27**, 395-407.

Rhoades, M. M. (1952). *In* "Heterosis" (J. W. Gowen, ed.), pp. 66-80. Iowa State College Press, Ames, Iowa.

Ris, H. (1942). *J. Exptl. Zool.* **90**, 267-322.

Ris, H. (1945). *Biol. Bull.* **89**, 242-257.

Ris, H. (1957). *In* "The Chemical Basis of Heredity." (W. D. McElroy and B. Glass, eds.) pp. 23-69. Johns Hopkins Press, Baltimore, Maryland.

Sampayo, T., Castro, D., and Malheiros, N. (1951). *Agronomia lusitana* **13**, 1-10.

Sandler, L., and Novitski, E. (1957). *Am. Naturalist* **91**, 105-110.

Sansome, E. R. (1933). *Cytologia* (*Tokyo*) **5**, 15-30.

Sax, H. J., and Sax, K. (1935). *J. Arnold Arboretum* (*Harvard Univ.*) **16**, 423-439.

Sax, K. (1932). *J. Arnold Arboretum* (*Harvard Univ.*) **13**, 180-212.

Sax, K. (1936). *Genetics* **21**, 324-338.

Schrader, F. (1931). *Z. wiss. Zool.* **138**, 386-408.

Schrader, F. (1935). *Cytologia (Tokyo)* **6**, 422-430.

Schrader, F. (1941). *J. Morphol.* **68**, 123-148.

Schrader, F. (1946a). *Biol. Bull.* **90**, 19-31.

Schrader, F. (1946b). *Biol. Bull.* **90**, 265-290.

Schrader, F. (1947). *Evolution* **1**, 134-142.

Schrader, F. (1953). "Mitosis: The Movements of Chromosomes in Cell Division." Columbia Univ. Press, New York.

Schrader, F., and Hughes-Schrader, S. (1956). *Chromosoma* **7**, 469-496.

Schultz, J., and Hungerford, D. A. (1953). *Rec. Genet. Soc.* **22**, 99 (Abstract).

Schultz, J., and Redfield, H. (1951). *Cold Spring Harbor Symposia Quant. Biol.* **16**, 175-195.

Schwartz, D. (1953). *Genetics* **38**, 251-260.

Schwartz, D. (1954). *Genetics* **39**, 692-700.

Schwartz, D. (1955). *J. Cellular Comp. Physiol.* **45**, Suppl. **2**, 171-188.

Serra, J. A. (1947). *Cold Spring Harbor Symposia Quant. Biol.* **12**, 192-210.

Serra, J. A. (1955). *In* "Encyclopedia of Plant Physiology" (W. Ruhland, ed.), Vol. I. pp. 472-506. Springer, Berlin.

Shinke, N. (1934). *Mem. Coll. Sci. Kyoto Imp. Univ.* **B9**, 366-392.

Singleton, J. R. (1953). *Am. J. Botany* **40**, 124-144.

Sinha, S. K. (1960). Ph.D. Thesis, Indiana University, Bloomington, Indiana.

Sisken, J. E. (1959). *Exptl. Cell Research* **16**, 602-615.

Smith, S. G. (1942). *Can. J. Research* **D20**, 221-229.

Smith, S. G., and Boothroyd, E. R. (1942). *Can. J. Research* **C20**, 358-388.

Sorsa, V. (1956). *Ann. Acad. Sci. Fennicae Ser. A IV* **33**, 5-64.

Sparrow, A. H., Moses, M. J., and Steele, R. (1952). *Brit. J. Radiol.* **25**, 182-188.

Sparrow, A. H., Pond, V., and Kojan, S. (1955). *Am. J. Botany* **42**, 384-393.

Stebbins, G. L. (1935). *Am. Naturalist* **69**, 81.

Stebbins, G. L. (1941). *Botan. Rev.* **7**, 507-542.

Steinitz-Sears, L. M., and Sears, E. R. (1953). *Genetics* **38**, 244-250.

Sturtevant, A. H. (1951). *In* "Genetics in the Twentieth Century" (L. C. Dunn, ed.), Chapter 6. Macmillan, New York.

Sturtevant, A. H., and Dobzhansky, Th. (1936). *Genetics* **21**, 473-490.

Swanson, C. P. (1942). *Am. Naturalist* **76**, 593-610.

Swanson, C. P. (1957). "Cytology and Cytogenetics." Prentice-Hall, Englewood Cliffs, New Jersey.

Swift, H. (1950a). *Physiol. Zoöl.* **23**, 169-198.

Swift, H. (1950b). *Proc. Natl. Acad. Sci. U.S.* **36**, 643-654.

Taylor, J. H. (1949). *J. Heredity* **40**, 86-88.

Taylor, J. H. (1950). *Am. J. Botany* **37**, 137-143.

Taylor, J. H. (1953). *Exptl. Cell Research* **4**, 164-173.

Taylor, J. H. (1957). *Am. Naturalist* **91**, 209-222.

Taylor, J. H. (1958). *Am. J. Botany* **45**, 123-131.

Taylor, J. H. (1959a). *Am. J. Botany* **46**, 477-485.

Taylor, J. H. (1959b). *Proc. 10th Intern. Congr. Genetics I,* pp. 63-78.

Taylor, J. H., and McMaster, R. D. (1954). *Chromosoma* **6**, 489-521.

Taylor, J. H., Woods, P. S., and Hughes, W. L. (1957). *Proc. Natl. Acad. Sci. U.S.* **43**, 122-128.

Thoday, J. M. (1954). *New Phytologist* **53**, 511-516.

Tobias, P. V. (1956). "Chromosomes, Sex-Cells, and Evolution in a Mammal." Percy Lund, Humphries, and Co., London.

Torvik-Greb, M. (1935). *Biol. Bull.* **26**, 25-34.

Upcott, M. (1936). *Cytologia (Tokyo)* **7**, 118-130.

Vasil, I. K. (1957). *Science* **126**, 1294-1295.

Wakayama, K. (1930). *Cytologia (Tokyo)* **2**, 27-36.

Walker, P. M. B., and Yates, H. B. (1952). *Proc. Roy. Soc.* **B140**, 274-300.

Watson, J. D., and Crick, F. H. C. (1953). *Nature* **171**, 737-738.

Wells, D. E. (1956). *Am. J. Botany* **43**, 761-768.

Westergaard, M. (1960). *Abhandl. deut. Akad. Wiss. Berlin Kl. Med. Jahrgang No. 1*, pp. 30-44.

White, M. J. D. (1941). *J. Genet.* **42**, 143-172.

White, M. J. D. (1942). "Cytology and Cell Physiology." Oxford Univ. Press, London and New York.

White, M. J. D. (1948). "Animal Cytology and Evolution." Cambridge Univ. Press, London and New York.

White, M. J. D. (1951). *Advances in Genet.* **4**, 267-330.

White, M. J. D. (1954). "Animal Cytology and Evolution," 2nd ed. Cambridge Univ. Press, London and New York.

Wilson, E. B. (1912). *J. Exptl. Zool.* **13**, 345-450.

Wilson, E. B. (1937). "The Cell in Development and Heredity," 3rd ed. Macmillan, New York.

Yos, J. M., Bade, W. L., and Jehle, H. (1957a). "Symposium on Molecular Structure and Biology Specificity" (L. Pauling and H. Itano, eds.). Am. Inst. Biol. Sci., Washington, D.C.

Yos, J. M., Bade, W. L., and Jehle, H. (1957b). *Proc. Natl. Acad. Sci. U.S.* **43**, 341-346.

CHAPTER 2

Mitosis and the Physiology of Cell Division

By DANIEL MAZIA

I. Introduction

The biological domain of the physical world has conservation principles of its own, operating within the larger ambit of the conservation principles of physics. The most general principle is that biological systems must reproduce themselves in order to sustain their very existence over long periods of time. The reproduction of biological systems may be referred to the reproduction of cells. Subcellular entities, such as viruses, cannot maintain themselves indefinitely without parallel reproduction of the cells in which they live. Likewise, the asexual reproduction of such organisms as flatworms is limited by the production of new cells, and it is perfectly obvious that all cases of sexual reproduction imply the generation of new cells after the mixing of genetic material from the parent cells.

Our general principle is founded on these facts, some of which will be discussed in more detail later: (1) an individual cell has a limited capacity for growth; (2) an individual cell has a limited life span, even in extreme cases such as spores; and (3) both these limitations are overcome by the reproduction of the cell, which we shall define as the production of two complete new cells from one old one. Facts giving this definition more than a figurative meaning will appear in the course of our survey of cell division.

The term "cell division" is used ambiguously in the biological literature. In some cases, it refers to the whole constellation of processes whereby two complete cells are produced from one. In others, it refers only to the culminating parturition and labor pains, the processes of mitosis and cytokinesis whereby nucleus and cytoplasm are literally divided. The ambiguity is not trivial or academic in significance. For example, the confusion resulting from a statement such as, "ionizing radiations inhibit cell division," can lead to meaningless experiments.

In reviewing the total picture of cell division, we shall take the position—to be elaborated below—that the whole history of the cell may be directed toward division, and where we refer to a *period of division,* in contrast to a *period between divisions,* the former term designates merely that part of the whole process during which the distribution of genetic material and the partitioning of the cytoplasm takes place. To avoid inventing a new term, we shall refer to those events that take place before the period of division as *preparations for division.* It will soon be evident that some of the most important acts in the over-all performance of cell division actually fall among the preparations. Furthermore, we shall take the position that the normal tendency of all cells is to divide, and, for purposes of analysis, we shall view cells that do not divide as being blocked at some point in their preparations for division. The stimulation and suppression of division will be considered an unblocking and a blocking of the normal trend.

Thus, the scope of this discussion of "cell division" is in fact the over-all drama of cell reproduction. We can usefully distinguish two classes of events. One comprises the *reproductive events,* during which the functional potentialities of the cell are doubled. The chief reproductive events we shall deal with are the doubling of the chromosomes and of the mitotic centers. The other general class of events we may call the *distributive;* these have to do with the partitioning of parental material between daughter cells.

We shall make a distinction between genetic reproduction and what we shall call *physiological reproduction.* The former is the actual doubling of chromosomal substance in a chemical sense, along with whatever allowance we wish to make for the doubling of genetic material localized in the cytoplasm. The hypothesis that a significant part of the genetic material resides in the cytoplasm, in some cases at least, has had its ups and downs and certainly still calls for open-minded attitudes. The writings of Ephrussi (1953, 1958) are recommended for a broad view of this question. *Physiological reproduction* will be defined as the doubling of the actual biosynthetic capacity of a cell, which we shall call its "growth potential." The distinction between genetic reproduction and physiological reproduction is called for by the fact that they follow different time courses (Section XIV).

This essay is not designed to give full documentation of the matters being discussed. Although references will always be given to support statements of fact, no attempt has been made to give all the relevant references. This is particularly true of the discussion of matters that were dealt with in the older literature, which has been summarized by Wilson (1925), Wassermann (1929), Tischler (1922, 1951), Milovidov (1949), Hughes (1952b), Schrader (1953), and others. It is sincerely hoped this summary will do justice to classic discoveries and will lead the reader back to the wealth of the classic literature. In doing so, he will find a valuable guide in Hughes' recent "A History of Cytology" (1959); only the originals can provide the illusion of immediate contact with what must have been a golden age in microscopical science. But the author feels that we are living in a second golden age, so far as this subject is concerned, and has attempted to convey a sense of rapid advance and deepening insight. If the reference list seems to be weighted in favor of recent work, it is not only because the coverage of recent literature is deliberately more complete, without attempting to be exhaustive—we *have* learned a great deal about cell reproduction in the last few years. We have gained some genuinely new insights but, even more, we have been able to translate quarrelsome ancestral speculations into experimental realities.

A conscious aim has been the discovery of generalizations or the germs of generalizations. In no field could this be more perilous, for one sometimes feels that "exceptions" have been the spice of life in the cytological past. If, however, we are willing to grant that the future of cell biology is longer than its past and that we "moderns" are really the pristine forerunners of that future, then the useful function of generalization is to discover any evidence of sense and plan that nature has been willing to provide us. Whether "exceptions" do destroy generalizations, suggest hidden complexities, or merely indicate the generosity of editors is a problem of judgment in each case.

II. The Plan of Cell Reproduction
A. *The Significance of Cell Division*

More often than not, questions beginning with "Why?" are inane and of no service in scientific discourse. In biology, they sometimes make sense because the science does possess a reference line for judgments of value and meaning; namely, the concept of *survival*. If we ask why cells—or at least their nuclei—must divide, the answer can be given in terms of what happens if they do not. The answer is, clearly, that they die, no matter what criterion of death we apply. Indeed, in some fields, such as microbiology, it is operationally useful to synonymize the loss of reproductive capacity with death. The first reason we can give for the necessity of cell division is an extremely simple one, involving the relations between division and cell growth. As we shall see, the capacity of a cell to grow is limited and is refreshed by nuclear reproduction. The simplest implication of growth is that it dilutes the existing contents of a cell with fresh substance. Regardless of the so-called "dynamic state" of the cell, cumulative and irreversible changes seem to exist which, collectively, constitute *aging* in its most fundamental aspect (cf. Lansing, 1952; Strehler, 1959). Thus division might be a necessity for survival only because it is, normally, a necessity for further growth and dilution of cell substance. If this were so, any other means of assuring growth and dilution would serve. That alternatives could exist was suggested by the famous study of Hartmann (1928) on what he called "Experimental Immortality." His experiments on *Amoeba proteus* were based on the fact that this organism, like most cells, will regenerate lost cytoplasm provided the nucleus is present. By amputating cytoplasm at intervals, and permitting the cell to regenerate before the next amputation, he could induce a periodic growth and dilution of cytoplasm—a kind of artificial cell division—without nuclear division. As long as the operations continued the cells did not "age"; they survived and continued to regenerate for many months, and there was no reason to think that they would not have gone on indefinitely. If cells normally possessed means of throwing away cytoplasm and regenerating new, cell division might not be a necessity for biological immortality.

The avoidance of aging is not the only justification of cell division as a necessity for survival. A more obvious reason is that cells sooner or later are bound to meet with accidents, and the tendency of organisms to produce more cells than the environment can support provides crude but effective insurance that a maximum number will survive in the long run. In sexually reproducing multicellular organisms we observe an admirable compromise whereby the reproducing population in the germ line is partially insulated against the hazards of the outside world by a population of specialized but nonreproducing cells which is renewed in each generation.

As we shall see, the restoration of the capacity for growth is a consequence of nuclear reproduction and is independent of the division of the cytoplasm. Continued nuclear division without cytoplasmic division is a way of life for many organisms and tissues, which exist as *syncytia* or *coenocytes*. We may ask why the subdivision of living material into small cells served by single nuclei tends to be the rule. The dimensions of cells are, in a rough way, quite uniform, no true cells falling below one micron and few being larger than one millimeter in average diameter. The upper limits are probably smaller than this if we exclude cells containing large amounts of storage material and if we restrict ourselves to those having diploid nuclear equipment. It is unlikely that this state of affairs represents a divine dispensation in favor of the manufacturers of microscopes, but it is highly probable [and the problem has been treated quantitatively in special cases, such as that of the nerve cell (Hill, 1928)] that limits of efficient cell diameter are set by rates of diffusion of metabolites. These may be overcome by limiting growth to one dimension, as in some of the coenocytic algae, by producing thin and reticulated plasmodia, as in some slime molds, or by developing internal "stirring," as in the large ciliates. But, by and large, organisms have solved their diffusion problems by producing small cells with single diploid nuclei, providing a large ratio of cell surface to volume.

An evolutionary consequence of cellularity is implicit in the designation of multicellular organisms as "higher" organisms. That single cells can develop a high level of variety and complexity of structure and function has been vividly demonstrated by the students of the Protozoa, who sometimes prefer the term "acellular" (cf. discussion by Corliss, 1957) to describe the extraordinary scope of differentiation found among the ciliates, for instance. If nothing else, these organisms tell us how far unicellular life has been able to evolve, and they enable us to imagine further evolutionary pathways that would be independent of cellularity. But it is all the more striking that the greatest range of versatility has been achieved by communities of cells, within which individual cells remain relatively simple but are diversified to serve the whole in specialized ways. In the development of a multicellular organism, cell division, beginning with the egg, is the essential step toward differentiation.

Although the question of the evolution of multicellular life falls outside the scope of our discussion, it is not entirely irrelevant. Commonly it is imagined that Metazoa originated by aggregation of cells into colonies in which functional specialization developed. But the students of the subject also call attention to a plausible alternative: the transformation of syncytial "unicellular" organisms—of which there are many —into multicellular systems by partitioning off the domains of individual nuclei. Considering the degree of cytoplasmic differentiation possible within a ciliate, it is imaginable that such a transformation could produce a rather complex organism whose further evolution would be along metazoan lines (cf. Hanson, 1958).

B. The Significance of Chromosomes

Our minimal image of a living cell includes a set of genes, but it does not necessarily imply that these are assembled into chromosomes. If fundamental genetic theory requires the assembly of genetic units into linkage groups, it still does not demand the gigantic groupings represented by micron-dimensioned chromosomes of plants and animals. We know of much smaller assemblies, having macromolecular dimensions, in bacterial viruses and bacteria. A strong case can be made for the genetic significance of the chromosome as a whole, as has been done by Goldschmidt (1955), although the question does not seem to disturb the serenity of most contemporary genetic theorists. Quite apart from genetic considerations it is possible to account for the significance of the chromosomes in terms of the mitotic mechanism.

If mitosis is a device for the distribution of sister genes to sister cells, the chromosomes may be viewed as a system in which the numerous genes are packaged into a small number of units. Estimates of the number of genetic units in a higher organism range upward from 10^4, depending on the method of counting and on whether we are considering "recons," "mutons," or "cistrons," following Benzer's (1957) definitions. Pontecorvo (1958) estimates the size of a gene ("cistron") in both *Aspergillus* and *Drosophila* to be of the order of 100–100,000 nucleotides. If we take 10^{-12} gm. as a round estimate of the amount of DNA in a representative haploid nucleus of a higher organism (Mirsky and Ris, 1951) and 750 as the molecular weight of a nucleotide pair, such an organism would carry about 10^4 to 10^7 genes. However imprecise such estimates may be, the numbers of units are immense in relation to the number of "packages" in which they are carried through mitosis. Haploid chromosome numbers of most plants and animals tend to fall in a range of 2–50 (e.g., McClung, 1940; Darlington, 1956), and we may make allowance for occasional instances where they fall in the hundreds without changing our conclusion very much.

The packaging of large numbers of genes in small numbers of chromosomes is intelligible in terms of the approximate generalization that the genetic elements, as such, cannot adequately participate in mitotic movements. This is shown unequivocally by the fate of chromosome fragments after irradiation or breakage from any cause; these "akinetic" fragments cannot make correct mitotic movements. The movements of chromosomes depend on specialized parts—the centromeres or kinetochores—and these parts are essential, whether we view them as motors or as points of attachment of fibers or as centers of electric charge or in the light of any of the other theories of movement (Section X, D). We shall deal with the kinetochores in more detail later (Section VIII, A).

Meanwhile, chromosomal organization can be defined, with respect to mitosis, as a device for attaching large numbers of genes to small numbers of centromeres or kinetochores. In the end, the chromosome number reflects the number of such motive centers, and not the amount of genetic material. The general constancy of chromosome number within a species attests to the constancy of the number of kinetochores. If chromosome numbers now prove to be more variable within an organism than had previously been supposed, this fact may be telling us something about genetic variability, but it may also reflect fluctuations in the behavior and reproduction of the kinetochores, about which we know so little. [The large literature on variation in chromosome numbers will not be discussed here. The origins of such variations (aneuploidy) in the germ line are discussed in Swanson's text (1957, p. 188), and somatic variations in animal tissues are discussed by Beatty (1954), Ford et al. (1958), Hsu (1959), and many other authors.]

Although we can make some sense of chromosomal organization in terms of the efficiency of handling the numerous genes as a small number of packages, we shall not be able to say exactly wherein the efficiency lies. Crude imagination suggests that the equipping of 10^5 chromosomal units with kinetochores, the establishing of 10^5 chromosomal spindle fibers, and the movement of that number of units into metaphase and through metaphase might be difficult, clumsy, and subject to error, but it would not be easy to defend the proposition. Conversely, we—or at least the writer—cannot give a good reason why chromosome numbers need to be as high as they are.

But the facts are clear enough. Chromosomal organization is a device for attaching large numbers of genes to small numbers of kinetochores; the latter are responsible for the mitotic movements of the chromosomes. In those organisms, i.e., the bacteria, in which there is some doubt as to the presence of microscopic chromosomes, there is also doubt as to the existence of a mitotic mechanism for distributing the genetic material (Section II, C, 7).

C. The Essential Mitotic Plan and Its Variants

The central feature of cell reproduction is the reproduction of the nucleus, although in the natural scheme of things the nuclear events may not be isolated so nicely. The dominance of the nucleus depends on a fact that was recognized by Strasburger (1893), but that we still do not understand at all: a single nucleus is capable of administering only a limited mass of cytoplasm. Strasburger's term "sphere of influence" (*Wirkungssphaere*) describes the situation well, and the relation of the nuclear sphere of influence to cell division was embodied in the concept of the *Kernplasmarelation* as developed by Hertwig (1908). The facts are simple enough; given one nucleus, a mass of cytoplasm can grow only to a limited extent, but the capacity for growth is refreshed once the nucleus has divided. In an approximate way, the nuclear dosage determines the total possible mass of a population or an organism.

There are various interpretations of the nuclear "sphere of influence" —none very precise. One is given by the "replacement hypothesis" of nuclear function (Mazia, 1952; reviewed by Brachet, 1957, p. 309). According to the hypothesis the functional synthetic units in the cytoplasm have a limited lifetime, after which they have to be replaced or, in more contemporary terms, have to receive fresh information from the nucleus. Obviously the number of active units in the cytoplasm reaches a maximum at the point of equilibrium between their breakdown and replacement. Thus, the fact that the output of a nucleus must have some limit restricts the cytoplasmic mass that it can administer.

All the variations of cell reproduction center around this relationship. Let us now list some of these:

1. Mitosis with Equal Division

In this scheme, which we shall arbitrarily use as a norm, nuclear division takes place by mitosis, the essential steps of which are: (a) the duplication of chromosome substance; (b) the "condensation" of the chromosomes, accompanied by the "disappearance" of the nucleolus; (c) the movement of sister chromosomes to opposite poles; (d) division of the cytoplasm, accompanied by the reconstitution of two complete nuclei, each with a full set of chromosomes and a nucleolus. In this standard case, we imagine that the daughter cells are equivalent in all respects.

2. Asymmetric Mitosis

This designation refers to cases where nuclear division takes place by mitosis, apparently normal, but the daughter cells are not equivalent. Often daughters are of unequal size, as in the much studied case of the grasshopper neuroblast (Carlson, 1940, 1952) or in the divisions of many animal eggs with spiral cleavage. More important is the fact that the several daughters may have a different future history, as in some of the divisions in plant meristems, the production of cells in hematopoietic systems of animals, the division of pollen, etc. One daughter may differentiate and not divide again while the other retains the tendency to divide and belongs to a "stem line." This type of cell reproduction is extraordinarily significant for the differentiation of multicellular systems, yet we know little or nothing about the fundamental origin of the asymmetry.

3. Mitosis with Delayed Cytokinesis

Here the nuclei divide repeatedly by mitosis, but the cytoplasm does not divide and a syncytium is formed. At a future time, cytokinesis takes place. The syncytium may be partitioned in such a way that a membrane forms around each nucleus. A familiar example from the plant world is cell formation in endosperms, and comparable cases are observed in sporogenesis and gametogenesis in a variety of Protozoa.

4. Division of Syncytia

There are multinucleated cells [e.g., giant amebae, some opalinids, and some ciliates among the Protozoa, surveyed by Grell (1956)] in which the nuclei undergo one mitotic division followed by cleavage of the cell into two daughters, each receiving half the nuclei. As will be mentioned later, whether or not the mitoses proceed synchronously depends on the type of cell. This design differs from the "normal" one in the important respect that cytokinesis cannot be clearly related to the mitotic apparatus (Section XII, B).

5. Endoreproduction

Under this heading we include a number of patterns of reproduction in which the nuclear material reproduces but is retained within a single nucleus. Cytokinesis does not take place. As the nucleus increases in genetic multiplicity, there is a corresponding growth of the cytoplasm. Clearly the separation of sister chromosome groups as such is not essential for continued reproduction of the cell. The patterns of nuclear reproduction are variable. In endomitosis in its narrower sense, the chromosomes go through a normal cycle of duplication, condensation, and reassembly into an interphase nucleus; the sister chromosomes separate visibly but do not move to distant poles. In interphase, all the chromosome sets are contained in a single nucleus. The form and the distribution of this mechanism have been reviewed thoroughly by Geitler (1941, 1953). Another system of endoreproduction is familiar from the well-known case of the dipteran larva, and this has been reviewed by Alfert (1954). Here the chromosomes duplicate and may show signs of going through a cycle of condensation and dispersion, but the sister chromosomes remain associated, forming large polytene chromosomes. By a dispensation of Providence, these polytene chromosomes remain condensed in a most useful banded form in *Drosophila* and other dipteran larvae favored by the geneticists.

Endoreproduction leading to the formation of giant cells may be achieved experimentally in various ways. A recent, interesting example is the production of giant cells in mammalian tissue cultures after inhibition of division by X-irradiation (Puck and Marcus, 1956). The general pattern of growth in such cells (including DNA synthesis) is comparable to that in normal cells, though slower (Whitmore *et al.*, 1958).

In mouse cells (Earle's L strain) and monkey kidney cells (Whitmore *et al.*, 1958) the time course of increase of proteins and nucleic acids in the growth to giant cells was exponential, although lower in absolute rate than in controls, whereas in human (HeLa) cells the absolute rates also were comparable to the normal rates over the equivalent of several generations. Clearly then, endoreproduction can override the limits of the sphere of influence of the nucleus. Nevertheless, there seem to be limits to the size that these giant cells can attain, and strict limits to their life span (Tolmach and Marcus, 1960). Some of the problems of nucleus-cytoplasm interaction are not solved by the endoreproductive mechanisms.

In practice, the most common method of bringing about endoreproduction in a variety of plant and animal cells is by the use of agents that "poison" the mitotic spindle while permitting the chromosome cycle to proceed. The most familiar agents of this kind are colchicine and its derivatives (Eigsti and Dustin, 1955) when used in appropriate concentrations. This so-called "c-mitosis" is not quite the same as endomitosis; the nuclear membrane breaks down, and the only aspect of normal mitosis that is missing is the anaphase separation of the chromosomes. The same results can be achieved with a great variety of chemical agents and by the imposition, in some cases, of low temperatures. A great literature exists not only on the mitotic abnormalities themselves, but also on the innumerable implications of genetic polyploidy.

Not only do these various observations tell us that the fundamental reproductive processes do not necessarily depend upon cell division, but we learn, conversely, that there must be definite processes, apart from general growth and nuclear reproduction, which decide whether or not a cell will go through division.

Where reproduction takes place by the variants of endoreproduction, the growth of the system obviously involves increase in mass by increase in cell size, and the number of cells remains constant. This design is actually used in the somatic growth of some animals, including, in addition to the familiar dipteran larvae, the nematodes and the rotifers. In the zoological literature, growth without increase in cell number is designated "eutely" (e.g., Rauther, 1930). The limitations of eutelic organisms illustrate the merits of the normal plan of reproduction by cell division. These organisms cannot, for instance, regenerate lost parts, being unable to make new somatic cells.

Finally, we may mention a process that falls midway between normal mitosis (without cell division) and endomitosis. Here the nuclei divide by mitosis but later fuse to form a single nucleus. This pattern of polyploidization in relation to physiological changes in animal tissues has recently been discussed by Alfert and Geschwind (1958).

6. Amitosis

The part played by the idea of amitosis in the history of our knowledge of cell division is illustrated by a quotation from O. Hertwig (English edition, 1909): "The older histologists were unable to discover what part the nucleus played in cell division. For many decades two opposing theories were held, of which now one and now the other obtained temporarily the greater number of supporters. According to the one theory, which was held by most botanists (Reichert [1847], etc.), the nucleus at each division was supposed to break up and become diffused throughout the protoplasm, in order to be formed anew in each daughter cell. According to the other (. . . Remak [1852], etc.) the nucleus was supposed to take an active part in the process of cell division, and, at the commencement of it, to become elongated and constricted at a point, corresponding with the plane of division which is seen later, and to divide into halves, which separate from one another and move apart. The cell body itself was supposed to become constricted, and to divide into two parts, in each of which one of the two daughter nuclei formed an attraction center."

Clearly the advocates of the second process, which came to be called "amitosis," were closer in principle to the truth to the extent that they preserved the idea of the continuity of the nuclear substance. But it was the persistent recognition of the fact that the nucleus disappeared from sight at the time of division, and intelligent concern about that fact, that led to the discovery of mitosis (cf. Section VI, A).

We now would consider the "disappearance" of the nucleus to be rather unessential to the definition of mitosis. The indispensable aspect of mitotic division of the nucleus is the anaphase separation of sister chromosomes, by any mechanism whatsoever.

By this criterion, we make the generalization that amitosis, the direct division of the nucleus without evident separation of sister chromosomes, is not common in plant and animal cells. So far as we know, such cells are incapable of producing genetically equivalent cells amitotically. But this does not mean that amitosis is never observed in higher organisms. A considerable number of cases have been described, but these generally have involved pathological conditions. The character and distribution of amitosis in animal cells has been discussed in detail in a recent monograph by Bucher (1959).

Among the ciliate and suctorian protozoa, an amitotic method of nuclear division is widespread and successful. Superficially, the division of the macronuclei in such forms follows the classic description of amitosis, as quoted above, and modern cytological methods fail to reveal anything equivalent to the mitotic separation of sister chromosomes. The key to success seems to be a high degree of redundancy of the genetic equipment. It is imagined that the macronucleus contains a number of "subnuclei" (Sonneborn, 1947) and that the requirements of genetic reproduction are met if each daughter cell receives at least one of these. For example, Sonneborn finds genetic evidence of the existence of about forty such "subnuclei" in the macronucleus of *Paramecium aurelia*. The method of reproduction of these hypothetical subunits has not been discovered. Their reproduction could involve a variant of mitosis, in which case the over-all process of cell reproduction would be not unlike that of multinucleated cells, such as the opalinids or giant amebae, with the difference that the nuclei are contained in a package that is capable of fission at the time of cell division. The possibilities are discussed by Nanney and Rudzinska (1960).

The macronucleus may take various forms: a compact sphere, a chain of beads, a long rod, etc. At the time of cell division, it elongates and pinches into two. This nuclear division may be quite accurate. In *Tetrahymena*, for instance, McDonald (1958) has measured the distribution of deoxyribonucleic acid (DNA), which is the most useful chemical tracer of chromosome substance, between daughter macronuclei, and he finds that the two daughters normally differ by only 0.1–14%, with a mean of about 5%. But we know that even this degree of equality is not necessary. In *Stentor*, for instance, where the macronucleus consists of a chain of about twelve beads, it can be shown by transplantation experiments that any one of these beads is adequate to provide for the genetic requirements of the organism (Tartar, 1957). In numerous cases macronuclear material is lost or divided unequally without detriment to the daughter cells (e.g., Scherbaum *et al.*, 1958).

This type of apparent amitosis represents a perfectly respectable and successful plan of cell reproduction, and it might even appear to be simpler and less liable to accidents than normal mitosis. [Incidentally, it provides cells with extraordinary resistance to radiation damage (Wichterman and Figge, 1954; Powers and Ehret, 1955) for reasons that are consistent with radiobiological "hit" theory.] Its obvious disadvantage is that it does not lend itself to meiotic recombination; for the purpose of recombination the ciliates discard their macronuclei and resort to mechanisms of the mitotic type (cf. Grell, 1956). We could also imagine that it might "overstabilize" the genetic equipment to the point where differentiation of daughter cells becomes difficult.

7. Uncertain Mechanisms. Bacteria

The distributive mechanisms in the division of bacteria, blue-green algae, and certain other groups of microorganisms are still extremely obscure. It is an unfortunate paradox that the study of genetic reproduction in bacteria has been the preponderant influence in forming our conceptions of the chemical nature of genetic material, the role of DNA, genetic fine structure, etc., while we know less about the distributive events of cell division in these cells than was known about plant and animal cells seventy-five years ago. It is at least certain that the cells possess nuclei. The nuclei are seen by staining for light microscopy (e.g., Robinow, 1957, 1960), have been the objects of numerous electron microscopic studies (e.g., Chapman and Hillier, 1953; Ryter and Kellenberger, 1958), and have been isolated (Spiegelman *et al.*, 1958) as bodies containing DNA. Tracer studies show that the DNA tends to be distributed equally between daughter cells at division (Fuerst and Stent, 1956; Painter *et al.*, 1958).

The bacterial "chromosome" is very well defined by genetic criteria; linkage mapping in *Escherichia coli* has led to the conclusion that there is but one "chromosome" in the genetic sense. A kind of chromosome behavior quite unknown in other cells has been discovered in *E. coli*: the transfer of chromosome segments from one cell to another in a predetermined order during mating (Jacob and Wollman, 1958).

As soon as we turn to the simplest questions concerning nuclear division in bacteria, we enter a realm of controversy. Most of the pictures one sees in the literature remind one of images of amitosis. Delamater (1953) has argued in favor of a mitotic mechanism, and he supports his view with photographs suggestive of a mitotic separation of chromosome bodies. More recently (Delamater, 1959) he has described the isolation of structures interpretable as nuclei containing chromosomes. A cautious conclusion at this time is that nuclear division in bacteria does take place within the confines of the nuclear interface, but some changes in nuclear structure, described by Robinow (1960) are associated with division.

For that matter, the physical image of the bacterial chromosome is quite uncertain, even though its genetic properties are so well known. The number of molecules of DNA in a bacterium (according to the physical chemist's criterion of a DNA molecule) is small; Zamenhof (1957) states that *Hemophilus* contains about 200 molecules per cell. The genetic evidence summarized by Jacob and Wollman (1958) is consistent with the image of the *E. coli* chromosome as a single linear sequence of nucleotide pairs. It has recently been claimed (p. 113) that DNA is synthesized continuously during the life of a bacterium in contrast with the situation in plants and animals, in which synthesis is interrupted during the period when the chromosomes are condensed for mitosis. This continuous synthesis in itself would argue against a typical mitotic cycle for bacteria.

The idea that an association of DNA and basic proteins is a typical feature of the chemistry of nuclei may be traced back to the great Miescher (1897), who discovered both these classes of molecules. So far as most cells are concerned, it is still a fundamental generalization of nuclear chemistry. Yet the very presence of histones in the bacterial nucleus is controversial at this time. Deoxyribonucleoproteins have been isolated from a number of bacteria. There is at least one report (Palmade *et al.*, 1958) that the protein has the properties of a histone in the case of *E. coli*. The protein associated with DNA in preparations isolated from *E. coli* by a somewhat different method (Zubay and Watson, 1959) did not resemble a histone in its amino acid composition. The deoxyribonucleoprotein isolated from tubercle bacilli (Tsumita and Chargaff, 1958 and earlier papers of a series) does not resemble a nucleohistone or nucleoprotamine at all. Not only is it uncertain whether DNA in bacteria is associated with basic proteins, but there is still some doubt whether it is necessarily conjugated to protein at all in some organisms. For example, Wilkins and Zubay (1959) obtained X-ray diffraction patterns from isolated nucleoproteins of *E. coli* that resemble those of free, "crystalline" DNA rather than those of plant and animal DNA-histone associations.

Thus there are reasons for thinking that the fundamental mechanism of nuclear division, beginning with the type of chromosomal "packages" employed in the transportation of genetic material, may be quite different in bacteria and in so-called higher organisms. The small size of bacteria has given rise to difficulties that have deprived the modern microbial cytologists of the head start given others by classic microscopical methods. This is most unfortunate in view of the extraordinary possibilities of cytogenetic correlation given by the remarkable advances of microbial genetics.

One other feature of cell division in bacteria is the rather flexible relations between nuclear division and cytokinesis. The production of multinucleated progeny is an extremely common result of physiological changes of all sorts.

Useful references on problems of bacterial cytology are reviews by Marshak (1955) and Vendrely (1955a), an interesting symposium volume (Miles and Pirie, 1956), and chapters by Murray (1960) and Robinow (1960).

D. Summary

The standard plan of mitosis is not the only means available to cells for imparting genetic information to sister cells in division. We have seen that ciliates and other organisms possessing macronuclei multiply successfully with an apparently amitotic system and that the mechanism of nuclear division in bacteria is not yet known. A summary of the "advantages" of the mitotic plan may enhance our appreciation of it at the expense of philosophical orthodoxy. (1) It is capable of handling very large numbers of genetic units with precision. (2) A high degree of redundancy of the genetic units is not required, as is the case with the macronuclear amitotic mechanism. (3) It provides a basis for systematic sexual reproduction. In multicellular organisms, mitosis produces the somatic cell population and provides, at the same time, a pool of potential germ cells. The actual gametes are produced by a meiotic mechanism the general mechanics of which are similar to those of mitosis (see Chapter I, this volume); this mechanism differs from mitosis only in certain essential details of chromosome behavior. Fertilization then produces a zygote that is equipped for immediate mitosis. In unicellular organisms having a regular sexual phase, there is the same cycle of mitosis, meiosis, and fertilization. Even in organisms in which a macronucleus may divide amitotically, sexuality requires micronuclei that reproduce by mitosis. (We could imagine a multicellular organism in which mitosis is restricted to the germ line, with amitotic somatic division according to the ciliate pattern. No such organism exists.)

We now know that sexual processes as such do not depend on the sequence mitosis→meiosis→fertilization→mitosis. The recently discovered sexual mechanisms of bacteria (summary, Lederberg, 1959) differ in a number of respects from the classic scheme, and if the bacterial chromosome were capable of handling a sufficient volume of genetic information, we could probably design a sexually reproducing multicellular organism which employed the bacterial system of fertilization and genetic recombination. Such an organism does not exist, and in any case would have no obvious advantages over the conventional organism in which sexual reproduction is based on the strategy of mitosis.

In the preceding section we have also noted various schemes in which the chromosomes go through a mitotic reproductive cycle without the corresponding division of the cells. All these devices have the same import: they are means of overcoming the limitations of the sphere of influence of the nucleus and thus permitting (or demanding) the production of large cells.

III. THE PREPARATIONS FOR MITOSIS

A. Interphase Events and Division Period; Time Map of the Mitotic Cycle

The view that the flow of events in the life history of the cell is continuous and that "phases" are artificial serves the needs of piety better than those of edification. Practical questions confront us: What events necessarily go in sequence? What events run in parallel? What are the transitions, crises, and "points of no return"? To approach these questions, let us attempt to sketch a "time map" of the reproductive history of the cell.

The process of mitosis itself may be divided into two stages: the establishment of the mitotic apparatus and the transportation of the chromosomes to the poles by this apparatus. The term "mitotic apparatus" had been used casually by Wilson (1925), and it was defined by Mazia and Dan (1952) as "the ensemble of structures constituting the 'chromatic' and 'achromatic' figures in the classical description of mitosis." A convenient starting point for a sketch of the general scheme of mitosis is not its beginning (for there is no one beginning) but the climax of metaphase, when the mitotic apparatus is completed and is about to perform the acts of chromosome movement that give it meaning. At this definite point in time, we can look forward and backward. Let us consider an idealized mitotic apparatus at metaphase (Fig. 1), exemplified by the form found in animal cells and some other cells, where the poles are physically represented by centrioles. Implicit in the design of the apparatus is the following minimal and general plan of mitosis:

1. Centers and chromosomes duplicate
2. Sister centers separate to establish the poles
3. Sister chromosomes move to sister centers.

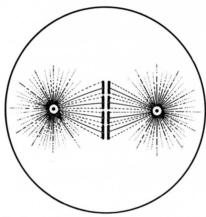

Fig. 1.   The idealized mitotic apparatus at metaphase. The polarization of the cell and the fibrous connections of sister chromosomes to sister centers guarantee that any mechanism whereby the chromosomes are pulled or guided apart by the fibers will result in the equipartition of the genetic material.

In the realization of this scheme, a great many different events may be distinguished, and more will be discovered. It is useful to locate those we know on the time map that is shown in Fig. 2. This map attempts to generalize the many variations in time relations of various parts of the mitotic process in different organisms. The possible time span of each process is represented. Where the beginning or end of a process is definitely fixed in relation to the whole, its diagrammatic representation comes to a point. Where the beginning or end cannot be fixed, the diagram is open-ended. We are referring to cells whose progeny will divide; the failure of cells to divide will later be considered as the blockage of one or more of the processes shown on the map.

The time map embodies the principles around which our discussion of mitosis will be built, as well as the particular processes that will be considered. The important principles are these: (1) The preparations for mitosis are going on continuously through the life of the cell; even as one division is taking place, preparations for the next have already started. (2) There are numerous preparations for a given division, all of which must be completed before the mitotic apparatus goes into action.

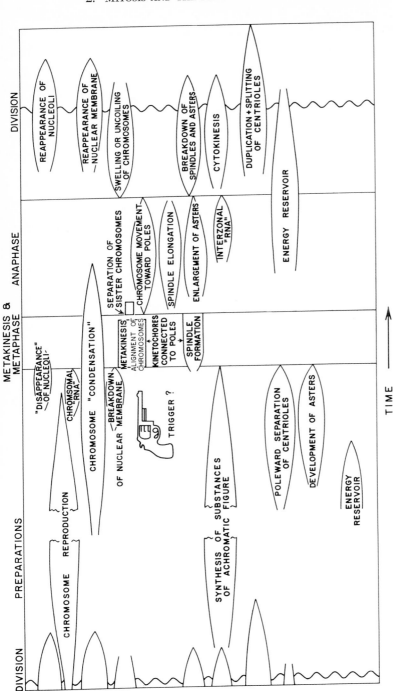

Fig. 2. A generalized plan of the time flow of events in mitosis. The time span for a given process represents the period during which it *may* take place; the actual interval will vary in different kinds of cells. The diagrammatic representation of each process converges to a point at the earliest time when it is known to begin or the latest time at which it may be completed. The representation is open-ended in cases where the time of initiation or termination of the process cannot be fixed.

(3) These preparations may take place in parallel, as well as sequentially. Some may be completed very early, but the cell must wait until all are completed. Let us designate this approach to the preparations for division as "the principle of parallel pathways." (4) The preparations converge on the point where the chromosomes begin to move, and the only fixed time points in our map of mitosis are metakinesis (the movement of chromosomes into their metaphase positions), the beginning of anaphase, and the end of anaphase.

These several generalizations, and especially the idea of parallel pathways in the preparation for division, are not original. Rather, an attempt is being made to formulate, in a definite scheme, views that have been developing in recent years among students of the cell (e.g., Mazia, 1956b; Scherbaum, 1957a; Swann, 1957). Not everyone will agree with this approach.

Our time map shows that some of the most important events of mitosis actually take place during the so-called interphase. The map itself is actually a summary of conclusions that will be developed in the following sections, and it is introduced this early only to provide guide lines. Our first problem is to sort out the events belonging immediately to the mitotic cycle from other activities of the cell.

B. Relations between Growth and Division

The period between divisions is occupied by two groups of events: preparations for division and, in the average case, growth of cell mass. (In this essay, the term *growth* will be used in this limited sense and will never refer to increase in cell numbers.) The over-all necessity for cell growth in conjunction with cell division is so apparent that perhaps it need not be mentioned; without it, cells obviously would diminish to a size at which they could no longer function as divisions succeeded each other. But the question is whether cell growth as a whole, viewed as an expansion of the metabolic machinery of the cell, is directly related to cell division. Only a small part of it appears on our map as syntheses preparing specifically for mitosis.

The idea of a causal relation between growth and division has much to recommend it. On a superficial view, cells do normally grow to a certain size before they divide. Hertwig's (1908) influential hypothesis concerning the significance of the nucleus-to-cytoplasm ratio (*Kernplasma-relation*) expressed the possibilities very convincingly. He imagined that as the nucleus-to-cytoplasm ratio falls below a certain value, i.e., as the cytoplasmic mass approaches the limits of the sphere of influence of the nucleus, a state of physiological instability sets in, which he described vividly as a state of "tension." It would be this state that precipitates the cell into division. In more fashionable language, we may refer to this as the concept of the "critical mass" (Mazia, 1956a). The famous experiments on "immortality" in *Amoeba* (Hartmann, 1928; confirmed by Prescott, 1956b) seem at first glance to support such a view (see Section II, A).

Such experiments illustrate another relevant fact that could be documented by many other cases: no matter how many times the cytoplasm is amputated, the cell is still capable of regenerating cytoplasm. This tells us that the limit to the sphere of influence of a nucleus is related to the amount of cytoplasm it can administer, and not to the exhaustion of the potentiality for growth.

We may also refer to experiments of Prescott (1955, 1956a) on *Amoeba proteus*, in which the growth in mass between divisions was measured by the Cartesian diver balance. Normally, the cells achieved exactly twice their "birth weight" before they divided, and normal division produced daughters of equal weight. Buf if sister cells were born unequal, they did not each double in mass. Rather, both the small daughter and the large daughter grew to the same mass before they divided, and this was the mass of the parent cell (Fig. 3).

All these experiments would seem to indicate that cells must reach a certain critical mass before they can divide. However, the defect of such experiments from the standpoint of the principle of parallel pathways is that the amputations reduce not only the total mass, but the fraction of the total cytoplasmic material that is being laid down specifically for division. Experimental designs in which the balance between total biosynthesis and biosynthesis specifically related to divisions remains undisturbed cannot test the critical mass hypothesis.

Further analysis forces us to reject the theory of the critical mass. Some of the examples to be cited suffer logically from the fact that size, not mass, was measured, but it is doubtful that determinations of mass would change the conclusions. Even normally, cells do not always divide at a fixed mass; as Swann (1957) points out in his valuable review, the relation is only approximate. We may cite an important older study, that of Adolph (1929), who found considerable variation in the size at which the ciliate *Colpoda* divided. The cleavage of animal ova tells us that the growth necessary to supply the needs of many cells may take place long before division; after this divisions can proceed in rapid sequence without further growth. The same situation may be produced artificially in *Tetrahymena* (Scherbaum and Zeuthen, 1954), where divisions may be headed off by a series of temperature shocks that do not block growth

(Section XV, B). When enlarged organisms are released from this regime, they can proceed without further growth through a series of synchronous divisions in nonnutrient medium (Hamburger and Zeuthen, 1957). Thus growth and division may be separated in time. In microorganisms which can be maintained under highly favorable nutritional conditions, cell size may vary at different points along the population-increase curve. For example, Scherbaum and Rasch (1957), have shown that in logarithmically growing *Tetrahymena* populations, size does not double between

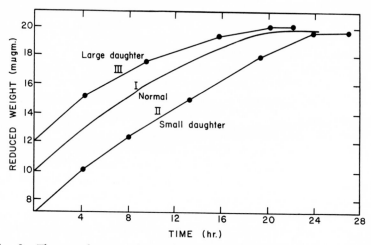

Fig. 3. The growth curve of *Amoeba proteus*, measured by the Cartesian diver balance. Each curve traces the growth of a single cell from the division which produced it to its own division. Curve *I* represents the typical situation; the parent cell had divided into equal halves, and the daughter doubles its mass before it divides. Curves *II* and *III* represent cells produced by an unequal division, induced by strong illumination. These cells do not double in mass, but reach the typical mature mass, as indicated in curve *I*, before they divide. After Prescott (1955).

divisions but increases by a factor of only 1.8. Thus, at each generation the size at which the cell divides is less, until the population levels off in its stationary phase.

In the large group of diatoms, reduction of cell size in successive generations is observed (Fritsch, 1935). The individual is contained in a pair of silicious shells. At division one daughter is contained in the larger "valve," and the other in the smaller. In the next generation the smaller daughter produces a daughter still smaller, and the process continues. In the end either the shell is discarded (in auxospore formation) to permit a phase of growth in size, or else the cells fail to divide again and die when their size has fallen below a critical minimum.

The division of organisms at less than normal size is, apparently, a common observation in experiments on nutritional limitation and inhibition in microorganisms. We may cite a recent study by Faed (1959) in which the growth-division relations in the fission yeast *Schizosaccharomyces pombe* were analyzed carefully. The cells were given a medium that was complete except for a source of nitrogen. Although they could not grow normally between divisions, they did divide once or twice, producing abnormally small cells (Fig. 4).

Another interesting example is given by experiments of Hirshfield and Pecora (1956) on the ciliate *Blepharisma*. The cells were cut at frequent intervals, as in the experiments on *Amoeba* cited above, but in this case the results were quite different. Divisions proceeded on schedule in nucleated fragments, regardless of reduction in size by cutting, until the cells were diminished to a size at which further amputations were fatal. Clearly division is determined by factors that may run parallel to cell size in some instances, but not by size itself.

At the other extreme, there are situations in which the growth of the cytoplasm seems to escape from the limitations of the nuclear sphere of influence and to continue without chromosomal reproduction. A familiar natural case is the growth of oöcytes in animals, which is in fact a preparation for later division without growth after fertilization. An experimental case which deserves more attention is that of amphibian embryos treated with nitrogen mustard (Bodenstein, 1947; Bodenstein and Kondritzer, 1948). In these embryos giant cells were produced without concurrent reproduction of the chromosomes. In this case—unlike that of the giant cells produced in cell structures by irradiation (Section II, C, 5)—the excess growth is not paralleled by an increase in DNA.

Even if we are uncertain as to the rigidity of the nuclear limitation of the capacity of the cell for growth, we may still imagine that in most kinds of cells the limit exists; the cells will grow so much and then will grow no more until they have divided. Recent work on bacteria has introduced a new and provocative concept, that of *unbalanced growth* (Cohen and Barner, 1954; Cohen, 1957). Strains of bacteria are available which have specific requirements for DNA precursors: thymine or deoxyribonucleosides, for instance. In *E. coli* mutants which require thymine, growth on a medium lacking thymine proceeds until the cells literally grow themselves to death. The mutants could reach a point in the imbalance between DNA and other cell constituents at which they could no longer be "rescued" by a supply of thymine. According to Cohen (1957), "cells which had lost the power to multiply had increased in length and diameter. They had at least doubled their protein and RNA

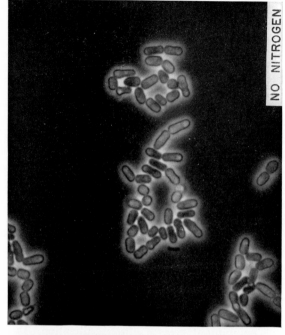

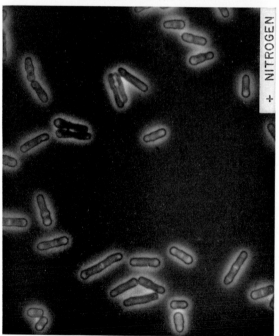

FIG. 4. Division of cells of a fission yeast, *Schizosaccharomyces pombe* in a normal inorganic medium plus 2% dextrose, but without a source of nitrogen. Controls (left photo) received nitrogen. The cells of the experimental group (right photo) divided once or twice, to produce abnormally small progeny. Apparently this cell can complete the preparations for division without the exogenous nitrogen sources that are required for normal growth between divisions. Photographs by J. N. Mitchison and D. Mazia; cf. Faed (1959).

content while their DNA content had increased at most by a few percent." This extreme consequence of unbalanced growth has not been observed in cells of higher organisms and cannot be said to be the rule even in bacteria. In an earlier and comparable experiment, Jeener and Jeener (1952; earlier references cited) found that the withholding of exogenous DNA from a strain of *Thermobacterium acidophilus* which requires DNA or its nucleosides leads to the growth of the cells, by elongation, to 35–40 times their normal size, with parallel synthesis of RNA to maintain its normal concentration. But these cells apparently do not grow themselves to death; even when they have reached such an abnormally large size they will divide and revert to normal nucleus:cytoplasm ratios when DNA is added.

All these observations of excess growth without division would seem at first to shake the validity of the concept of the nuclear sphere of influence even though it serves us so well in many contexts. Before it is rejected, however, we must recognize that we have been equating the nuclear control of growth with the DNA content or with the ploidy of chromosome numbers. An alternative hypothesis is that the nuclear factors that determine the growth potential of a cell are not necessarily measured by the DNA content or the chromosome number, although they are certainly linked to the genetic elements and most often run parallel to them. That this is an experimentally pertinent hypothesis will be shown in Section XIV.

Conclusions

There is, of course, an important relation between growth and division; it is not to be found in the idea that growth causes division, but in its antithesis. The meanings of the limited sphere of influence of a nucleus and of the refreshment of synthetic capacity by nuclear reproduction are focal questions of cell biology. Some of these matters will be discussed in Section XIV on physiological reproduction.

C. *Evidences of Specific Preparations for Division; Time Requirements*

In the normal situation we cannot separate the preparations for division completely from the less specific aspects of growth; for example, syntheses of routine enzymes might be limiting for syntheses directly concerned with division. But there are experimental and normal systems where the growth background is of little significance, and the time spent between divisions is attributable to preparations for division.

In *Amoeba proteus*, where the generation time is about 24 hours, Prescott has been able to deduce the limitations imposed by growth in two ways. One (Prescott, 1959) has been through studies on generation time of sister cells when unequal division was induced by an ingenious procedure. If the cells were illuminated strongly at the time of division, the cytoplasm streamed away from the light as cytokinesis took place, and unequal daughter cells were produced. These cells grew to the mass of their parents before dividing again. The generation time was inversely proportional to the "birth weight" (Fig. 5). By extrapolating the data to

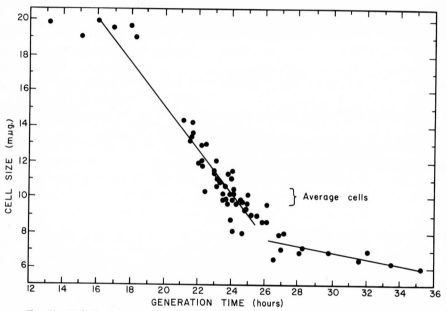

Fig. 5. Relation between size at "birth" and generation time in *Amoeba proteus*. Ordinate represents "reduced weight" of cells just after parental division. The cells in the range of 6–5 mμg. were obtained by light-induced unequal division. The cells whose initial weight was about 20 mμg. were obtained by suppression of the cytoplasmic division of the parent cell, after which one of the two daughter nuclei was removed. After Prescott (1959).

a point where "birth weight" equals mature weight, we may ask: How much time must be spent between divisions even if no growth is required? The answer is 16 hours or two-thirds of a normal generation time. A second way (Prescott, 1959) involves the use of amebae in which nuclear division takes place without cytokinesis. If one of the two nuclei is removed just after division, we have a cell with adult cytoplasmic mass containing a "newborn" nucleus. Studying the generation time of such cells, Prescott found that about 16 hours elapsed before division. These experiments are interpreted to mean that the *preparations for division*, entirely apart from growth, extend over a *large portion of the interphase period.*

The technique of synchronizing divisions in *Tetrahymena* (Scherbaum and Zeuthen, 1954) has provided a valuable tool for the evaluation of preparations for division. The normal generation time of this organism grown under favorable conditions is about 3 hours. As we have mentioned, the organisms may be "fattened" by a temperature cycling regime, after which they may go through a series of synchronous divisions without further growth. But the minimum time required from the last heat shock to the first division is about 70 minutes, and no way has yet been found to shorten it (Fig. 103). This interval, about *half a normal generation time,* is interpreted as being a period during which the cell completes those preparations for division that were inhibited during the temperature cycling. It is known that in this system (Scherbaum, 1957b; Scherbaum, *et al.,* 1959; Iverson and Giese, 1957) DNA synthesis continues during the temperature treatment. Therefore it is an admirable system for studying other specific (and endogenous) preparations or division, and it is under study in a number of laboratories (cf. Hamburger and Zeuthen, 1957; Scherbaum, 1957a; Plesner, 1958).

Finally, we may consider natural situations in which no reason other than specific preparations for division would seem to account for the existence of an interphase, since there is no growth. In a system like the sea urchin egg, the interphase during cleavage is very short compared to the time actually elapsing from prophase to telophase, but it still is (Ågrell, 1958) 25% of the total time between divisions. Here we know that one of the obvious preparations, the duplication of the chromosomes, has to take place. In meiosis, it is difficult to imagine what preparations need take place between the first and second meiotic divisions. In plants, at least, the nuclei commonly do go through an interphase between those divisions, according to information kindly given by Dr. Arnold H. Sparrow, but there are cases, e.g., *Trillium* (Swanson, 1943), where it is reported that interphase may be omitted.

Conclusions

Preparations for division may be distinguished from over-all cell growth. In the normal growth-division cycle these preparations extend over a large proportion of the time between divisions. In certain natural and experimental systems preparations for a series of divisions may take place before any division is seen, with the result that the interphase time is greatly reduced.

TABLE I

THE TIME OF DNA SYNTHESIS IN THE MITOTIC CYCLE

Species	Tissue	Time of DNA synthesis	Method[a]	Author	Conditions
Rat	Liver	Interphase	C	Price and Laird (1950)	Regeneration
		Late interphase	A	Kleinfeld (1953)	Regeneration; estimated synthesis time 90 min.
	Small intestine crypts	Telophase to early interphase	A	Pasteels and Lison (1950)	—
		Interphase	A	Alfert and Swift (1953)	—
Mouse	Embryo heart	Late interphase	A	Richards et al. (1956)	—
	Embryo liver	Late interphase	A	Swift (1950a)	—
	Liver	Late interphase	C	Barnum et al. (1956)	Max. P^{32} incorp. into DNA preceded mitotic max. by 6 to 12 hr.
	Spermatocytes	Interphase	A	Swift (1950a)	—
Grasshopper	Embryo neuroblasts	Mid-telophase through interphase to early prophase	B	Caulden (1957)	Thymidine-C^{14} uptake in *Chortophaga*; synthesis time 80 min.
	Early embryo	Interphase	A	Swift and Kleinfeld (1953)	—
	Spermatocytes	Interphase	A	Swift and Kleinfeld (1953)	Synthesis during pro-chromosome stage

[a] A = Feulgen microphotometry; B = radioautography; C = biochemical techniques.

TABLE I (*Continued*)

Species	Tissue	Time of DNA synthesis	Method[a]	Author	Conditions
Tradescantia	Root meristem	Mid-interphase	A	Swift (1953)	—
	Microsporocytes	Early prophase	A	Swift (1950b)	Synthesis during leptotene
		Early prophase	A and B	Moses and Taylor (1955)	Synthesis during leptotene
	Microspore	Late interphase	A	Swift (1950b)	—
		Late interphase	A and B	Moses and Taylor (1955)	—
	Generative nucleus	Early interphase	A	Woodard and Swift (1958)	—
Tulbaghia	Microspore	Very early interphase	A and B	Taylor (1958)	—
Trillium	Microsporocytes	Mid-prophase	C	Sparrow *et al.* (1952)	Synthesis during pachytene
		Interphase	B	Howard and Pelc (1951)	—
Vicia	Root meristem	Mid-interphase	A	Woodard and Swift (1958)	—

[a] A = Feulgen microphotometry; B = radioautography; C = biochemical techniques.

D. Identification of Specific Preparations for Division

In this section we shall consider briefly those processes that have been recognized as preparations for division. It is to be expected that more such processes will be discovered.

1. Reproduction of Chromosome Substance

a. Time of chromosome reproduction. The availability of methods for the estimation of the amounts of chromosomal substances (especially by microspectrophotometric methods; Walker and Richards, 1959) and the time course of their synthesis (by tracer methods) has made it possible to determine at what point in the cell cycle the synthesis occurs. The determination depends on the fact that DNA and the histones are the most characteristic constituents of chromosomes; they serve as useful *tracers* of chromosome substance in nuclei at stages when the chromosomes themselves are morphologically obscure. The concept of DNA and histones as tracers carries no necessary implications as to their functions.

An enormous amount of information on the timing of the synthesis of chromosomal substance is now at our disposal. Table I, for which the writer is indebted to Dr. Hewson Swift, gives only a sampling of this body of information. To this we may add Fig. 6, which shows the probable time course of nuclear DNA synthesis in representative plant, animal, and protozoan cells.

The main conclusion is clear enough; the normal expectation is that the DNA content of the nucleus will double—nearly exactly—before division. This generalization appears to hold not only for cells dividing by recognizable mitosis, but also for synchronized bacterial populations (measurements of DNA per cell in synchronized populations; Maruyama, 1956) and for ciliates [e.g., photometric studies by McDonald (1958) on *Tetrahymena*]. The localization of the period of DNA synthesis in the

---

Fig. 6.   The time course of DNA synthesis in representative plant, animal, and protozoan cells, as determined by a variety of methods.

A. DNA synthesis in root-tip cells of *Vicia faba*, the broad bean. The experimental points represent data obtained by the photometric measurements of Feulgen staining and are calculated from the statistical distribution of DNA contents of the nuclei in the dividing population, shown in histogram at lower right. The dotted line shows the time course of DNA synthesis in the same material as determined by Howard and Pelc (1953) by the autoradiographic method, employing P^{32}. The results of the two methods agree. After Deeley *et al.* (1957).

B. DNA synthesis in Krebs ascites tumor cells. The time course is calculated from the distribution of DNA values, measured by the photometric method after Feulgen staining. After Richards *et al.* (1956).

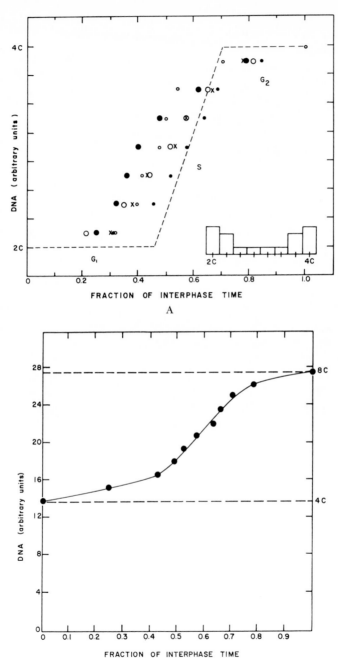

FRACTION OF INTERPHASE TIME

A

FRACTION OF INTERPHASE TIME

B

period before division does not depend on cytochemical techniques alone; it is also illustrated biochemically in cases such as that of mouse liver (Barnum *et al.*, 1956), where diurnal waves of mitosis may be recognized. Here it is found that a wave of DNA syntheses precedes the wave of mitosis by 6–12 hours.

It has been shown (Bloch and Godman, 1955a, b) that the histone and DNA levels run parallel in the course of the increase in chromosomal substance, a fact which suggests that, in effect, the material is being synthesized as nucleoprotein.

At present, the only generalization we can make is that the major part of DNA and histone synthesis in plant, animal, and protozoan cells takes place during interphase. It is now clear that there is no uniformity in the time of the beginning or ending of these syntheses. This will be clear even from the small sample of available data that is given in Table I and Fig. 6. DNA synthesis has been reported to begin as early as telophase and as late as prophase. In many animal and plant cells it seems to begin only some time after division and to be completed some time before division. In one ciliate, *Tetrahymena* (Walker and Mitchison, 1957), it appears to extend throughout the entire interphase period, but in another, *Paramecium* (Walker and Mitchison, 1957; Kimball and Barka, 1959), it seems to be confined to the latter part of interphase. If we were to regard chromosome synthesis as being quite independent of other preparations for division, these different patterns would merely be telling us that other preparations for division take either more or less time than does the doubling of DNA and histone. But considerable significance has been attached to the frequently observed fact that the syntheses begin only some time after division and are completed a relatively short time

---

Fig. 6. C. Time relations between synthesis and mitosis in cultures of connective tissue of rat heart, illustrating an autoradiographic method. The cultures were exposed to tritiated thymidine for a 1-hour period at various times after the beginning of the outgrowth of the culture. All were fixed after 24 hours. Autoradiographs of all cells in mitosis at 24 hours were examined to see whether there had been DNA synthesis during the hour when they were given labeled thymidine. It is concluded that synthesis begins 13–14 hours before metaphase and ends 3–4 hours before metaphase. After Harris (1959).

D. DNA synthesis in two ciliates, by a photometric method similar to that used for A and B, above. The lower curve shows a linear time course for *Tetrahymena* macronuclei in contrast with the upper curve for macronuclei of *Paramecium caudatum*, which shows a lag in early interphase and possibly the completion of DNA synthesis before division. Similar results were obtained for micronuclei of *P. caudatum* (Walker and Mitchison) and for macronuclei of *P. aurelia* (Kimball and Barka, 1959). After Walker and Mitchison (1957).

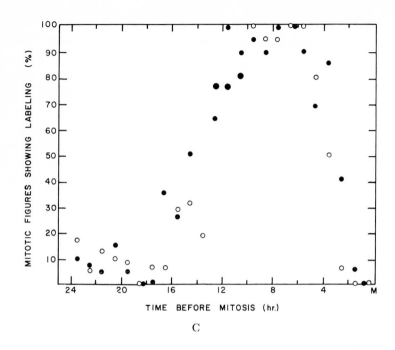

C

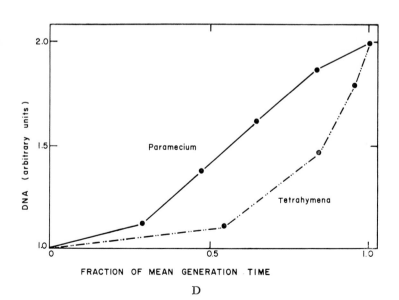

D

before division. The former may be a useful guide to processes controlling DNA and histone synthesis that may be related to the "decision" as to whether a cell of a higher organism will or will not divide again (cf. Section XVI, A, 1). Wherever there is a delay between the completion of the doubling of chromosome substance and the onset of division, we are bound to conclude that the completion of these syntheses is not a direct cause of division, that the cell must "wait" for something else to happen.

Conversely, we could cite numerous pieces of evidence that there is no synthesis of chromosome substance during the period of mitosis when the chromosomes are in motion. The observations of Pätau and Swift

TABLE II

THE DNA CONTENT OF NUCLEI AND OF SISTER GROUPS OF CHROMOSOMES
DURING MITOSIS (ONION ROOT TIP)[a]

Stage	DNA content (arbitrary units), total	Daughter groups	
Late interphase	19.1	—	—
Early prophase	17.5	—	—
Middle prophase	19.1	—	—
Late prophase	20.5	—	—
Metaphase	24.3	—	—
Early anaphase	17.3	—	—
Middle anaphase	23.0	—	—
Late anaphase	23.0	—	—
Very late anaphase (chromosome groups contracting)	20.4	10.4	10.1
Early telophase	18.4	9.7	8.7
Middle telophase	19.4	9.7	9.7
Late telophase	17.9	8.8	9.1

[a] These data were obtained by photometric measurements on Feulgen-stained preparations by the "two-wavelength method" (Pätau and Swift, 1953).

(Table II) illustrate this generalization, and it was elegantly demonstrated in the pioneering autoradiographic study of Howard and Pelc (1953), who found that P^{32} did not appear in the chromosomes of *Vicia faba* unless the exposure to the isotope was long enough to enable cells in interphase to pass into division.

We can associate the period of DNA synthesis with that part of the cell's life during which the chromosome material is contained within a nuclear membrane. There is at least some experimental evidence suggesting that the status of the chromosomes themselves during mitosis is incompatible with DNA synthesis. When cells are blocked during mitosis by colchicine (Taylor *et al.*, 1957) or by mercaptoethanol (Bibring, cited by Bucher and Mazia, 1960) they fail to synthesize DNA, even though these agents have no appreciable effect on DNA synthesis during interphase. However, various reports (Table I) that DNA synthesis may begin in telophase or extend into prophase argue against the simple assumption that chromosomes must be in the fully extended interphase condition in order for DNA synthesis to take place.

In view of the recent evidence (Kornberg, 1959a, b) implicating a complex enzyme system in DNA synthesis, it would not be surprising if the internal environment and metabolic machinery of the nucleus as a whole were to decide when chromosome reproduction can begin. After all, self-duplication does not imply autonomy.

In bacteria, where we do not yet have adequate cytological guideposts, the timing of DNA synthesis is not entirely clear. There is now evidence that organisms such as *E. coli* and *Salmonella typhimurium* growing under ordinary conditions, synthesize DNA continuously, without evidence of an interruption during division (Schaechter *et al.*, 1959; Young and Fitz-James, 1959; McFall and Stent, 1959; Abbo and Pardee, 1960). This is shown by the fact that almost all the cells in a culture contain labeled DNA after a very short period of exposure to tritiated thymidine (Schaechter *et al.*) and by the "radioactive suicide" method (McFall and Stent). In the latter case, the incorporation of P^{32} of high specific activity into DNA can be demonstrated by the fact that the decay of the phosphorus will "sterilize" the cells when they are stored at low temperature. It was shown that exposure to P^{32} of an asynchronous population for a fraction of a generation time led to the death of most of the cells, and it could be calculated that any period of the life cycle during which there was no DNA synthesis must be very short relative to the generation time.

In synchronized bacterial populations (e.g., Maruyama, 1956; Scott and Chu, 1959) the situation may be different; a definite periodicity of DNA synthesis is observed.

By a rather intricate experimental approach, Maaløe and Hanawalt (1961) appear to have demonstrated that DNA synthesis in *E. coli* does proceed in distinct rounds of duplication with brief interruption. They also conclude that the initiation of each round depends on some event, linked to protein and/or RNA synthesis, which is not required for the completion of the doubling of the DNA. If the interruption of the DNA synthesis coincided with nuclear division, it would provide a point of similarity between bacterial division and mitosis.

   b. Causal relations between chromosome reproduction and cell divi-

sion. Chromosome reproduction, reflected as DNA synthesis, is so implicit in the over-all sense of cell division that attempts to correlate it with the causation and prevention of division are inevitable. It is possible to limit cell reproduction by limiting net DNA synthesis, and it would appear that this is a common form of control. Some of the basic relationships are best shown in experiments on bacteria, e.g., *E. coli* (Cohen and Barner, 1954) where mutants incapable of synthesizing thymine are grown in the absence of thymine. Division appears to be impossible, but other types of synthesis continue uncurbed, and, as we have seen, the "unbalanced growth" leads to death. In higher organisms, antimetabolites presumed to interfere specifically with DNA synthesis inhibit division (Biesele, 1958). In a great many differentiated tissues of plants (e.g., Deeley *et al.*, 1957) and of animals (e.g., Vendrely, 1955b; and many others) the DNA level is found to be the diploid, i.e., the level at which the cell came out of the division that produced it. In general DNA synthesis may be viewed as an anticipation of division, though it does not predict it infallibly. In Section XVI we shall consider cases where cells which have completed the doubling of DNA fail to divide, presumably because something else is limiting the division.

Is DNA synthesis to be viewed as *causal* to a given division or merely as a prerequisite? Various facts argue against an immediate causal relation. One, the fact that DNA synthesis in many cases is completed long before division has been interpreted (Mazia, 1956a, b; Swann, 1957) as excluding the idea that it constitutes a stimulus or trigger. There are also the numerous cases where DNA sufficient for several divisions accumulates, after which the divisions take place in sequence without intervening synthesis. This is seen, for instance, in the so-called "light cells" of *Chlorella* (Iwamura, 1955). In the course of an appropriate regime of illumination the cells grow large and their nuclei accumulate abnormally large amounts of DNA. These cells then may divide four times to produce sixteen "dark cells," which in turn are capable of repeating the cycle. A comparable sequence is observed in *Tetrahymena* after temperature cycling (see Section XV, B). Thus DNA synthesis need not determine a given division.

From this we might expect that polyploid cells could easily divide without DNA synthesis to give diploids. In the well-studied case of tobacco pith cells in culture (Pätau *et al.*, 1957) it is shown that such is not the rule. More commonly, polyploidy is maintained by the intervention of chromosome duplication between divisions. It is interesting that the degree of ploidy does affect the probability that a cell will divide, and this in turn depends on physiological conditions. In plant tissues, where the matter has been studied in some detail, diploid cells normally have a greater tendency to divide, and polyploidy is often associated with differentiation (Pätau et al., 1957; Torrey, 1958). However, the division of polyploid cells can be stimulated by hormonal factors, such as kinetin (6-furfurylaminopurine).

Cases where polyploid cells may divide without intervening DNA synthesis to yield daughters of lower ploidy are most important because they demonstrate again that DNA synthesis need not be involved immediately in the drive of the cell to division. A striking example is seen in the transformation of normal differentiated plant cells into tumor cells that results from bacterial infection. In a study by Rasch et al. (1959) it has been shown that during the production of the crown gall tumors in bean stems (Vicia faba) by infection with Agrobacterium rubi, "some normal nuclei of the higher DNA classes (with 2, 4 or 8 times the DNA content of diploid nuclei) were reduced to diploid levels by successive cell divisions without intervening DNA synthesis."

At the extreme, even cells that are not initially polyploid may divide without a preceding doubling of DNA to yield daughters of less than diploid DNA content. Such a case has been described by Lindner (1959) for mouse acites tumors treated with 5-fluorouracil. The daughter cells of division following treatment contained half the normal amount of DNA, but the normal number of chromosome threads. They were abnormal in other respects, not relevant here, and their capability of further division was far below normal. Apart from the striking dissociation of division from DNA synthesis, the apparent subdivision of the chromosomes during the experiments is most interesting and is relevant to the theory of the multiplicity of the chromosomes, to be discussed in Section VI, B, 2.

c. Conclusions. As a generalization, we may say that DNA synthesis, viewed as a tracer for the doubling of chromosome substance, is a normal feature of the pathway to division and that cells which will not divide do not increase their DNA content. But cells which have doubled their DNA do not necessarily divide, and not all inhibitors or stimulants of division act through DNA synthesis. Endomitotic situations, natural and experimental, tell us that the whole cycle of chromosome reproduction may proceed without the entrance of the cell into division. The relation of DNA to the control of division will be treated in Section XVI. Now we need only stress these facts as illustrating the point of view embodied in our time map: the various preparations for division are dissociable, though they may interact, and no one of them may be dominant.

We are not sure that the doubling of the chemical constituents of

chromosomes is a full measure of reproduction. To make two chromosomes from one involves substances other than DNA and histone. It
is conceivable that there is a step of final assembly of macromolecules
into a chromosome over and above the chemical replication of the genetic
material. The reproduction of that part of the chromosome which is most
essential in mitosis—the kinetochore—is not reckoned with in the cytochemical studies. In short, we are not yet prepared to fix the time of
completion of total chromosome reproduction in relation to division.

2. Reproduction of the Mitotic Centers

The act of mitosis involves a polarization of the mitotic apparatus,
which in turn defines the destinations of the chromosomes and the plane
of division. In the archetypal form of animal mitosis, as symbolized in
Fig. 1, the poles may be sharply defined by what we shall call the "mitotic
centers." That these may be embodied physically in a "polar corpuscle"
was discovered in 1876 by Van Beneden, who used this expressive term.
Since that time, the polar corpuscle has received many other names:
"central corpuscle," "division center," "central body," "centriole," etc.;
these terms are not exact equivalents because many of them imply the
preconceptions of their creators as to the nature of the centers. The confusion arose legitimately from the wide variation in the microscopic
structure of the poles; Wilson (1925, Fig. 321) illustrates no less than
eight fundamental morphological variants, and there are many others.
If we can speak of a typical pattern, it is that of a large "centrosphere"
containing one or more smaller "centrioles," which are described (Wilson,
1925, p. 674) as "granule(s) of extreme minuteness, staining intensely
with iron hematoxylin, crystal violet, and some other dyes, and often
hardly to be distinguished from a microsome save that it lies at the focus
of the astral rays." This compact form of the centriole probably corresponds to the centrioles of rather constant structure that now have been
seen with the electron microscope, as will be described below. But it was
not always found by the older microscopists, and it is not certain whether
its electron microscopic counterpart is to be found even in animal cells
of all kinds.

In their original status as extranuclear particles possessed of the
power of self-reproduction and as elements that controlled the polarity of division, the centrioles were naturally exciting at a time when such
ideas were new. The excitement was enhanced by Boveri's theory that
the essential event of the fertilization of the animal egg was the introduction of the centriole by the spermatozoon. As efforts to find centrioles
in plant cells were frustrated, as their morphology seemed more and

more variable, and as Boveri's theory apparently collapsed with the discovery of artificial parthenogenesis, interest waned. Indeed the summaries given by Heidenhain (1907) and Wilson (1925) come close to giving a complete survey of our knowledge until the 1950's, although we shall cite a few important works of the intervening decades. Today, centrioles are exciting to us again.

a. The concept of the centers. i. Definition and structure. Through most of this chapter, the rather noncommittal term "center" will be used in an operational sense to define those functions that are associated with centrioles when centrioles can be seen. The operational meaning of the center is that of a body defining a mitotic pole, whether it is visible or not. The implication is that there is an external point toward which the chromosome moves, regardless of the mechanism of movement. It is further implied that the centers are self-reproducing bodies in the sense that they are derived from other identical bodies, although they cannot meet the second criterion of a self-reproducing body, which has to do with mutation (Pontecorvo, 1958).

As has been mentioned, the structure of the centers as seen by light microscopy is highly variable; only in favorable cases can any definite centriolar structure be ascertained. Examples are certain flagellates (cf. Fig. 13), and various animal cells in which rod-shaped or V-shaped centrioles have been seen (reviewed by Costello, 1961). At the other extreme, distinct centrioles may not be seen at all or may be seen only in certain stages of mitosis, but their positions are pointed by the astral rays. Electron microscopy now provides a consistent morphological conception of a centriole as a characteristic body composed of nine tubules in cylindrical array (Fig. 7). The tubules are each about 200 A. in diameter and 5000 A. long, and the cylinder which they circumscribe is about 1500 A. in diameter (de Harven and Bernhard, 1956; Amano, 1957; Bessis et al., 1958; other structural details are discussed in these papers). Centrioles of this form are commonly observed as pairs, and it is most interesting that the "sisters" are generally observed to lie at right angles to each other, not parallel. This orientation may be preserved as sister centrioles separate to form poles; thus the axes of the centrioles determine the axes of division (Costello, 1961).

The cylindrical structure has now been found in many kinds of animal cells, although variants have already been reported. For example, De Robertis and Franco Ruffo (1957) describe centrioles of a quite different pattern in grasshopper testes, "round or oval shaped masses of 1–2 μ . . . composed of very dense granules . . . of about 160 Å diameter tightly packed in a dense matrix."

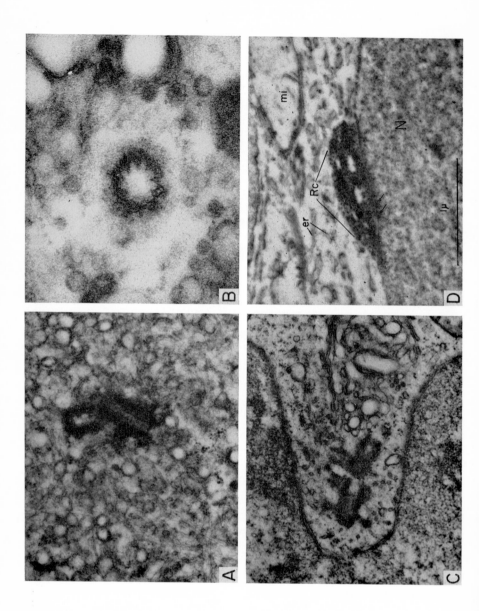

Now that the electron microscope has given some idea of the structural complexity of compact centrioles corresponding to the classic "granule of extreme minuteness," it is legitimate to inquire into the polar structure in forms in which the optical microscope detected either no centrioles or obscure masses whose presence was indicated by the astral rays.

ii. Mitotic centers in plant cells? We cannot evade the fact that centrioles have not been seen in great numbers of organisms, especially the higher plants. In morphological terms, we can only ask whether centrioles may be found in such organisms now that electron microscopy provides new criteria of identification. The functional criteria of a polar organ apply equally well to plant and animal material. For example, multipolar mitotic figures may be induced in plant cells as in animal cells, e.g., induction of such figures by treatment of onion root tips with alcohol (Barthelmess, 1957). In such cases, not only do groups of chromosomes move toward the several poles, but also their metaphase orientation with respect to the poles is quite like that seen in multipolar figures in animals, which are attributed to extra centrioles. In animal cells the centrioles are often indistinct but are identified as the foci of asters. In more recent literature on plant mitosis it has been claimed that asters may be induced, e.g., by treatment of root tips with aminopyrin (Oestergren *et al.*, 1953), or may be observed by appropriate

---

FIG. 7. Four views of centrioles, stressing various features as shown by the electron microscope.

A. A pair of centrioles of an embryonic mouse fibroblast in interphase, showing the centriole as a cylinder bounded by tubules. One of the members of the pair is cut in longitudinal section. Note that the two centrioles do not lie parallel to each other. The surrounding cytoplasm contains a reticulum of elongated elements which may conceivably represent the aggregation of fibrous material that will be assembled into spindles as asters, but there is no direct evidence of this. Photograph by courtesy of Dr. W. Bernhard. Magnification: $\times$ 43,000.

B. Cross section of a centriole at high magnification, showing a helicoidal structure of the tubular elements making up the wall of the cylinder. Photograph by courtesy of Dr. W. Bernhard. Magnification: $\times$ 98,000.

C. Centrioles in a mouse spleen cell, in interphase. The pair of large centrioles, lying near the nuclear surface, appears to be proliferating a pair of smaller centrioles at right angles to the cylinder surfaces. Photograph by courtesy of Dr. E. De Harven (Bernhard and de Harven, 1960). Magnification: $\times$ 33,000.

D. The "ring centriole" (*Rc*) in early spermatids of a grasshopper, *Laplatacris dispar*. At more advanced stages of spermiogenesis, the centriole has the "typical" structure seen in A–C. Photograph by courtesy of Professor E. De Robertis (De Robertis and Franco Ruffo, 1957). Magnification: $\times$ 22,000.

means without experimental treatment (Oestergren, 1954; Lima-de-Faria, 1958).

If centrioles had never been seen in animal cells, the hypothesis of the existence of centers might well have evolved as a general hypothesis to account for the metaphase orientations and the direction of chromosome movements in normal and multipolar mitosis. There is no simpler answer to the question, "How do the chromosomes know where to go?" This does not make it a true hypothesis, and not all cytologists even consider it a useful one. A summary of arguments *against* the hypothesis that plant cells contain centrioles is given in a review by Lepper (1956).

We may mention the phenomenon of *divergent* mitosis as one that in some respects calls for the assumption of some kind of center and in other ways argues against a simple view of the center. In typical mitosis in animals that possess centers, the chromosomes move as though they were converging on a common point. There are, however, cases where the individual chromosomes behave as though they are polarized independently, and in extreme cases their paths diverge, rather than converge, at anaphase. Indeed, Walters (1958) has recently described divisions in hybrids of the genus *Bromus* (a grass) in which one pole is convergent while the other is divergent. Some examples of nonconvergent division spindles are shown in Fig. 8. It is important to note that nonconvergent chromosome movements have been observed both in plants and in animals. In certain insect groups (Hughes-Schrader, 1948a, 1955; Cooper, 1939) they are seen only in meiotic divisions; mitotic figures are convergent. In plants where meiotic figures are normally convergent, divergence may be a phenotypic expression of a mutant: for example, ultraviolet irradiation of maize pollen gave rise to a recessive mutation *dv* (divergent) which, in the homozygous condition, brought about a highly divergent meiotic movement (Clark, 1940; cf. Fig. 8, B). The convergence of chromosomal fibers may be disturbed experimentally, e.g., by extreme flattening of the dividing cells (cf. Fig. 9).

Obviously, the existence of nonconvergent mitosis throws doubt on any generalization calling for the polarization of mitosis by unique, compact "polar corpuscles." But at the same time it argues for the conception that something exists at the poles which determines the destinations of the chromosomes. They do not move at random. Divergent anaphases occur consistently where they occur at all, and they are obviously governed by the genetic background, as in the case of the *dv* gene in maize. In those animal cells in which nonconvergent divisions are seen in male meiosis, we are inclined to assume the persistence of the centers through these stages, unless we abandon the hypothesis of the continuity of the centers entirely. For these spermatocytes produce spermatozoa, the spermatozoa have tails, and sperm tails are believed to be derived from centrioles. Moreover, these same animals show normal convergent spindles during mitosis. To attribute the direction of anaphase movement of chromosomes to the metaphase configuration is to beg the question

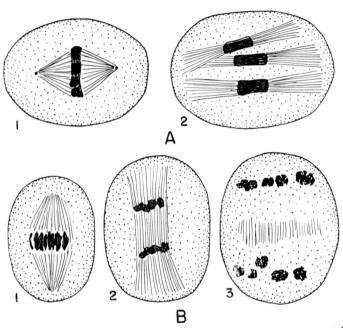

FIG. 8.   Some examples of divergent division figures.   A1. Spermatogonial mitosis in the coccid *Llaveia bouvari.* A2. First meiotic metaphase, to be compared with A1. In A1, note convergence of mitotic spindle, with compact centriole represented. In meiosis (A2), each chromosome appears to be polarized independently. After Hughes-Schrader (1931). B1. Normal first meiotic metaphase in maize. Spindle is convergent. B2. Nonconvergent anaphase in first meiotic division in maize carrying gene for "divergence." B3. First meiotic telophase in "divergent" maize. The several groups of chromosomes will form "karyomeres." This results in multiple spindles in the second meiotic division. If, however, a spore receives a full complement of chromosomes, distributed among several nuclei, these will enter the first microspore division synchronously and will produce a single normal mitotic figure. B1–B3 drawn after Clark (1940).

because it is just as difficult to understand the movement *into* metaphase without assuming some activity at the poles as to understand the poleward anaphase movement. In general, the existence of nonconvergent mitosis in certain consistent forms and as a genetically controlled phenomenon supports the idea of a specialized organization of the poles but disallows the hypothesis that the centriole is necessarily a single unit. A simple alternative is that the centers (or, if one prefers, the "spindle organizers" in cases where the poles are not centralized) are compound structures (Walters, 1958; Lettré and Lettré, 1958, 1960). The subunits might ordinarily be clustered in a compact centriole or might be arrayed in a line or plane to give nonconvergent figures. Ideally,

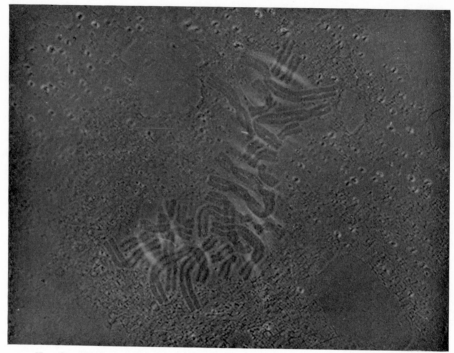

FIG. 9.   Divergence of chromosomal fibers resulting from the extreme flattening of an endosperm cell of *Haemanthus*. This may be compared with the convergent arrangement in an unflattened cell (Figs. 37, 69). Photographed through polarization microscope; chromosomal fibers are birefringent and appear bright. Photograph by Drs. S. Inoué and A. Bajer.

we would imagine that the numbers of such subunits would bear some relation to the numbers of chromosomes. While such a proposal might be frowned on in principle as a hypothesis whose function is to save another hypothesis, it has some heuristic significance, for the morphological and functional polar termination of the spindle fiber is a definite problem in the structure of the mitotic apparatus. The spindle fiber does not terminate in a vacuum, and at the very least we are required to discover how it is "anchored." The structure of the normal compact centriole, which is now being resolved more and more finely by electron microscopy, may serve as a guide to less compact polar structures.

b. Origin of centers. It generally has been thought, since their discovery in the nineteenth century, that centrioles are permanent and self-reproducing bodies. Many observers have traced the centers through the life histories of various cells by microscopic methods (e.g., Pollister, 1933), and the recent electron microscopic studies, already cited, have not failed to find them at any stage which was examined (e.g., Bessis *et al.*, 1958).

i. Cases of apparent de novo origin. "Cytasters." Controversy concerning the possible *de novo* origin of centers originated in the discovery of "cytasters" in activated sea urchin eggs (Morgan, 1896), after which they were discovered in eggs of other animals including Amphibia (cf. Brachet, 1957, p. 163; Briggs and King, 1959, p. 559). In the sea urchin egg, Harvey (1936) and Lorch (1952; Lorch *et al.*, 1953) have shown that cytasters may be induced even after removal of the nucleus, and Lorch has also described their development in sea urchin blastomeres from which the whole mitotic apparatus including the normal asters has been removed micrurgically. The question of cytasters has been discussed most seriously in relation to the problem of artificial parthenogenesis. "Activation" of the egg may produce a number of cytasters in the cytoplasm. Some of these do not interact with the chromosomes, but they do persist and divide. Typically one cytaster does engage the chromosomes, and a monopolar mitotic figure is formed (Fig. 10). This can give rise to a typical bipolar figure, after which mitosis and development proceed normally. Occasionally, more than one monopolar spindle can be seen in the same egg, and multipolar spindles are seen commonly. In multipolar spindles, it is uncertain whether several cytasters of independent origin have engaged the female chromosome, of whether the multiple poles are the progeny of a single one. Figure 10 illustrates the appearance and behavior of cytasters.

In short, successful artificial parthenogenesis implies that the egg cytoplasm has given rise to fully functional centers, which not only engage the chromosomes in a normal mitotic apparatus, but also may reproduce even if they are not associated with chromosomes. This, then, has been the factual background for questioning the generalization that the centers are self-perpetuating bodies and do not arise *de novo*.

It is commonly assumed that cytasters form without reference to a true centriole; Brachet (1957) states this view: "The main interest of this abnormality lies in the fact that, in eggs, asters may form around almost any cytoplasmic granules; thus, the formation of an aster does not require

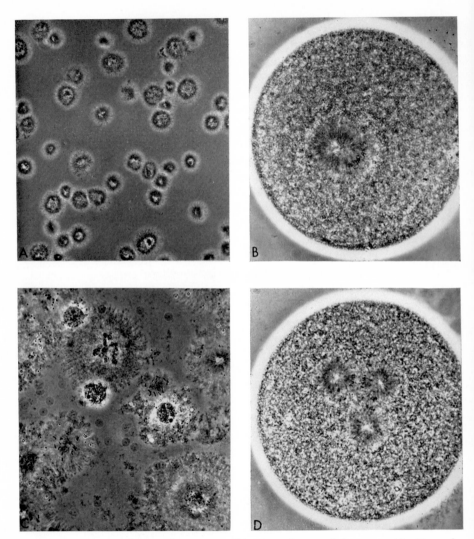

Fig. 10. "Cytasters" in parthenogenetically activated eggs of the sea urchin *Strongylo-centrotus purpuratus*. Phase contrast views of material prepared by the alcohol-digitonin method for isolating of mitotic figures (Section IX, B, 1). A. Isolated cytasters (low power). B. Single cytaster in an incompletely dispersed egg. The aster has engaged the chromosomes and has formed a monopolar metaphase. C. Isolated monopolar figures, as in B, showing chromosomes in several stages of their mitotic cycle. D. Cell in which three cytasters have engaged the chromosomes in a tripolar mitotic figure. Experiments of Dr. Ellen R. Dirksen.

the presence of a specific centrosome in this case." The paradox depends on the assumption that the egg lacks centrioles, which is fortified by the fact that normally the mitotic apparatus seems to arise on connection with centrioles introduced by the spermatozoon.

The question whether cytasters are organized around true centrioles or around particles of other kinds has now been answered by the work of Dirksen (1961). An electron-microscopic examination of cytasters in parthenogenetically activated sea urchin eggs has shown the presence, in the cytasters, of typical centrioles of the kind illustrated in Fig. 7, A–C, identical in structure to the centrioles seen in normal cleavage of the same eggs. Clearly, then, the problem of the origin of cytasters is a problem of the origin of centrioles.

Let us reconsider the question of the presence of centrioles in the egg. One of the remarkable generalizations of classic cytology is the so-called "Henneguy-Lenhossék hypothesis" (Henneguy, 1898; von Lenhossék, 1898; discussed by Wilson, 1925, pp. 690-700). According to this, mitotic centers and the "basal granules" of cilia and flagella are homologous or identical bodies. To express it differently, this class of particle may serve alternatively in the origin of the spindle fibers or flagella or cilia or may, as in the case of certain flagellates, serve both functions simultaneously.

As predicted by the hypothesis, the fine structure of basal granules of cilia often corresponds to the typical cylindrical structure of centrioles, described on p. 117 (Rouiller and Fauré-Fremiet, 1958; Nanney and Rudzinska, 1960, Figs. 2 and 3). Perhaps even more striking are the photographs by Sotelo and Trujillo-Cenoz (1958), who trace the origin of cilia in neural epithelial cells of the chick embryo from basal granules, which in turn are observed to be mitotic centrioles that have taken up a position near the cell surface. Comparable observations had already been made by Henneguy and others in the nineteenth century, but their interpretation was questionable as long as the particles were characterizable only as staining dots.

Let us recall that both the centrioles and the basal granules (Lwoff, 1950) have been viewed as self-reproducing bodies on the basis of a great variety of evidence. What is under consideration is the one celebrated case where such a particle is alleged to arise *de novo*: the formation of cytasters in animal eggs. Let us also recall the elementary zoological fact that these animal eggs will produce cilia and flagella at later stages of development, whether they have been fertilized by spermatozoa or have been activated parthenogenetically. If we do not admit that the parthenogenetic eggs contain particles that are destined to become basal granules, we must conclude that the latter too arise *de novo* in parthenogenesis. If the eggs do contain these particles, they could be converted to centers under special conditions, just as the reverse occurs in the formation of cilia and flagella. Thus, an alternative to the hypothesis of the *de novo* origin of centers in the case of the cytasters is the hypothesis that they arise from presumptive basal granules in the cytoplasm, if there is more than one such granule, numerous cytasters could be produced, which is the case.

Indeed, the assumption that the egg contains no centriole of its own deserves re-examination. If centrioles are permanent and self-reproducing structures, it seems odd that they should "die" after their operations in the meiotic divisions in the ovary, though they survive spermatogenesis. The commonly accepted view that the centers of the dividing egg are contributed by the spermatozoon may have some other explanation. For that matter, the long-rejected hypothesis that the egg has a centriole which joins the sperm centriole (Fol, 1891) has come again under discussion in connection with the theory of mitosis that will be discussed later (Lettré and Lettré, 1959).

A second hypothetical source of true centrioles may be mentioned here. There is a great deal of evidence arguing for a homology between centrioles and the kinetochores of chromosomes (Schrader, 1953). The strongest support is Pollister's demonstration in the snail *Viviparus* that kinetochores may in fact be transformed into centrioles. In this remarkable case, it was noted that a certain number of the spermatids contained an abnormally small amount of chromosome material and a correspondingly large number of centrioles; the latter could not only be counted, but also were made evident by the presence of supernumerary tail filaments (Fig. 11).

The correspondence between the number of chromosomes lost and the number of centrioles gained could easily be accounted for by the interpretation that kinetochores had taken over the role of centrioles and that

FIG. 11. The homology between centrioles and kinetochores. Typical and atypical spermatogenesis of a snail, *Viviparus malleatus*. In the typical line, the chromosomes all have kinetochores and the centriole is seen as a single particle, reproducing before each division. The spermatids have a normal chromosome complement and the single centriole gives rise to a single flagellum. In the atypical line most of the chromosomes have lost their kinetochores, and there is a corresponding increase in the number of centriolar particles at the mitotic centers. The distribution of the chromosomes is erratic in the divisions, and they are not included in the nucleus at telophase. The extra centrioles, presumably derived from the lost kinetochores, reproduce and separate like normal centrioles and after meiosis give rise to extra flagella. After Pollister and Pollister (1943).

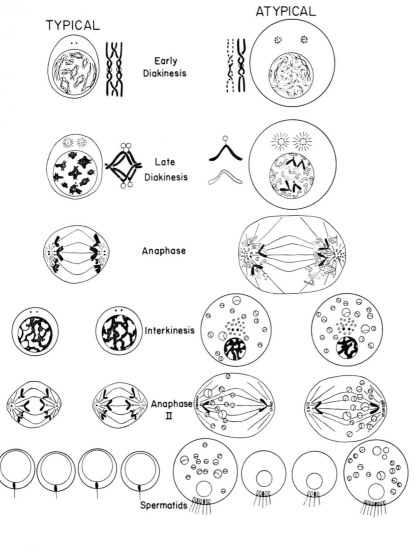

Akinetic chromosomes

Chromosomes with kinetochores

Flagella derived from normal centrioles

Flagella whose basal bodies are derived from kinetochores

the defective chromosomes could no longer participate in division. From Pollister's description of the chromosomes, it is evident that they cannot replace the lost kinetochores. This view is consistent with the opinion that these bodies, which we now see in their three roles as kinetochores, centrioles, and basal granules, are to be regarded as self-reproducing.

The origin of centrioles from kinetochores would not account for the formation of cytasters in eggs, for these may be produced in anucleate fragments. It is brought up here only to complete a general discussion of the possible origins of centers.

Considerable space has been devoted to this discussion of the relatively obscure instance of the cytasters. The issue is far from trivial. Our conception of the reproductive organization of cells depends on the recognition of those elements which are *permanent* and *self-reproducing* and those which are not. The problem has been considered primarily from the point of view of the geneticist, which emphasizes "mutability" (e.g., Pontecorvo, 1958), and the concept of "structural information" (Ephrussi, 1958). In genetics, the question has been whether there exists a general class of extranuclear particles, enjoying names such as "plasmagene" and "cytogene" when they are in fashion, which plays a significant role in hereditary transmission and perhaps in differentiation. Work on the subject has provided substantial insight into the role of the cytoplasm in heredity (Ephrussi, 1953, 1958; Nanney, 1957), but palpable self-reproducing particles have seldom materialized. On the other hand, it is difficult even to assign meaning to the question whether centrioles, "basal granules," and kinetochores are mutable, but there is no doubt of their physical existence and only small doubt of their self-reproduction in a naive material sense. When they reproduce, a second particle arises next to the first, and if the one is not already present another will not appear. It might be imagined that this kind of self-reproduction is a second-order consequence of a nuclear event; for example, that the pre-existing particle may be merely a necessary site at which molecules duplicated in the nucleus may be assembled. This is not the case, for it was shown long ago that centers may duplicate and form bipolar spindles without chromosomes, even when the nucleus is entirely absent. A long series of observations to this effect, beginning with Boveri in 1896, is cited by Wilson (1925, p. 176). The earliest experiments on sea urchin eggs were quite simple. If the eggs were shaken during division, all the chromosomes went to one pole in some cases, although both daughter cells received their normal complement of centers. It was then easily possible to observe the multiplication of the centers in cells containing no chromosomes.

The most perfectly studied case of an extranuclear reproducing particle is that of the basal granules (or "kinetosomes") of ciliates, as described by Lwoff (1950) and others, for here the major differentiations of the organism are transmitted by these particles. But we have seen that three kinds of particles may in fact represent a single type of particle expressing itself in different ways. A kinetochore may become a centriole, a centriole may become a basal granule, and as we have suggested, the cytaster may represent a presumptive basal granule turned centriole. In their twin aspects, as self-reproducing entities and as indispensable organizers or oriented fibrous structures, these are remarkable particles indeed and worthy of a prominent place in anyone's thoughts about the plan of the cell.

c. *The multiplicity of the centers and their method of reproduction.*
i. *Experimental evidence.* The oldest approach to the reproduction of the centers is through microscopic recognition and counting. During the first vogue of the centers (very well summarized by Heidenhain, 1907) a great deal of attention was paid to these problems, and Heidenhain's summary (pp. 223-224) supplies an illuminating background to our discussion. In free translation, he says: "(1) The centers of cells consist of two or more central bodies (centrioles) and a substance uniting them (substance of the 'centrodesmose'); such a group of centrioles I call a 'microcenter'. (2) The centrioles are sharply bounded solid granules of very minute size, which possess the capacity to assimilate, to grow, and to multiply by budding (unequal division). (3) Typical cells contain only one group of central bodies, consisting of 2–4 centrioles; the giant cells of bone marrow, however, contain several groups of central bodies, each with several to many centrioles. (4) The sphere (centrosphere) described by Van Beneden is not a constant feature either of the cell or of the centers, but is a specially structured portion of the cytoplasm. (5) The centrioles will probably be seen in cells of all species. (6) The substance of the centers is specific in character. (7) The central spindle and the centrioles comprise a unit, for the central spindle derives from the differentiation and growth of the 'centrodesmose.' "

It should be explained that the term "centrodesmose" refers to the material between sister centers (Fig. 12) as they separate, and "central spindle" refers to the continuous pole-to-pole connections of the mitotic apparatus which may form independently of chromosome-to-pole connections. We shall treat the central spindle in some detail later (Section VIII).

It is probable that Heidenhain was essentially correct in his conclusion that the centers are basically duplex, although the issue became confused as later microscopic studies often failed to disclose compact, stainable, and countable centrioles, even where the presence of centers was clearly indicated by asters (summarized by Schrader, 1953). For example, the studies of Cleveland (1938, 1953) on the very large and complex centrioles of certain flagellates, where microscopic identification is less difficult, have confirmed the conclusion that cells which contain centrioles at all contain at least two of them, with the important reservation that one may be "young" and the other "old." This is illustrated in

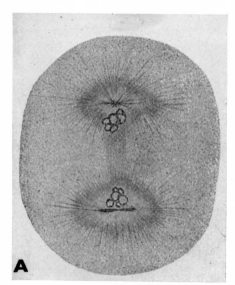

Fig. 12. The *centrodesmose*, or bridge which connects centers in the initial stages of their separation. A. Drawing by Boveri (1900) of telophase in the sea urchin *Echinus microtuberculatus*. B. Isolated mitotic figures of the sea urchin *Strongylocentrotus purpuratus* in phase contrast. The connections between the centriolar particles within the centrospheres are shown. The stage of the chromosomes with respect to the centers is not normal in this photograph, which was taken from an experiment on mitotic blockage. From Mazia *et al.* (1960).

Fig. 13. The duplex character of the centers is also shown in most of the electron microscopic studies of vertebrate cells to which we have referred (Fig. 7).

"Center" is a functional concept, describing an agency that is responsible for polarizing the mitotic apparatus. Stainable and resolvable particulate centrioles provide the structural basis for the activity of centers, when such structures can be found, but their absence cannot imply the absence of the function. Even when the particles are present and can be counted, we are still left with unanswered elementary questions; e.g., does the presence of two bodies mean that the pair of them is required in order to form a single pole?

It has become possible to deal with the question of the multiplicity of the centers in an experimental, functional way that does not depend on resolving them visually. In these studies (Mazia *et al.*, 1960) the

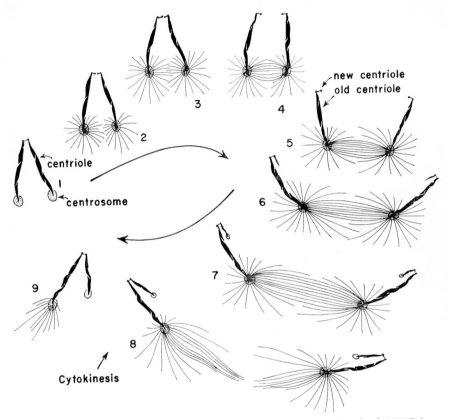

Fig. 13. The life cycle of the flagellate *Barbulanympha*. After Cleveland (1957a).

center was simply defined as a potential pole. The material used, eggs of sand dollars and sea urchins, does not have clearly defined centrioles in the microscopic sense, but the presence of asters is an aid in identifying the centers. The basic experimental observation is simply that when these cells are blocked by means of mercaptoethanol ($HSCH_2CH_2OH$) at about the beginning of metaphase, and the block is removed some time later, they divide into four (Fig. 16). Since a four-polar figure has been generated from a bipolar figure, as confirmed by direct observation

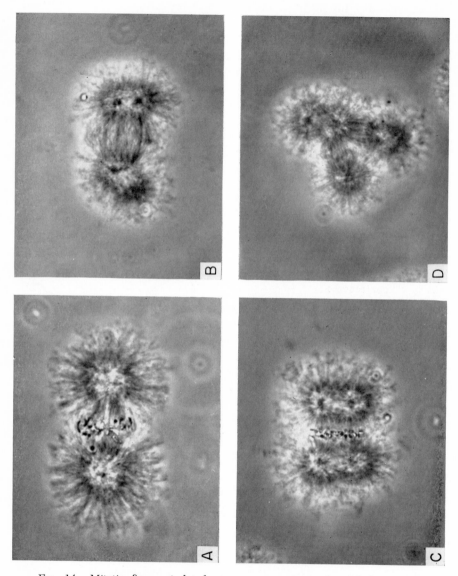

Fig. 14. Mitotic figures isolated at successive times after blocking eggs of *Strongylocentrotus purpuratus* at metaphase by means of mercaptoethanol. The sequence of stages in the generation of a four-polar figure from a two-polar figure is shown.

(Fig. 14), we may ask whether the centers accomplished an additional duplication during the block or whether we are merely observing the splitting of what were originally duplex centers. If the latter were the case, then each of the four daughter cells would be receiving only half the usual complement of "centriolar" units. That this indeed happens is shown in a remarkable way. The cells enter division and form only half a mitotic apparatus, a perfect monopolar figure (Fig. 15); in short, the

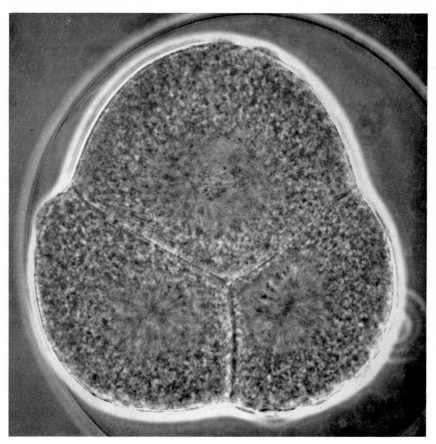

FIG. 15. The first mitosis following four-way division after blockage by mer-captoethanol (cf. Fig. 14). In this egg, one of the furrows failed, so that the upper cell received two centers while the lower two received one each. The latter form mitotic figures with only one pole, from which it was concluded that they had re-ceived only half the normal number of centriolar units. These cells cannot divide, but will return to interphase, undergo another cycle of replication of centriolar units, and will re-enter mitosis with two poles. The interpretation of the experiment is diagrammed in Fig. 16 (cf. Mazia *et al.*, 1960).

cells tell us by forming half a mitotic apparatus that they have received only half the normal number of pole-determining units.

Thus we conclude, without actually seeing centrioles, (1) that the cells enter division with four potential centers; (2) that the poles of a normal bipolar figure contain two units; and (3) that each of these units is capable of forming a pole when it is permitted to split from its sister by the blockage of other mitotic events. This operational "titration" of centers confirms Heidenhain's view of their normal duplicity, and adds the information that one unit may be adequate to form a pole.

ii. Interpretations. The reproductive cycle of the centers. In the literature the reproductive process of the centers is commonly described as a "division" and is sometimes illustrated as a fission procedure. We have seen, however, that Heidenhain spoke of it as a process of "budding" or unequal division. The most detailed microscopic observations have been made in more recent times by Cleveland (summarized in his 1957b paper). He has traced the complete life histories of the very favorable centrioles in a number of parasitic flagellates of woodroaches. These centrioles may be as long as 24 μ and may have a quite complex structure. A most important and perhaps unexpected finding is that these centrioles do not divide at all, in the common sense of the term. Rather, the "parent" centriole generates a tiny body, an "infant" centriole, so to speak, which remains connected to it by a strand and which grows to mature size and form. This may be what Heidenhain had observed in less favorable material. The cells studied by Cleveland contain four centrioles at the time of division, each pair consisting of one "old" and one "new," and never less than two (Fig. 13).

There is reason to think that this method of the reproduction of the centrioles is employed also in vertebrates, where they possess the cylindrical form described earlier. A remarkable electron microscopic observation by de Harven and Dustin (1960) (Fig. 9c) can be interpreted as being the image of a pair of "new" centrioles in the process of growing from their parents.

Here we have at least fragments of concrete information about the method of reproduction of a palpable intracellular particle. So far as the evidence goes, it tells us that the centrioles reproduce by what we may call a "generative" mechanism; that is, the parent body gives rise to a small "germ" or "seed" which determines the further growth of a complete mature copy of the original. "Generative" reproduction comprises three steps: the "conception" of the "germ" or "seed," which may be viewed as a replication mechanism at the molecular level; the growth of the daughter body; and the splitting apart of the two, or "parturition."

This may be contrasted with the more familiar "fission" mechanism, often postulated for the reproduction of chromosomes, in which the synthesis of a copy and the splitting apart of the sister products are viewed as inseparable events. At first glance, it might seem that the generative model is excessively complicated, but, if the ultimate information must be reproduced by some kind of template system, the reproduction by fission of a relatively large, three-dimensional body, such as a centriole, is difficult to imagine. To take the best-studied example—bacteriophage —it has now become unthinkable that the complete and complex phage particle would reproduce by fission; the known mechanism is the replication of molecular phage DNA, which then determines the synthesis and assembly of the complete phage.

In any event, the method of reproduction of the centrioles is not likely to be decided on the basis of intellectual attractiveness. The facts at present point to a generative method.

One of the consequences of the generative model is that "conception" (in the sense of the synthesis of the "germ" or "seed" of the new particle) is a separate event from the final "parturition" or splitting apart of parent and copy. In Fig. 13, it is suggested that these events appear to take place at about the same time; as the fully grown "new" centriole separates from its parent, both seem to have generated the tiny particles from which their progeny will grow.

In the studies of Mazia *et al.* (1960) it was shown experimentally that determination of "new" potential centers and separation of "old" centers from their progeny take place at about the same time—telophase or early interphase—and yet are dissociable events. Their conclusions are contained in Fig. 16. Without going into the rather intricate evidence, the basic facts are as follows. At the time of metaphase, the cells contain four potential poles, yet produce four actual poles only when blocked for a sufficient length of time. We have seen above that the production of four actual poles does not depend on an extra duplication. It must depend on the splitting of the pair of units at each of the original two poles. Therefore the splitting event does not depend on "conception" of new units. We may now imagine one reason why the mercaptoethanol block is necessary in order to obtain four actual poles; other mitotic events must be delayed while the two "new" potential poles complete their development and can split from their parents. If the new potential poles have been determined but have not yet split away, the pair consisting of parent and offspring can give rise to only one actual pole. This is shown when the time of blockage is too short (Fig. 14A) and in the case of the monopolar figures shown in Fig. 15. Cells containing monopolar

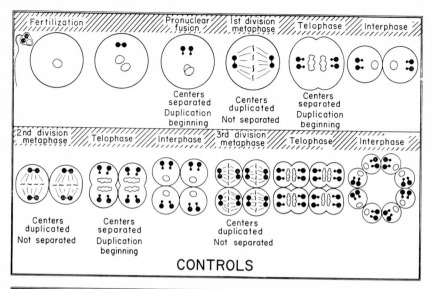

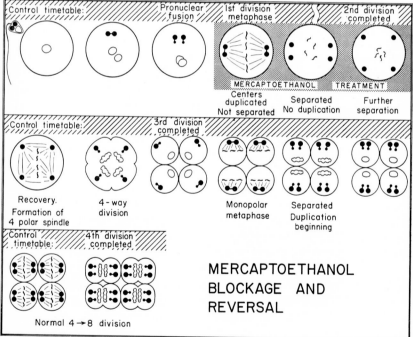

FIG. 16. Above: Diagrammatic interpretation of the reproductive cycle of the centrioles in sea urchin eggs. Below: Interpretation, on the basis of the scheme shown above of the four-way division following blockage with mercaptoethanol and of the subsequent formation of monopolar figures in the four daughter cells. From Mazia *et al.* (1960).

figures cannot divide, of course. They proceed to interphase and then re-enter mitosis with the normal number of poles. From this it is deduced that the poles of the monopolar figures actually contained two units as shown in Fig. 16, but that these function as one because they have not yet reached the stage at which they split.

Although we know that the splitting event does not depend on the duplication event, we do not know whether new units can be conceived if the old have not separated.

d. Reproduction of the centers as a preparation for division. Our original question was: Where on our time map does the reproduction of the centers belong, and is it to be regarded as a preparation for division? The question has become more complicated, since we may have to distinguish between replication in a chemical sense and the physical splitting of the products. Moreover, if the critical event in replication is a molecular event, we cannot depend on the visible detection of the "young" centriole to tell us when it was generated.

If we define the center operationally as a potential pole, a simple extension of experiments with mercaptoethanol gives an answer (Mazia *et al.*, 1960). The division of echinoderm blastomeres into four on recovery from blockage with mercaptoethanol was used to demonstrate the presence at metaphase of four units capable of forming poles. If this be true, then there must have been an earlier stage at which there were only two potential poles in the cells, for we have seen that they do not replicate while in mercaptoethanol. If the cells are blocked at these earlier stages, they should divide only into two upon recovery. This is the case, and it enables us to establish the time of transition from two potential poles to four. The observed time corresponds to late telophase or very early interphase. Indeed, the duplication of the centers may be considered to be the earliest event attributable to a given mitotic cycle.

Because of the precession of duplication in the chemical sense and the splitting event, we might even say that the true replication of the centers for a given mitotic cycle took place early in the parental generation or even late in the grandparental. In any case we have good reasons to believe that the units which will determine the poles of a given division have completed their reproduction, including both replication and splitting, well before the cell enters prophase, and that the establishment of the actual poles depends on the migration of these units. Indeed, the newer findings only confirm and refine the conclusion of Wilson (1925, p. 140) that "a separation of the two halves of each centriole," which takes place at telophase, "is clearly a preparation for the next division following, and might appropriately be reckoned as a prophasic event."

e. Chemical and experimental aspects. Almost nothing is known about the chemistry of the centers. The question of the presence and amounts of nucleic acids is crucial, for the centriole is one of the few known cytoplasmic particles of widespread occurrence having the ability to reproduce itself. It cannot be said that the centrioles ordinarily stain for either DNA or RNA. Stich (1954) has reported that the mitotic centers of *Cyclops* eggs contain RNA. Amano (1954) interprets the staining of centrioles in various vertebrate cells by Fe hematoxylin as indicative of RNA but cites earlier failures to demonstrate them with the ultraviolet microscope. Dirksen (1961) failed to demonstrate RNA or DNA in the centers of sea urchin eggs in autoradiographic experiments using tritiated precursors at high specific activities over several generations. Such negative results cannot be decisive. If the generative scheme of reproduction does apply to centrioles (p. 134) we need expect the truly replicating "germ" in centriole to contain only a few replicating molecules, while the rest of the centriole need contain none.

For a more detailed analysis isolation methods obviously would be desirable. Fortunately, it would not be necessary to restrict such a study to cells that contain only one or two centers lost in a great mass of cytoplasm. The midpieces of spermatozoa have long been known to contain centrioles which, as we have mentioned, provide the mitotic centers for the division of the eggs. The ratio of the mass of these to the total cell mass is very much more favorable than in ordinary cells. A beginning was made by Fischer *et al.* (1952), who reported the isolation of "centrioles" from trout sperm but gave no chemical data.

The isolation of the mitotic apparatus (to be discussed later) lays the foundation for the further separation of the centers from dividing cells. Using a new method for direct isolation of relatively "native" mitotic apparatus from living cells (Section IX, B, 1), Mazia (1959a) found that regions of the centers may be set free by dissolving the fibrous components with strong salt solutions and collecting them by centrifugation. Even such preliminary steps toward the isolation of the centrioles, i.e., the separation and concentration of the regions containing them, might provide useful chemical information.

f. Conclusions. There can be little doubt that the reproduction of the centers is one of the events of the mitotic cycle, in animal cells at least, that is completed before division. Indeed, there is good evidence that this reproductive event takes place during the previous division. It is also reasonably certain that the centers are normally duplex, though it has now been shown that a single unit is adequate to establish a functional pole. The *splitting* of a center, an event necessary for the establishment of poles, is a process distinct from its reproductive "conception."

We do not yet know the role, if any, of the centers in the control of division in normal situations. The evidence suggests that the replication of the centers precedes that of the chromosomes and may perhaps be regarded as the first event assignable to a given cell division. It is logically possible that any antecedent event stands in a causal or regulatory relationship to those that follow, and we are bound to ask, for instance, whether the reproduction of chromosome substance depends on the reproduction of the centers. This question has recently been investigated by Bucher and Mazia (1960), using sea urchin eggs. The facts available were (1) that mercaptoethanol does not inhibit the synthesis of DNA if it is applied during the period of synthesis and (2) that mercaptoethanol blocks the duplication of the centers though not their splitting (Mazia *et al.*, 1960). It was therefore possible to test whether eggs whose centers had not yet duplicated and were prevented from duplicating could synthesize DNA. The answer was clearly that they could. Chromosome reproduction does not depend on previous reproduction of the centers, and both must be regarded as parallel but separable preparations for division.

The question remains whether the reproduction of the centers may be a target of antimitotic action by chemicals, radiation, and other means. This reproduction is one logical candidate for the role of the sensitive system in cases where DNA synthesis seems to be insensitive. Such a case, according to some recent views (e.g., Kelly, 1957), is the antimitotic action of ionizing radiations.

Finally, it should be stressed that although the evidence that the centers are genuine self-reproducing systems is strong, our information on the presence, kinds, and amounts of nucleic acids in them is restricted to observations of their staining properties in a few cases.

3. Preparation of the Substance of the Mitotic Apparatus

The mitotic apparatus as a whole occupies a large proportion of the volume of the dividing cell. Estimates of its density by interference microscopy and refractometry (Mitchison and Swann, 1953; Ross, 1954) and by X-ray absorption (Stich and McIntyre, 1958) would suggest that it is not much lower than that of the cytoplasm as a whole. Therefore, microscopy alone tells us that a great deal of the substance of the cell is invested in the mitotic apparatus at the time of division. The isolation of the mitotic apparatus has made this problem accessible to direct chemical study, and Mazia and Roslansky (1956) determined that one isolated mitotic figure of a sea urchin egg (in the first metaphase or anaphase period) contained about 11% of the total protein of that cell. In this discussion, we are considering the mitotic apparatus as a whole, including all spindle and aster components, and we are assuming that all of it is involved in division.

Thus a cell entering division must either synthesize a very large amount of new substance or must assemble the mitotic apparatus from substance already present before division. Some classic lines of thought favored the latter view. According to the views of several pioneer cytologists, cells contained a distinct fibrous component, variously termed "kinoplasm" (Strasburger, 1900), "archoplasm" (Boveri, 1888), etc., which might be randomly distributed before division, but which was assembled into a mitotic apparatus at the time of division. Boveri, for instance, thought that the centrioles attracted and oriented the "archoplasmic" fibers. In these older views, the fibrous component was thought to be of microscopic dimensions, and we have a considerable descriptive literature based on fixation images.

We might attack the problem by searching for a phase of active protein synthesis at the beginning of division or just preceding it. If this phase exists, it should soon be found as more attention is paid to the biochemical sequences in the cell cycle. A few existing fragments of evidence may be mentioned. When chloramphenicol at a rather high concentration was applied to newt fibroblasts 30 minutes or more before the spindle would have formed, the mitotic figure was defective; the spindle was very short, and the chromosomes were not aligned in a metaphase plate (E. W. Taylor, 1959). Unfortunately it was not demonstrated that chloramphenicol actually was inhibiting protein synthesis in these animal cells. In synchronized yeast cultures, Sylvén *et al.* (1959) find that the dipeptidase and cathepsin activities increase strikingly just before division and decline during division. A relationship of these enzymes to protein synthesis is uncertain, but these findings may possibly be related to transformations and rearrangements of existing proteins in the preparations for division.

Rather than seek direct evidence of the synthesis of the substance of the mitotic apparatus at the time of division, we might, conversely, search for them in cells preparing for division. Isolation of the mitotic apparatus (Section IX, B, 1) has made this possible. The problem was unexpectedly simplified by the finding (Mazia and Dan, 1952; Mazia, 1955) that the mitotic apparatus is dominated quantitatively by a single protein containing about 5% RNA. So far as the cells under study, sea urchin eggs, were concerned, the question was simply whether this protein was present before division. Immunochemical characterization proved to be the most useful tool. It was demonstrated by H. A. Went (1959a, b; Went and Mazia, 1959) that an extract of unfertilized eggs contained at least one and probably more antigens that matched those of the dissolved mitotic apparatus, along with many that did not. Conversely, the dissolved mitotic apparatus yielded no antigens which were not present in the unfertilized egg. The experimental argument is illustrated in Fig. 17. The first conclusion is that the protein of the mitotic apparatus is produced before division and is merely assembled at the time of division. In a sense this conclusion supports the older cytological concepts, but it

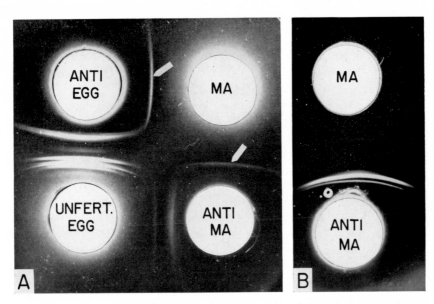

Fig. 17. A. Immunological evidence that the proteins of the mitotic apparatus are present in the cell before division. In this case, it is shown that the unfertilized sea urchin egg contains the antigens which are present in the isolated mitotic apparatus. The photograph represents an agar gel with four cells containing the following substances: *Anti-egg* = antiserum to an extract of unfertilized eggs; *Unfert. egg* = an extract of the proteins of the unfertilized egg such as was used to induce ES in a rabbit. *Anti-MA* = antiserum to the isolated mitotic apparatus. *MA* = The solution of dissolved mitotic apparatus such as was used to induce the *anti-MA*.

The bright bands between any two wells represent the precipitates formed by the counterdiffusing antigens and antibodies. The fusion of bands between two antigen wells and one antibody well is considered evidence of the identity of the antigens yielding these bands. It is seen that the unfertilized egg shares one or more antigens with the mitotic apparatus and that the isolated mitotic apparatus contains no antigens that are absent from the egg. After Went and Mazia (1959) and Went (1959b).

B. Evidence of the presence of at least four antigens in the isolated mitotic apparatus. *MA* and *anti-MA* prepared as in A, but a serum of higher activity was used. Data of H. Sauaia.

is not quite the same. The "archoplasm," etc., appears to have been a concept of microscopic morphology, and the idea that the fibrous mitotic apparatus was assembled from molecular precursors did not enter the picture.

In the normal sequence of synthesis and assembly we can expect the substance of the mitotic apparatus to be present as "free" molecules, as submicroscopic fibers, and ultimately as oriented fibers resolvable by the light microscope with appropriate methods such as polarization microscopy. The existence of the intermediate stage is suggested by observations of an abundance of fine filaments, not well oriented with respect to each other or to the centriole, in the vicinity of the centrioles of cells that are still in interphase (Fig. 7A). Their existence would harmonize data on the time sequence of viscosity changes (the "mitotic gelation"; Section IX, A, 1) and the development of an organized mitotic apparatus.

In an egg, it is conceivable that one will find sufficient protein in storage to supply all the needs of an early embryo for the formation of mitotic apparatus. We can even suppose that the protein is returned to a "pool" at the end of division and is used again at the next division. But in a growing system, the cell will come out of division with, at most, half the amount of the protein needed for forming a mitotic apparatus at the next division, and the deficit must be made up by synthesis between divisions. It seems probable, then, that *the preparations for division must include the synthesis of proteins concerned specifically with mitosis.* Conversely, the presence of such proteins may provide a useful criterion of cells preparing to divide. We can understand why interphase is so short in cells such as eggs, which carry a reserve of "precursor" proteins to the mitotic apparatus, and can well imagine that their synthesis may be a limiting and decisive factor in the ability of other kinds of cells to divide.

a. Conclusions. The mitotic apparatus is assembled from proteins synthesized before division, and is not synthesized at the time of division from smaller units. In growing systems the synthesis of proteins specifically participating in the assembly of the mitotic apparatus is a prerequisite to division and might limit division.

4. "Energy Reservoirs"

It would seem obvious that mitotic division is a process requiring the expenditure of energy, although we may easily exaggerate the magnitude of the requirement because human laziness leads us to associate movement with hard work. Yet the period of division is not a period of intense respiratory activity; if anything, the reverse is true (Section XIII, B). A variety of experiments involving inhibitions of respiration and oxidative phosphorylation (reviewed by Krahl, 1950; Swann, 1957) and restrictions of energy sources (reviewed by Bullough, 1952) lead to a second generalization: mitosis can be prevented if these are imposed before division, but cannot be stopped once it is under way. Moreover, the "point of no return" is fairly consistent from one type of cell to another. In mammalian epidermis (Bullough, 1950) it is identified as an "antephase," a period just before definite chromosomal prophase. In various invertebrate eggs (Krahl, 1950; Swann, 1957; Butros, 1956) the critical point is said to come around prophase, but it has not been identified exactly in these cells where the mitotic events proceed so rapidly. In synchronized *Tetrahymena*, where the division is seemingly amitotic and where DNA synthesis and other conspicuous aspects of growth have been completed beforehand, the "minimum" inhibition by dinitrophenol (Hamburger and Zeuthen, 1957) occurs when the cell is about three-fourths of the way toward division. These generalizations lead logically to the hypothesis that the energy for a given division is stored in the course of the preparations for that division and does not depend on oxidations that take place during the division itself. A further hypothesis, developed most fully by Swann (1954b, 1957), is that the completion of filling of the "energy reservoir" is a controlling factor in division. Oversimplifying the hypothesis, we imagine that the "spilling" of the reservoir sets the division machinery into motion (Fig. 18).

The properties of the postulated "energy reservoirs" are not simple. In Swann's experiments on sea urchin eggs it was observed that the imposition of a metabolic block (e.g., CO poisoning) for a given period of time caused a delay of division by just that length of time. The cells were "frozen" in their advance toward division. It would follow that the energy store was not one that could be drained off by other cell processes. Further, although the imposition of a respiratory inhibition *during* division has no effect on that division, it does delay the next one (Swann, 1953; Hamburger and Zeuthen, 1957). It would follow that the hypothetical reservoir for the next division is already filling while that for the current division is being drained, with no evidence of mixing. In the *Tetrahymena* system the delay produced by a given period of inhibition increases as the cell approaches a critical point (Fig. 19), and the results are interpreted in terms of "setback in time."

Exploration of obvious "energy reservoirs"—typified by adenosine triphosphate—has not yet been decisive. Swann (1953) states that the ATP level does not change in a significant way during division in the sea urchin eggs, and he suggests (1957) the exploration of less familiar high-energy grouping, such as thiol esters. In *Tetrahymena* Plesner (1958) has described a rather striking increase in total nucleoside triphosphates just before division in synchronized population (Fig. 20); the increase involves a build-up of ATP followed by an apparent shift from ATP to GTP. This interesting observation, to which we will return later, does not have all the expected characteristics of the "energy reservoir." The time

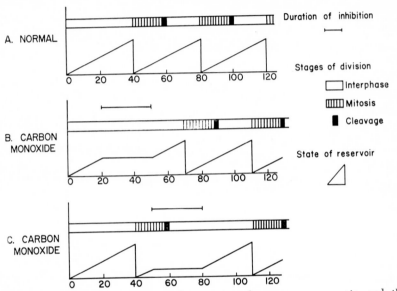

Fɪɢ. 18. Diagrams to illustrate the concept of an energy reservoir, and the interpretation of experiments on which the concept is based. A. The normal situation. According to the hypothesis, the energy reservoir is filling continuously up to a critical point at which division is precipitated, draining the reservoir. It begins to refill as soon as it is drained, during the period of mitosis. B. Carbon monoxide inhibition before the critical point is reached. Under inhibition, the level of the reservoir remains constant, and after release from inhibition, it begins to increase immediately. Thus, the delay in division is equal to the duration of the inhibition. C. Carbon monoxide inhibition after critical point is reached, during the period of mitosis. The current division is completed, but the next division is delayed for a length of time equal to the period of inhibition. After Swann (1954b).

course does not quite parallel the linear rise predicted from the experiments with inhibitors (Fig. 19). The levels of nucleoside triphosphate drop precipitously *before* division, and not during division as would be required of an immediate energy source.

The attractive feature of the notion of an energy reservoir is that it gives one simple explanation of the oxidative requirements of cells preparing for division and of the apparent lack of such requirements during division. But as soon as we examine the detailed properties of the postulated reservoirs, the picture is no longer simple, and we are compelled to postulate specialized and compartmentalized energy stores of unknown composition. Let us, then, consider an alternative and logically equivalent way of looking at the information. Viewed naively, the data might only be telling us that the energy requirements (or dependence on

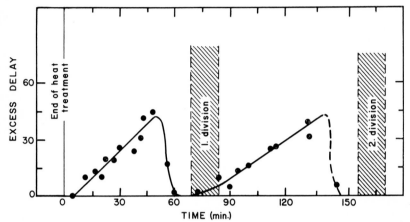

Fig. 19. "Excess delay" of division in *Tetrahymena* resulting from a brief (20 minutes) exposure to $5 \times 10^{-5}M$ dinitrophenol. Excess delay is relative to time of exposure; if an exposure of 20 minutes gives a delay of 20 minutes relative to controls, excess delay is zero. It is seen that inhibition of oxidative phosphorylation delays division at all stages, the smallest delay being equivalent to the time of exposure to DNP. Points show the time at which the DNP was introduced following the last heat shock used to synchronize the cells. The shadowed time intervals represent the times of synchronous divisions of the controls (compare Fig. 103). It is seen that inhibition of oxidative phosphorylation delays division at all stages before a given division. If DNP is introduced during a division it delays the next. The magnitude of the delay increases to a maximum up to 25 minutes before a given division, then decreases sharply. These experiments have been interpreted as indicating a build-up of an energy reservoir which is committed to division at 25 minutes before the cells actually begin to divide. After Hamburger and Zeuthen (1957).

oxidative phosphorylations) of preparations for division are large, whereas those of the division process itself are small and can be met by the residual activity that is always found in inhibition experiments.

When we speak of "energy" in a biological context, we are generally referring to a sequence that involves the "activation" of a system, after which it carries out some operation in an apparently spontaneous way. Rather than thinking of an "energy store" in the form of a pool of some "high-energy compound," we may imagine that the mitotic apparatus *is* the energy store, not in the sense that it contains an identifiable high-energy fuel (though it may), but in the sense that its potentialities are the result of energy expenditure during the preparations for its formation, and that these preparations could not have been completed without such an expenditure. Such a view provides a simple interpretation of the

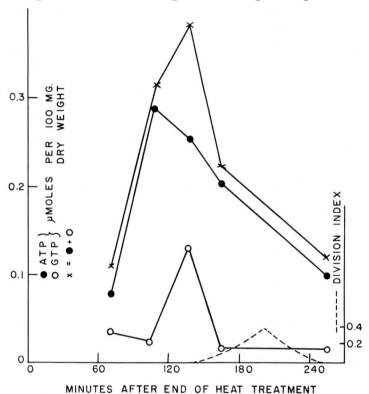

Fig. 20. Nucleoside triphosphates in *Tetrahymena* cells that are approaching the first synchronous division following a series of heat shocks. It is seen that these high-energy compounds increase rapidly during the latter part of the preparations for division and decline sharply before division. Data of Dr. Paul Plesner (cf. Plesner, 1958).

data we have discussed. The "point of no return" becomes the time at which some energy-dependent syntheses are completed. If they are inhibited before completion, they can either be merely arrested or be set back. The evidence that the "energy reservoir" for a division begins to fill during the preceding division can be translated in terms of synthetic events that do take place during the preceding division, such as the duplication of the centers.

However, the possibility of stating the problem of energy storage in alternative forms does not detract from the essential insight that we owe to Swann and others. From the standpoint of the cell's economics, the price of mitosis in energy is paid before mitosis begins (p. 354).

a. Conclusions. It is possible to make the generalization that the energy requirements for the division cycle as a whole are met largely during the time of preparations for division, not during division. The hypothesis that division depends on the preparatory filling of an "energy reservoir" is open to several interpretations, one of which is that the "reservoir" is a pool of high-energy "fuel."

5. General Summary

It is now certain that some of the most essential events which belong strictly to the mitotic cycle take place well before the period of division. These include the two best-known reproductive events of the division cycle: (1) the reproduction of the centers, which comes first, and (2) the reproduction of the chief substances of the chromosomes, DNA and histone. Nothing is known about the reproduction of kinetochores, viewed as a chemical process. The reproduction of the nucleolus, which has some special features, will be discussed in Section XIV.

In addition to these reproductive events the preparations for division include (3) the provision of the bulk of the substance of the mitotic apparatus and (4) the payment of the energetic cost of division.

It is likely that other specific preparations will be discovered. In what we may call the principle of parallel pathways, which was summarized at the beginning of this section, stress is laid on the fact that specific preparations for division may proceed in relative independence from each other and from cell growth. In principle we may accept the platitude that every aspect of cell division is related to the cell as a whole, which at least defends us from surprise when we discover that almost anything that we do to the cell may have some effect on its division. But if analysis is our objective, we allow ourselves the artifice of isolating certain processes and designating them as immediate, specific, and independent in relation to cell division.

IV. THE TRANSITION PERIOD

A. When Does the Division Period Begin?

The difficulty of deciding just when division begins has often been discussed. Theoretically, it may be meaningless; our map tells us that events clearly assignable to the division process (e.g., chromosome reproduction, reproduction of the centers, and the preparation of the material of the mitotic apparatus) are taking place during the so-called "interphase." Logically, we could establish the beginning of division as the time when the chromosomes first begin to move into the mitotic apparatus, at which time it is no longer possible to stop division except by damaging the mitotic apparatus itself. Practically, it is convenient to use the striking chromosomal changes of prophase, because they are easy to detect and because most cells do proceed smoothly into division once these changes are under way. This practical measure does not stand up to generalized criticism, for several reasons. In some organisms (e.g., the flagellate *Holomastigotoides;* Cleveland, 1949) chromosomal prophase events take place at the beginning of what we commonly call "interphase," not at the end. Chromosomal prophase may be reversed by experimental treatment, e.g., by puncture of plant cells (Wada, 1932) or by irradiation of animal cells (Carlson, 1950). In any case we have as yet no precise means of deciding when prophase begins in most kinds of cells.

In terms of our map the question we are asking is whether we can distinguish a transitional event *following the completion of all the other prerequisites for division.* The dividing cell differs from the interphase cell in so many ways that it makes little sense to argue that these changes have no beginning. Several authors (e.g., Mazia, 1956a) have spoken of "triggers" setting off the division process. Such facile figures of speech have their hazards, and the ambiguities of the use of this one would justify the strictures of the terminological purist. A trigger fires an instrument that is fully "cocked," and the trigger to mitosis implies events restricted to the transition period that we are discussing. It would not apply, for instance, to the important case where a cell had not yet doubled its DNA. That cell requires the order "Load!", not the order "Fire!" We do not know whether a trigger to division, in the present sense, exists, and on our time map it is displayed as questionable. The alternative hypothesis is that the entrance into division is a necessary consequence of the completion of all the preparations, in which case the last preparation *completed* by a given cell would be the precipitating event for division of that cell. More will be said about triggers and stimuli in Section XVI.

One approach to these unsolved problems is to look for evidence of transitional events as the cell enters division.

B. Evidences of Transitional Events

1. Visible Changes

In the earlier cytological literature some stress is placed on a phenomenon termed "Teilungswachstum": a rapid increase in the volume of the nucleus just at the end of interphase. Such a growth has been described in many other cases (e.g., the cleaving *Crepidula* egg, Conklin, 1912); various types of animal cells in culture (Hughes, 1952b, pp. 56-61); in rat liver nuclei (Carrière *et al.*, 1961); in ciliates (Popoff, 1908) and *Amoeba proteus* (Prescott, 1956b). In other well-studied cells it is not seen—for instance, in the endosperm mitosis filmed by Bajer (1958a). That the nuclear growth may be a genuine anticipation of division is shown by some measurements made by Prescott (1956b). In his studies of the effects of amputation of cytoplasm on the division of Amoeba (Fig. 100), Prescott measured nuclear volumes and observed that whenever division was interdicted by the amputation of cytoplasm, the nuclear volume decreased. In other words, when the cell as a whole was set back in time with respect to the next division, the nuclear volume was set back too. As the cell grew again, the nuclear volume increased, only to be set back at the time of the next amputation. This reversal of nuclear growth can hardly be attributed to the genetic material unless it is assumed that the latter may be "desynthesized." It is more likely that the nuclear growth before division is related to other processes that fall under the heading of preparations for division.

We have, then, occasional visible indications of changes in the nucleus associated with the transition into division. Thus far, we can say little about corresponding changes in the appearance of the cytoplasm, for the cytoplasm itself offers us few morphological variables until we reach the level accessible only to the electron microscope. As we shall see (Section XIII, C, 1), there is evidence from electron microscopy that cytoplasmic structure is greatly modified when the cell enters division, but at present we have no picture of the time course of the transitional events.

We can, however, feel reasonably sure that the entrance into division is not ordinarily a decision made autonomously by nuclei when they have reached a certain stage of preparation. The assurance comes from the frequent instances of cells containing more than one nucleus, where, typically though not universally, all the nuclei enter prophase at the same time (Section XVI, B). The synchrony of entrance into prophase is seen even in cases such as plant hybrids (e.g., Holden and Mota, 1956) in which the several nuclei can fall out of synchrony in the later phase of division. There are, therefore, aspects of the transition into division which may be referred to conditions pervading the cell as a whole.

2. *Physical and Chemical Changes*

We do not, as yet, recognize any generally characteristic changes in the chemistry of the nucleus that augur the coming prophase. In most cells DNA synthesis has ceased by the end of interphase. There are some fragments of evidence that the nuclear RNA is active during the transition period. Even before RNA was given a name—and long before it received an alphabetical nickname—the accumulation of basophilic material before division in some kinds of nuclei had been described. Conklin (1912) refers to the accumulation of a "chromatic sap," which passed into the cytoplasm at the time of division. The appearance of RNA-containing particles, apart from the nucleolus, has been described as "amongst the earliest changes which can be observed in (chick embryo osteoblast) cells about to divide" (Jacobson and Webb, 1952). In the mitotic and microspore divisions of *Tradescantia*, autoradiographic studies show a striking increase in nuclear RNA activity in the period just before the divisions (Moses and Taylor, 1955). We cannot say that such changes in nuclear RNA just before prophase are universal and cannot yet interpret them; they stand as one of the few known changes associated with the transition period.

The initial steps in the assembly of the mitotic apparatus may well be critical to the transition from interphase into division. By the end of prophase the cell is ready to form its definitive mitotic apparatus very quickly. We can well imagine that there is an earlier time at which the assembly begins, whether it is preceded or accompanied by synthesis. In physical terms the polymerization of the macromolecules composing the bulk of the mitotic apparatus into larger units, and the further associations of the larger units, might well be expressed as a gelation in the cytoplasm. The importance of such a "mitotic gelation," coming in advance of the appearance of an organized mitotic apparatus, has been stressed especially by L. V. Heilbrunn (e.g., 1952, 1956). Measured as a sudden increase in cytoplasmic viscosity (Fig. 96), this gelation anticipating the appearance of the mitotic apparatus has been observed in several kinds of cells. It is discussed in more detail later (Section XIII, E). Numerous studies, especially from Heilbrunn's laboratory, have shown that agents which prevent this gelation block mitosis.

In types of cells in which the initial assembly of the substances of the mitotic apparatus takes place in the nucleus, we will not necessarily expect to find a mitotic gelation in the cytoplasm. Such cells should be particularly useful for identifying the time of the assembly, for the process will be segregated from the cytoplasmic background and may appear as an absolute increase of nuclear substance. A good case in point is the *Cyclops* egg. In Table VIII the data on the mass of the nucleus of this cell, obtained by X-ray absorption method, show a sharp increase in mass during the "antephase," the period before prophase. Stich and Mc-Intyre (1958) interpret this increase as evidence of rapid synthesis of material in the nucleus at this time, but the possibility that it represents the accumulation of material synthesized elsewhere at an earlier time is not excluded. The material is identified as protein containing about 5% RNA, which corresponds to the composition of the major protein of the isolated mitotic apparatus of sea urchin eggs (Section IX, B). This "antephase" event in the nucleus of the *Cyclops* egg clearly can represent the assembly of material for the mitotic apparatus, which forms within the nucleus in this cell.

Many cytologists have felt it necessary to postulate the existence of a transitional phase between typical interphase and frank prophase. They base their conclusions on general cell behavior, reactions to chemicals, radiation, metabolic inhibition, etc., and have given it various names— "antephase" (Bullough, 1952), "preprophase" Hughes, 1952a), "predivision period," etc. It is strange that we have so little that is definite to say about it. The obvious aspects accessible to direct study are the early stages in the assembly of the mitotic apparatus, the initiation of chromosome coiling, and the changes in the finer organization of the cytoplasm, to which we come later.

3. Conclusions

It seems useful to postulate the existence of a transitional period during which the interphase (or "resting") cell is transformed into a dividing cell. We shall see (Section XIII) that these two stages of the life history of cells do differ in almost every way. Some fragments of evidence associate the transition with changes in nuclear size, nuclear ribonucleoprotein, and cytoplasmic viscosity. A possible starting point for analysis is the hypothesis that the transitional event is the initial assembly of substances to be organized into the mitotic apparatus.

V. THE TIME COURSE OF MITOSIS

A. Intermitotic Time and Mitotic Time

The relation between mitotic time and intermitotic time can be measured directly on cells in culture (e.g., Fell and Hughes, 1949). Various indirect methods are available for obtaining comparable information on cells in tissues. The basic "measurable" in these methods is the *mitotic index,* the fraction of cells observed at some stage of mitosis at a given time. For instance, the mitotic time may be derived from the rate at which the mitotic index increases when the cells are blocked with colchicine or comparable agents (Eigsti and Dustin, 1955) or from the rate at which it decreases after irradiation doses which prevent new cells from entering division (Lushbaugh, 1956). Such methods depend on the assumption that the cells of the population are entering mitosis at a steady rate. In the not infrequent cases where division seems to take place in waves, depending, for instance, on the time of day (Laughlin, 1919; Bullough, 1952), the mitotic time may be obtained from analysis of the distribution of mitotic stages in the course of a wave. Lushbaugh (1956) has tabulated a large number of mitotic times of cells in mammalian tissues as given by these methods, and it appears that seldom are they less than 20 minutes or more than 40 minutes at body temperature, a time of 30 minutes being representative.

Various formulas are available for calculating the intermitotic time from the mitotic index and the mitotic time. An approximation of the relationship is given by the formula IT = MT/MI (Hoffman, 1949), where IT = intermitotic time, MT = mitotic time, and MI = mitotic index.

A formula attributed to Crick is used by Hughes (1952b) to plot the relation of mitotic time, intermitotic time, and mitotic index. With the above abbreviations, it reads:

$$\frac{MT}{MT + IT} \times \log_e 2 = \log_e \frac{1 + 2\,MI}{1 + MI}$$

A few values selected from Hughes' Fig. 30 are presented in Table III, which shows the expectations from this formula.

According to Edwards et al. (1960) this equation becomes inaccurate when the mitotic index (or frequency of any phase of the cell cycle) becomes large. In their derivation, the right hand side of the equation becomes simply $\log_e(1 + MI)$.

TABLE III

CALCULATED RELATIONS BETWEEN MITOTIC TIME, INTERMITOTIC TIME, AND MITOTIC INDEX[a]

Mitotic time (hours)	Mitotic index (% of cells in division)	Intermitotic time (hours)
1	2	34
	5	14
2	2	67
	5	27
3	2	>110
	5	41

[a] Data from Hughes (1952), Fig. 30.

In cases where the only means of obtaining information on the reproductive rate of a cell population is by a count of the frequency of mitosis —as in most studies on plant and animal tissues—these time relations can be the source of confusion. A high "mitotic index" can mean either an increase in the number of cells entering division, a protraction of the mitotic time, or the existence of a "wave" of divisions.

Let us tabulate a few representative values in Table IV, which is by no means a complete record. At first glance, the only conclusion that could be drawn from these data would be that there was no consistency. There is, however, a generalization that can be made if we compare growing systems, e.g., animal cell cultures or plant meristems, with systems that divide without doubling in mass during interphase. In cells that grow between divisions—and the cases given in Table IV are merely illustrative of a larger number—the intermitotic time is long. In nongrowing systems, such as eggs in early cleavage, the interphase time is very short. An intermediate example may be the grasshopper neuroblast. This cell undergoes a series of unequal budding-like divisions that produce ganglion cells; it does not double in mass between the divisions of the parent cell (Carlson, 1952).

The intermitotic time, then, may normally be geared to the growth of cells between divisions. This would have to be the normal situation in the long run, for if daughter cells consistently divided before attaining the mass of the parent cells, they would diminish to the vanishing point in successive generations. Further, it has recently been shown by Sisken and Kinosita (1961) that variations in intermitotic time in mammalian cells in culture may be attributable to the time between the preceding division and the beginning of DNA synthesis (the so-called G1 period) rather than to the duration of the period of DNA synthesis or of the G2 period between the end of DNA synthesis and the beginning of division.

Another generalization can be made in spite of the inexactness of the various methods of measuring mitotic and intermitotic time: in most cell populations, the rate of increase in cell numbers is a function of the duration of the intermitotic period. Conversely, the duration of mitosis seems to be relatively constant for a given kind of cell and is not significantly dependent upon the conditions dictating the increase in cell numbers. In short, the multiplication of cells ordinarily reflects the rate at which they enter division, but not the rate at which they go through division.

B. Velocity of Mitosis

If we were compelled to state a "typical" value for the duration of the mitotic process—in order to orient the student who is not interested in variations from the general—a reasonable figure would be from 30

TABLE IV

REPRESENTATIVE VALUES FOR MITOTIC TIMES AND INTERMITOTIC TIMES IN VARIOUS
TYPES OF CELLS[a]

Cell	Time in minutes		References
	Intermitotic	Mitotic	
Vicia faba root meristem (19°C.)	1300	150	L. H. Gray (1951)
	1400	186	Evans and Savage (1959)
Pisum sativum (peas) root meristem (20°C.)	1350	177	R. Brown (1951)
Chick fibroblasts (38°C.)	660–720	23	Strangeways (1923)
Mouse spleen cultures	480–1080	43–90	Fell and Hughes (1949)
Rat jejunum (in animal)	2000	28	Widner *et al.* (1951)
Jensen rat sarcoma (in animal)	720	27	Widner *et al.* (1951)
Rat corneal epithelium (in animal)	14,000	70	Friedenwald and Sigelman (1953)
Chortophaga (grasshopper) neuroblast	27	181	Carlson and Hollaender (1948)
Drosophila egg	2.9	6.2	Rabinowitz (1941)
Psammechinus (sea urchin) embryo, 2–4 cell stage (16°C.)	14	28	Ågrell (1958)
Psammechinus embryo, 200–300 cell stage	110 (approx.)	32	Ågrell (1958)

[a] Various methods are represented.

minutes to 3 hours. Of 16 cases tabulated by Hughes (1952b) only one falls below this range and one above. Milovidov (1949) summarizes the results on more than 30 kinds of plant and animal cells and cites only 4 or 5 cases where mitosis took longer than 3 hours and 2 cases where it took less than 30 minutes. The reader is welcome to decide whether or not we are dealing with a modest generalization that ultimately may be useful when we can relate rates to mechanisms; at least it can be said that an order-of-magnitude guess at the expected length of a mitotic process is unlikely to go far from the mark.

It is interesting to consider the shortest durations reported, tabulated below.

Genus	Mitotic time (minutes)
Drosophila, egg (Huettner, 1933)	9–10
Acanthamoeba (Comandon and de Fonbrune, 1937)	19.5
Chilomonas (Maltaux and Massart, 1906)	5 (at 35° C.)
Chlamydophrys (Belar, 1921)	15–16

A feeble thread holding these cases together is the fact that in all the chromosomes are very small and the mitotic apparatus is small.

A relation between cell size and the speed of the mitotic process is seen in the study of Makino and Nakahara (1953a) on ascites tumor populations (MTK-sarcoma I) in which cell size was variable. They report data (see tabulation) based on direct phase contrast observations.

Cell diameter (microns)	Duration of mitosis, beginning of prophase to the end of telophase (minutes)
19	119
16	83
14	77
13	70

C. Duration of Various Phases

The duration of the various phases of mitosis has been determined by direct observation in many cases and has been deduced in others from the relative frequency of occurrence of the phases. The latter type of information may be converted to absolute values if the actual duration of some part of the cycle (e.g., mitotic time or intermitotic time) is known. A useful method of statistical analysis applicable to cases where the relative lengths of various stages are altered experimentally is given by Guttman (1952).

TABLE V

SOME EXAMPLES OF DATA ON THE DURATION OF THE MITOTIC PHASES, REPRESENTING DIRECT OBSERVATIONS (OR CINÉ RECORDS) OF LIVING DIVIDING CELLS

Cell	Minutes					References
	Prophase	Metaphase	Anaphase	Telophase		
Yoshida sarcoma (35°C.)	14	31	4	21		Makino and Nakahara (1953a)
MTK-sarcoma I (35°C.)	10	44	5	18		—
Mouse spleen in culture	20–35	6–15	8–14	9–26		Hughes (1952b)
Triton liver fibroblast (26°C.)	18 or more	17–38	14–26	28		Hughes and Preston (1949)
Chortophaga (grasshopper) neuroblast (38°C.)	102	13	9	57		Carlson and Hollaender (1948)
Pea endosperm	40	20	12	110		Bajer and Mole-Bajer (1954a)
Iris endosperm	40–65	10–30	12–22	40–75		Bajer and Mole-Bajer (1954a)
Micrasterias rotata (desmid)	60	21–24	6–12	3–45		Waris (1950)

Hughes (1952a) and Milovidov (1949) have tabulated some of the published data on the relative duration of the several phases of mitosis. Table V adds a few more data from the recent literature; all these data are based on direct observations of mitosis in living cells.

Milovidov (1949) summarizes a large number of observations on cells of all kinds (Table VI); he expresses the longest and shortest durations of the several phases. So far as this writer is aware, there are no more recent data that would extend this range.

TABLE VI
EXTREME VALUES FOR THE DURATIONS OF THE MITOTIC PHASES[a]

Phase	Minimum (min.)	Maximum (min.)
Prophase	2	270
Metaphase	0.3	175
Anaphase	0.3	122
Telophase	1.5	140

[a] From Milovidov (1949).

After all deference is given to variability, it is still possible and useful, in the author's opinion, to think of "typical" or "representative" values for the durations of the mitotic phases. Values of the magnitudes shown in Table V recur most frequently. We can make the generalization that anaphase tends to proceed rapidly; if we examine the various tabulations, instances where anaphase takes more than 10 minutes at normal temperatures are rare. Metaphase, too, tends to be rather brief, even though its span is more difficult to define than that of anaphase. Against the overall time scale of the cell cycle, the moving about of the chromosomes appears as a rather violent operation sometimes pausing in metaphase, and this activity has been dramatized in the various beautiful films of mitosis.

D. Temperature Dependence

As would be expected, the duration of the entire life cycle of a cell, the duration of the division period, and the relative durations of the various phases of mitosis depend on the temperature. For the mitotic process itself, temperature analysis could be especially revealing because we may be dealing with two distinguishable categories of temperature dependence: (1) the usual relation between temperature and reaction rates, as expressed in the Arrhenius equation and its later formulations (e.g., Johnson et al., 1954) and (2) the various relations between temperature and the physical state of gels and polymers.

Thus far our information about temperature and mitosis is descriptive, not analytical, and may be illustrated by some of the better-studied cases in the literature. As an example of the temperature dependence of the total cell cycle and of the mitotic period, we may take some recent data on *Vicia faba* (Fig. 21). Over most of the range it would appear that mitosis itself is somewhat more sensitive than the interdivision events.

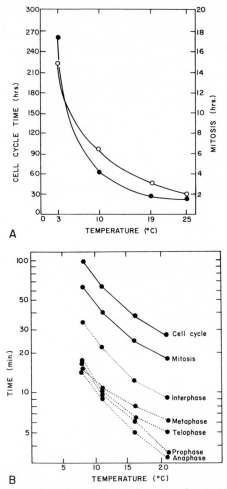

FIG. 21. Temperature dependence of the duration of mitosis (–o–) and of the time taken by a complete mitotic cycle (–●–) in two kinds of cells. A. *Vicia faba* seedling root tip meristem (Evans and Savage, 1959). B. Sea urchin egg. *Psammechinus miliaris* at 2–4 cell stage. Duration of mitotic stages is also shown (Ågrell, 1958). In *Vicia*, the cells grow between division. In the sea urchin egg, there is no growth during interphase and the only obvious preparations for division are the reproduction of the chromosomes, the separation of the centers, and the mobilization of preformed substances for the mitotic apparatus.

The temperature dependence of the duration of mitosis seems to follow a similar pattern in a variety of unrelated cell types (Table VII).

For most of the stages of mitosis the temperature phase-duration relationship is about what would be expected from commonplace kinetics. The period of greatest interest is metaphase, for we do not know what is happening in this period. It appears to be a pause in the flow of chro-

TABLE VII

DATA ON THE TEMPERATURE-DEPENDENCE OF THE DURATION OF THE MITOTIC
STAGES IN SEVERAL TYPES OF CELLS

Cell, authors, and method	Temp. (°C.)	Minutes			
		Pro-phase	Meta-phase	Ana-phase	Telo-phase
Yoshida sarcoma; Makino and Nakahara (1953a). Direct observation	27	34	105	8	44
	30	20	80	5	50
	35	14	31	4	21
Pea seedlings, root meristem; R. Brown (1951). Total generation time by counting number of new cells produced by given length of root tip in 24 hr; relative duration of phases estimated from frequencies	15	126	24	5	22
	20	78	14	4	13
	25	54	14	3	11
	30	42	11	2.5	10
Two species of sea urchin; Ågrell (1958). Total cycle observed directly; duration of phases calculated from frequencies					
Echinus esculentus (2–4 cell stage)	4	70	40	48	65
	8	35	25	22	30
	12	19	17	12	18
	17	8	15	7	11
Psammechinus miliaris (2–4 cell stage)	8	18	17	16	18
	12	15	16	14	16
	16	6	8	5	7
	21	2	6	1	5
Vicia seedlings, root meristem; Evans and Savage (1959). Rate of entry of cells into mitosis determined by colchicine method; total generation time calculated from this; relative duration of phases estimated from frequencies.				Anaphase and Telophase	
	3	500	160	220	
	10	245	54	80	
	19	115	18	54	
	25	66	18	30	

mosome movements, and later we shall consider the hypothesis that it represents the time lag between the arrival of chromosomes at the equator and the splitting event that enables sister chromosomes to move apart. In the pioneer studies of Ephrussi (1927) it was suggested that the duration of metaphase in sea urchin eggs (*Paracentrotus*) and in *Ascaris* eggs was considerably less sensitive to temperature than the length of other phases. It can be seen in Table VII and Fig. 21 that this has been confirmed for sea urchin eggs by Ågrell (1958). In ascites tumor cells, on the other hand, metaphase events appear to be extraordinarily sensitive; they are speeded up by elevation of temperature from 35 to 38°C. and are slowed down by a further rise to 40°C. In *Vicia faba* metaphase is very sensitive up to 19°C., but it is little affected by a further increase of temperature to 25°C.

These facts are of practical interest, to those working on cell populations in mitosis, as a guide to the prediction of the consequences of temperature variations. They also have some theoretical implications. We see that decreasing the temperature to about 5°C. will decrease the velocity of the whole mitotic process and of its several phases but will not stop it entirely. Such a "physiological zero" would not have been unexpected if the mitotic apparatus were a gel whose function was extremely sensitive to its viscosity, and its viscosity very sensitive to temperature. The data say that the over-all temperature dependence of what must be a most complex network of chemical reactions and structural interactions falls in line with the expectations of simple chemical kinetics. For example, the data of Evans and Savage (1959; cf. Table VII) for the temperature-velocity relationship of the whole mitotic process in *Vicia faba* make an almost perfect straight line when the logarithm of the velocity is plotted against the reciprocal of the absolute temperature according to the Arrhenius equation. The "free energy of activation," whatever it may mean in such a complex system, calculates out as about 14,000 calories.

A good deal of information could be expected from really systematic temperature analyses of mitosis, but the analyses should not be confined to the experimental design in which the cells are kept at a given temperature through the entire division period. The duration of a given phase will depend greatly on what happened during the preceding phase. For example, the length of metaphase may depend on changes in the kinetochores which were taking place earlier. The "true" temperature dependence of metaphase, if such a term is permissible, would be given by experiments in which the temperature was shifted from the normal value only at the beginning of this phase.

E. *Phases and "Points of No Return"*

The standard phases of mitosis are derived from the landmarks most useful to the practical microscopist and need not be discarded if they turn out to be artificial upon closer scrutiny. In minimizing their reality we sometimes go to the other extreme of insisting that the mitotic cycle be viewed as a continuum in time. This is not a particularly instructive point of view. It is much more useful to regard "the cell," passing through its life history, as being a quite different cell at different times. We seek not only to identify the phases of its history and the activities characteristic of each phase, but also to determine when the critical transitions take place and the nature of the "decisions" involved. Such an approach is not limited to the normal cell as a whole. It would be even more significant, from a practical research standpoint, to find that the several activities that characterize a given phase are dissociable, so that one activity may proceed into the next phase while another is held in the earlier phase.

The idea of such transitions and "decisions" is meaningful if we can identify them, and identification can sometimes be made in terms of what we shall call "points of no return," which can be defined experimentally. If the cell can be prevented from making a given transition before a certain time, but can no longer be blocked after that time, the "point of no return" is identified. It is even more striking in practice that the agents which interdict the beginning of a given event will often have little effect on its completion once the decision is made.

A number of "points of no return" in the mitotic cycle are known, and others surely will be discovered. Let us list some of them.

1. Chromosome reproduction. Cells that will not divide have generally the DNA content which they received from the parent. Once the "decision" to begin the synthesis is made, synthesis goes on until the DNA content is doubled, and the cell usually, but not always, goes on into mitosis. The prevention of DNA synthesis is a normal occurrence, but once begun it is extraordinarily difficult to interrupt.

2. Energy supply. As we have mentioned, there is a "point of no return" around prophase, at which the progress into mitosis is no longer inhibited by poisoning oxidations and phosphorylations (Section III, D, 4).

3. Entrance into anaphase. Sometime during metaphase the mitotic apparatus becomes relatively insensitive to a number of agents affecting spindle structure and proceeds through anaphase in their presence. It is as though the structure was "locked" (Section IX, D).

4. Entrance into cytokinesis (Section XII, B). Up to a certain point in anaphase, cytokinesis seems to depend on the mitotic apparatus. Once the cleavage mechanism is determined, it becomes relatively indifferent to the mitotic apparatus.

5. Dependence of mitosis on the nucleolus (Section VI, B, 4). Before a certain time in mid-prophase, damage to the nucleolus arrests the progress of the cell toward division. After a "point of no return" nucleolar damage does not interrupt mitosis.

It would be important to know whether there is a critical event that determines the beginning of prophase condensation or whether the condensation follows inevitably from the completion of the reproduction of the chromosomes. The condensation is the most familiar expression of the beginning of mitosis, and it also happens to be the one event that seems to be reversible experimentally (p. 148 and discussion in Ducoff and Ehret, 1959, p. 35).

In defining the timing of mitotic events, we also learn that the familiar time marks of the cell cycle may be misleading. With respect to growth, a generation runs from the end of one division to the end of the next. But our analysis of mitosis shows that events are taking place during a given generation which are directly related to the division in the following generation. For example, we have seen that the traditional view that the reproduction of the centrioles for a given division takes place during the preceding division is correct (Section III, D, 3). It is conceivable that this is true in a sense for the reproduction of the chromosomes (Section VI, B, 2). Moreover, experimental impacts that take place during a given division may affect the next one in a consistent way. Thus, exposure of cells to CO after the "point of no return" in a given division will delay the next by an interval corresponding to the time of exposure to CO (Section III, D, 4). Similarly, there is a "point of no return" for the delay of a given division with ultraviolet irradiation, and irradiation after that point delays the next division (Blum and Price, 1950; Rustad, 1960).

VI. The Mobilization of the Mitotic Apparatus

A. Introduction. History

The actors in the mitotic process and the stage on which they perform belong to the world of microscopic dimensions; we are in a micron theater, as well as in an angstrom theater. Our problem involves large bodies moving over long distances according to plans that are intelligible in what could be described as teleological terms if these were respectable; let us say that the deployments of mitosis are intelligible in terms of a definite preconceivable outcome. For these reasons we can draw on the results of some ninety years of microscopic investigations that depend on observational methods and skills that have not improved drastically and on imaginative intelligence that has not improved at all. The works of the "old masters" have not been superseded. Works such as those of Strasburger (1880), Flemming (1882), or Henneguy (1896) are to be regarded as sources of firsthand information and stimulating ideas, and not merely as venerable relics of interest to historians. Later syntheses, such as those of Wilson (1925 and earlier editions) and of Tischler (1922), summarize the vast accumulation of cytological data; Wilson's work is certainly one of the classics of biological literature in the English language.

The story of the discovery of mitosis is interesting and well documented. Contemporary historical accounts will be found in the works of Strasburger (1880), Mark (1881), Flemming (1882), Henneguy (1896), and others. Detailed and critical recent accounts are given in papers by Baker (1953, 1955) and by Katznelson (1959). The discovery of mitosis as we understand the process has been attributed to various nineteenth century microscopists, often to Flemming. It is now clear from various accounts, including Flemming's own, that several workers had arrived at the definitive picture by 1878–1879.

The major stages in the discovery of mitosis were: (1) the discovery of the cell and of the fact that cells multiply by dividing. Interesting historical accounts of the early period of cell research are given by Conklin (1939) and by Baker (1953). Among the original descriptions of cells and cell division, a classic in English is the paper of Robert Brown (1833) in which the nucleus is described and named. (2) The setback resulting from the influential theory of free-cell formation (Schwann and Schleiden, 1839). In this theory the obligatory derivation of cells from other cells was denied; instead, it was imagined that cells crystallized out of a fluid called the "cytoblastema." (3) Appreciation of the fact that cell division involved nuclear reproduction, and attempts to observe nuclear reproduction (ca. 1845–1875). As mentioned (Section II, C, 6) this involved a conflict between the extremes of direct nuclear division (amitosis) and the notion of "karyolysis." Observers who detected, correctly, the disappearance of the nucleus in living material postulated that it disintegrated completely and that new nuclei were reconstructed in the daughter cells. During these years many of the details of mitosis were actually described, but they were not interpreted in their correct sequences and relationships. The work of Schneider, published in 1873, is often cited as an instance where almost all the stages of mitosis were observed and figured, but not interpreted. (4) Definitive description of mitosis. In less than a decade, 1870–1880, the picture of mitosis crystallized as a result of new observations and enhanced insight into older ones. In accounting for this great event in the history of biology, historians will doubtless disagree as to the part played by new personalities, new methods, and the sheer maturity of microscopical science. The technical advances were the rapid introduction of methods of fixation and staining not much worse than those now in use and the production of achromatic microscopical optics of high quality.

Our newer microscopic methods—notably the use of phase contrast, interferometric, and polarization optics—have supplemented the older data with improved observations on living material. Microscopic cytology has gone through frequent and tolerably wholesome phases of scepticism during which the "reality" of practically every aspect of the mitotic process has been questioned, but history has been kinder to the more careful practitioners of the classic cytological methods than to the connoisseurs of artifact.

The difficulties attending experimental analysis of the mitotic process in terms of molecular functions are obvious. The process involves a number of large structures, deploying over long distances in a seemingly purposeful way and with a high degree of coordination. The size of the structures takes us into the dark domains of the physical sciences that lie between molecular and microscopic dimensions. The structures themselves are complex. We are required to account for changes in form and for movements that are so highly coordinated as to be expressible most readily by teleological language or by the invention of special "forces." The mitotic equipment is interwoven with the cell as a whole, interacts with the cell as a whole; it is transitory and unstable, appearing when "needed" and then disappearing from sight. Moreover, the rich literature of microscopic cytology tells us that although the essential plan of mitosis is a unified one, its visible expression in different kinds of cells is highly varied. Of physical and chemical theories there is no lack, for the sources of frustration mentioned above were bound to challenge the imaginative souls who have built up the science of cytology. Hypotheses are bound to accumulate in the absence of means of testing them, and there is no aspect of mitosis which has not been the subject of many alternative speculations, all together invoking the greatest variety of physical and chemical phenomena.

B. Prophase

1. General Description

If the term "prophase" is to be defined at all for purposes other than the arbitrary scoring of mitotic stages, it may be viewed as including all the visible events in the mobilization of the mitotic apparatus. Its beginning is necessarily ill defined, but it can be said to terminate when the chromosomes begin their movement toward their metaphase positions.

The most conspicuous proceeding of prophase is the "condensation" of the chromosomes, now generally viewed as the imposition of several orders of spiralization or coiling upon greatly extended interphase chromosome threads. The functional significance of the condensation is clear enough; it solves in a straightforward way the problem of effecting mitotic movement of chromosomes cleanly with minimum resistance and risk of entanglement. Although the typical prophase condensation of chromosomes provides the most convenient means of recognizing cells that are entering mitosis, it is not universally geared in time to the other events. For example, in *Holomastigotoides* (Cleveland, 1949) the chromosomes go through their uncoiling, duplication, and "prophase" coiling immediately after division, after which a long delay ("resting period") ensues before the next division. Nor is the completion of prophase, as defined above, linked to the completion of the condensation of the chromosomes. In many cases, it continues beyond the metaphase period (cf. Section 2, C, below).

A second major problem of prophase is the establishment of the poles for the forthcoming division. In forms where centers are recognizable, the polarization is a matter of the separation of the sister centers. The time at which the actual movement is observed varies from one type of cell to another. In some cases, e.g., the sea urchin egg, this separation has progressed considerably by the time telophase is completed (Fig. 22, A.). At the other extreme the major part of the movement is associated with prophase, and sometimes with late prophase (Fig. 22, B). The movement may be relatively rapid. Thus, the establishment of the poles may be one of the first or one of the last events of prophase.

The other conspicuous events in the familiar description of prophase are the disappearance of the nucleolus and the attenuation (and sometimes the dissolution) of the nuclear membrane. These generally take place toward the end of prophase (which is all we can say in discussing the time scale of a phase whose end we can define but whose beginning is undefinable). Entering now into separate discussion of these prophase processes, we must admit that the causal or coordinating links between these events are not known. Yet such links must exist, for the several prophase events proceed in a characteristic sequence in each kind of cell.

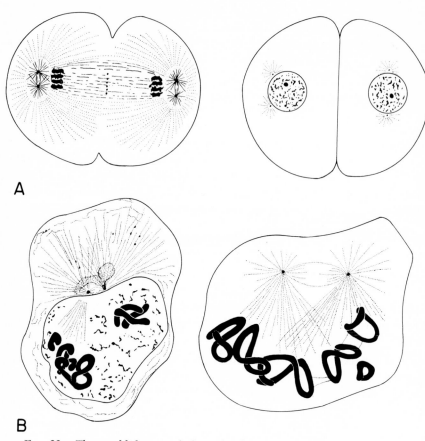

Fig. 22. The establishment of the poles by the separation of the centers in animal cells. A. Early separation. In the sea urchin egg, the centers have moved apart appreciably by the end of a division, establishing the poles for the next division. B. Late separation. Cells of the newt are illustrated. Quantitative data on this separation are given in Fig. 32. The centers move apart rapidly at late prophase or early metakinesis. After Wilson (1925).

2. Chromosomes in Prophase

a. Chromosome coiling. It now seems to be agreed generally that the prophase "condensation" of the chromosomes is to be explained by their progressive coiling. The recondite subject of chromosome coiling has been reviewed comprehensively by Kaufmann (1948) and by Manton (1950), and it is discussed in some detail in Swanson's (1957) recent text.

The theme of helical structure pervades the description of chromosomes even down to molecular dimensions, but its deeper meaning remains elusive. So far as the sense of mitotic prophase is concerned, the imposition of "major" coils upon the extended chromosome thread that may in itself be wound in "minor" coils and the "super" coiling that is sometimes (Cleveland, 1949) imposed upon the "major" coils provide a very neat device for producing a compact chromosome.

In the simplest view the contraction of the chromosome would be interpreted entirely in terms of the coiling of a primary thread of constant length, but we are cautioned (Swanson, 1957, pp. 196–207) against the assumption that the length of primary thread is necessarily constant.

We do not know the driving mechanism of prophase coiling. The hypotheses—which are for the most part impressions or opinions—fall into two groups. The one stresses the possible role of a "matrix" which is distinguished from the primary genetic threads, the other looks to the properties of the genetic thread itself for the explanation of coiling.

In its morphological aspect the matrix is seen in favorable cases as a sausagelike body within which the chromosome is coiled. Breakdown of the matrix, as described by Cleveland (1949) and others, results in uncoiling, and its build-up and contraction accompany the condensation of the chromosome threads. Approached through chemistry, the matrix is seen to be that part of the chromosome which is not essential to the integrity of the primary genetic threads and which can fluctuate normally or be removed experimentally without interrupting the linear continuity of the chromosome. In the next section we shall consider evidence that material is deposited in and removed from the chromosome in the course of mitosis.

Some recent thoughts on chromosome coiling focus attention on the properties of the primary chromosome thread, without invoking an accessory matrix.

Even before the proposal of helical models of the structure of DNA by Pauling and Corey (1953) and Watson and Crick (1953), cytologists were tantalized by the fact that chromosomes could be described as "coiled-coiled-coils" and asked whether this helical principle might not be built into the ultimate molecules of the chromosome. Yet we do not understand the transitions, if any, from the properties of DNA and its associated proteins to the coiled chromosome.

An interesting discussion of the physical problems involved has been given by Anderson (1956a), who has developed a hypothetical mechanism of chromosome coiling based on properties of bundles of nucleohistone threads. Apart from the biochemical speculations, Anderson demonstrated how coiling might be the expected result of the contraction or longitudinal translation of the individual fibers in a bundle where the fibers interact with each other. Among the other models of a chromosome in which coiling is expected on purely mechanical grounds and without invoking a matrix is the "ribbon" chromosome discussed in a speculative way by J. H. Taylor (1957).

We are led to one frontal experimental approach to coiling by the question: Can coiling be induced by changing the chemical environment of the chromosome? The above-mentioned hypothesis of Anderson predicted that polycationic compounds would induce chromosome coiling or prevent uncoiling. It finds support in observations on isolated interphase nuclei (Anderson 1956a), where the addition of arginine brought about the formation of prophase-like threads. Similar observations have been reported by Philpot and Stanier (1957) who obtained prophase-like images in isolated nuclei upon elevation of ionic strength, decrease of pH, or the addition of Mg ions, protamines, or histones. Davidson and Anderson (1960) have produced disturbances of chromosome condensation in living *Vicia* root tip cells by exposures to the polyamines, putrescine and cadaverine. The uncoiling of chromosomes at the end of anaphase was suppressed and the chromosomes were abnormally condensed at metaphase.

Useful information is available from studies of experimental uncoiling of chromosomes, which has been an important tool in the study of chromosome structure (Kuwada, *et al.*, 1938; Sigenaga, 1940). The most interesting generalization is that uncoiling is brought about by alkaline conditions, e.g., by exposure of cells in division to ammonia or KCN solutions. Sigenaga also has induced uncoiling of *Tradescantia* chromosomes by exposing pollen mother cells to 0.4–0.5 M neutral salt solutions. Experiments on the "reversal of prophase" by irradiation, puncture of the cell, etc., may be taken as examples of the uncoiling of chromosomes (p. 148). The chromosomes can recover and coil again.

b. Untwisting and splitting in relation to the duplication of chromosomes. The preparation of the chromosomes for mitosis involves more than the doubling of their substance: two equal and separable bodies must be produced, and their production involves the splitting and unwinding of the daughter chromosomes.

The theme of coiling that pervades our view of the chromosomes from the molecular to the microscopic levels confronts us with the problem of the untwisting of the sister units. Most of the thinking has assumed that chromosomes reproduce by a *fission* mechanism. If this implies that a coiled thread is split along its long axis, then the sister units will be "plectonemically" related to each other and cannot be separated without untwisting. This problem arises even in speculation about the duplication of molecular DNA, and ingenious hypotheses have been constructed to account for the unwinding of the helixes (e.g., Levinthal and Crane, 1956). Some of the hypothetical models of the nucleic acids and protein relationships in chromosomes avoid this difficulty (e.g., D. Schwartz, 1955; J. H. Taylor, 1957), and there is at least one speculation that rejects the fission model of chromosome reproduction entirely (Schmitt, 1956).

i. Observations. In reality, chromosomes often enter prophase with their arms visibly split. The sister threads represent the products of the molecular duplication that has taken place earlier, and in that sense they represent two chromosomes. Presumably, they are associated at the kinetochore region, and perhaps along their arms. Cytologists often prefer to designate the units as "chromatids" before metaphase and "chromosomes" after metaphase. This distinction is not merely a symptom of the cytologists' love of terminology. On the contrary, it will be seen to be a fact that the supposedly duplicated chromsome has the functional significance of only one chromosome before the sister units have separated and of two chromosomes only after the separation (Section XIV).

Naturally, the problem of unwinding sister chromosomes exists at all the levels at which winding exists. Direct observation has been limited to the microscopic levels. In the flagellate *Holomastigotoides*, in which the chromosomes are visible throughout the entire cycle, it is seen that the chromosomes still retain the ultimate "minor" coils of the primary microscopic thread at the time they reproduce, even though the higher levels of coiling tend to be lost as the chromosomes become extended at telophase. The reproduction of this coiled thread produces a pair of coiled strands wound around each other. The sisters are seemingly unwound as a result of torsion generated by the contraction of the strands. As shown in Fig. 23, this apparent torsion may develop at various points along the chromosomes, and it seems unlikely that the unwinding begins at the ends.

In more familiar situations we cannot see the earlier stages, but we do often observe that chromosomes enter prophase visibly split, with the sister units "relationally" wound around each other. We might imagine that the forces of anaphase movement could separate them, even though the relational coiling exists. It has been seen, in motion pictures of *Haemanthus* endosperm, that the sister chromosomes are still twisted around each other at a fairly advanced stage of prophase condensation, then simply unwind just as though they were being rotated at their ends (Fig. 24). It is difficult to imagine how this comes about.

ii. The multiplicity of the chromosomes in relation to duplication and splitting. Our image of the splitting of the already reproduced chromosomes in mitosis depends very much on the number of units of which a chromosome is composed. On the one extreme, a genetic approach would best be satisfied by the hypothesis of a single chain of genetic units, for this would best fit the evidence that a single event within molecular dimensions may express itself as a mutation. On the other extreme, the fine-structural approach (e.g., Kaufmann and McDonald, 1956; Ris, 1956; Steffensen, 1959; Kaufmann, 1960).

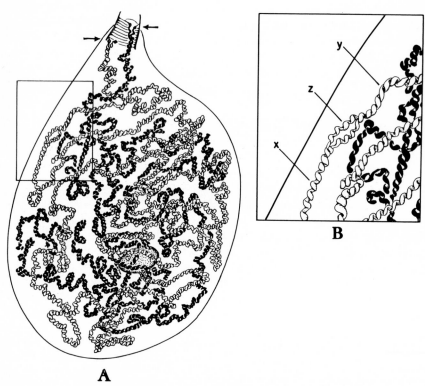

A

B

FIG. 23.   Relation between chromosome duplication and coiling in the flagellate *Holomastigotoides tusitula*, a form in which the chromosomes, two in number, are visible throughout the entire cell cycle. (Another remarkable feature of this organism is that chromosome duplication and prophase coiling follow immediately upon the preceding telophase, after which the cell goes through a "resting period" before the next division.) Drawing on left (A) shows an early prophase. Drawing on right (B) is an enlarged view of a region in which duplication and unwinding of the daughter strands seems to be taking place. At x, the chromosome appears to be single. At y, it is visibly double, but the two strands are wound around each other. At z, and near the centromeres (kinetochores), the pairs of strands seem to be unwinding. After Cleveland (1949).

tends to resolve the chromosome into a hierarchy of strands down to the molecular level, leaving open the possibility of a high degree of multiplicity of each unit of genetic information. At the cytological level, the hypothesis that the chromosome is composed of a relatively small number of strands has received attention. Perhaps the favored hypothesis has been that it is composed of two strands; in accordance with this hypothetical structure the prophase chromosome would be described as comprising two chromatids each composed of two "half-chromatids." This view has been favored partly because it accounts for "half-chromatid breaks" in

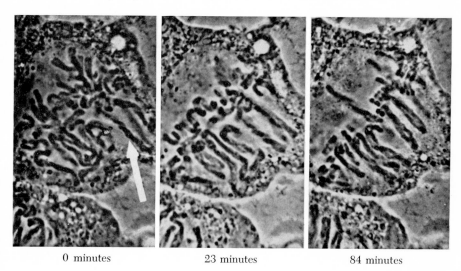

| 0 minutes | 23 minutes | 84 minutes |

FIG 24. The unwinding of sister chromosomes at prophase in *Haemanthus* endosperm. The chromosomes indicated by the arrow at zero time consists of two parts, tightly wound around each other. The unwinding seen in the later frames takes place during metakinesis. Photographs are from time lapse films by Dr. A. Bajer.

experiments on the effects of radiations (e.g., Swanson, 1957; Oestergren and Wakonig, 1954). There is direct evidence in favor of this view; the double chromosome is often seen clearly, especially at anaphase (e.g., Manton, 1945). Such an observation is illustrated in Fig. 25, A. In the flagellate *Holomastigotoides*, in which so many details of chromosome behavior can be seen, Cleveland (1949) finds forms whose chromosomes are consistently single or consistently double at the microscopic level, and this difference is observed even as a characteristic of varieties of the same species (Fig. 25, B).

Recent speculations on the molecular structure of chromosomes have given rise to still other meanings of the multiplicity of chromosomes. For example, the ingenious hypothesis of J. H. Taylor (1957) postulates that the double helixes of DNA run perpendicular to the long axis of the chromosome, the longitudinal continuity being maintained by a pair of protein threads. One strand of each DNA double helix is anchored in one

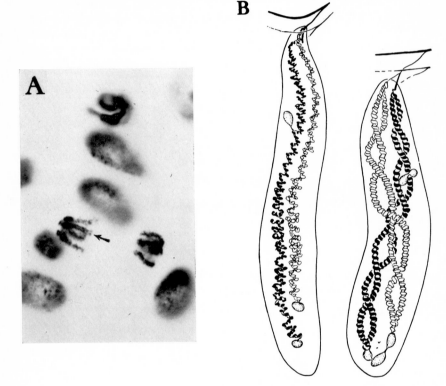

SINGLE   DOUBLE

FIG. 25. The doubleness of chromosomes. A. Chromosomes of *Crepis capillaris* root tips at anaphase. At this stage, it is reasonably certain that the chromosomes have not begun to replicate for the next division. Photograph by courtesy of Dr. Walter Plaut. B. Single-chromatid and double-chromatid chromosomes in *Holomastigotoides*. Drawings show nuclei at telophase. Nucleus at left has single-chromatid type of chromosomes; that at right shows the double-chromatid type. After Cleveland (1949); cf. Cleveland (1961) for phase contrast photographs of double-chromatid structure.

of the protein threads; the other, in its mate. If this interesting model prove to be correct, it might describe the molecular structure of a so-called half-chromatid but would not be equivalent to the microscopic bipartite chromosome of Fig. 25.

So far as the immediate problem of mitosis is concerned, the question of the multiplicity of the chromosomes formulates itself in this way: no matter how many molecular strands are present in the chromosomes, by prophase they are split accurately into two resolvable bundles, and these become separable at anaphase. Subunits, such as are shown in Fig. 25, may be resolved at favorable stages and in favorable material, but normally they remain together before prophase. The mechanism determining which strands separate may involve the kinetochores, as is commonly supposed, or associations between the arms, or a combination of these. The problem is one of the relations between the duplication process and the splitting process, just as it was in the case of the centers (Section III, D, 2).

One complete morphological description is given by Cleveland (1949) for the cases of flagellates containing double-chromatid chromosomes. The chromosomes come out of telophase composed of two strands, "relationally" wound around each other. These strands duplicate, even before they unwind. Each strand produces daughters that are wound around each other, so that two superimposed generations of "relational" coiling are observed at one stage. The duplication of the chromosomal subunits before division is not accompanied by a visible doubling of the kinetochores. The kinetochores are seen to double at late telophase, and this doubling determines a precession whereby the products of duplication in one generation will be separated in the next.

The hypothesis that the chromosome is a duplex structure in the sense that it contains two equivalent strands that may be separated at a later generation finds strong support. It cannot be denied that even further subdivision will be possible, in line with electron microscopic evidence of the existence of many strands.

iii. Distribution of parental substance between daughter chromosomes. A number of investigators have studied the distribution of "old" and newly synthesized DNA between sister chromosomes at mitosis. In an early study, that of Plaut and Mazia (1956), it was concluded that newly synthesized DNA could be distributed unequally between daughter nuclei of the plant *Crepis capillaris* in the first division following synthesis. The statistics of the distribution were satisfied by the interpretations (1) that the chromosome before duplication consists of at least two (and conceivably three) units, (2) that these "old" units duplicate to produce daughter units consisting largely or entirely of "new" DNA, and (3) that the duplicated chromosome is split at random in mitosis, so that the new subunits may or may not be distributed equally between daughter nuclei. In these experiments the new DNA was labeled with C¹⁴, which does not permit the autoradiographic resolution of individual chromosomes. The introduction of tritium labeling made this possible, and J. H. Taylor *et al.* (1957), experimenting with *Vicia faba,* concluded that the new DNA was equally distributed between daughter chromosomes at the first division following synthesis and went to only one of each pair of granddaughters at the second division. However, LaCour and Pelc (1958, 1959) did observe cases of unequal distribution of new DNA in *Vicia faba* at the first division following synthesis (see Fig. 26). The number of cases in which the new DNA was unequally distributed between sister chromosomes at the first division was in-

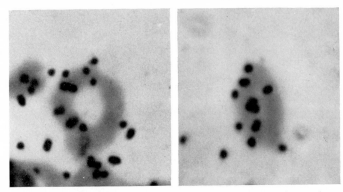

FIG. 26. A case where the "old" DNA and the DNA newly synthesized by a chromosome during the preceding interphase are separated at mitosis. *Vicia faba* roots were exposed to colchicine and tritium-labeled thymidine, then fixed and processed for autoradiography. The silver grains over one sister chromosome indicate that it has received the "new" DNA. Photograph by courtesy of Drs. L. F. LaCour and S. R. Pelc (LaCour and Pelc, 1959).

creased when the roots were exposed to colchicine during the period of DNA synthesis, as well as during the interval between synthesis and division. This variability was attributed by LaCour and Pelc to an effect of colchicine on the separation of chromosomal subunits, the "splitting" step in reproduction.

Perhaps it is safe to conclude, even while admitting the polemic status of the question, that chromosome reproduction does sometimes follow the mother-daughter relationship, providing one cell with an old chromosome and the other with a new one.

Unfortunately, it has been imagined that such experiments represent critical tests of the Watson-Crick (1953) hypothesis concerning the mechanism of duplication of molecular DNA. Although they are not entirely irrelevant, they cannot possibly be decisive, and this question is better dealt with by direct studies on DNA molecules, such as the experiments of Meselson and Stahl (1958), Cavalieri and Rosenberg (1961), Sueoka (1960), and others.

Thus far, the experimental designs pose the single question: How is the DNA synthesized by a chromosome before a given division distributed between its daughters and granddaughters? It is seen in Fig. 27, which is a diagram of the possible results of such experiments, that the distribution of newly synthesized (and labeled) DNA will depend on (1) the method of replication itself and (2) the way in which the products split at mitosis if the reproducing chromosome is composed of more than one unit ("half-chromatid"). Following the terminology of Delbrück and Stent (1957), we may consider *dispersive, semiconservative,* and *conservative* methods of reproduction.

In the *dispersive* scheme no unit retains its integrity; the molecules that are newly synthesized before a given division are uniformly dispersed among the progeny of all following divisions. The *semiconservative* scheme, of which the famous Watson-Crick hypothesis for molecular DNA replication is the prototype, predicts that the newly synthesized material will be equally distributed at the first division, but that it will not be subdivided at further divisions. In the *conservative* plan the parent unit retains its integrity, and all the newly synthesized material goes to the daughter unit, which remains intact at further divisions. We need not consider the dispersive method in connection with chromosomes. In fact, a fundamental conclusion from all the work done thus far, independent of all other interpretation, is that some linear unit of the chromosome does remain intact through an indefinite series of replications. Where it does not, the deviation has the characteristics of crossing-over (J. H. Taylor, 1958). The essential features of the semiconservative and conservative schemes will be evident from the diagrams; the black areas represent units labeled before the first division.

Let us stress the point that the units postulated in the diagrams are "cytological" units, chromatids and half-chromatids; the least equivocal term for such a chromosomal thread is, perhaps, *chromonema*. Presumably the nucleotide chains in each unit will exist in pairs, according to the present image of the DNA molecule, but the numbers or arrangements of the pairs do not enter the discussion. We see that the expected distributions in the cases where the chromosome is composed of a single chromatid are rather limited. If the replication is semiconservative, the sisters *must* be equally labeled after the first division and unequally labeled after the second. If replication is conservative, the sisters *must* be unequally labeled after the first division. But as soon as we introduce

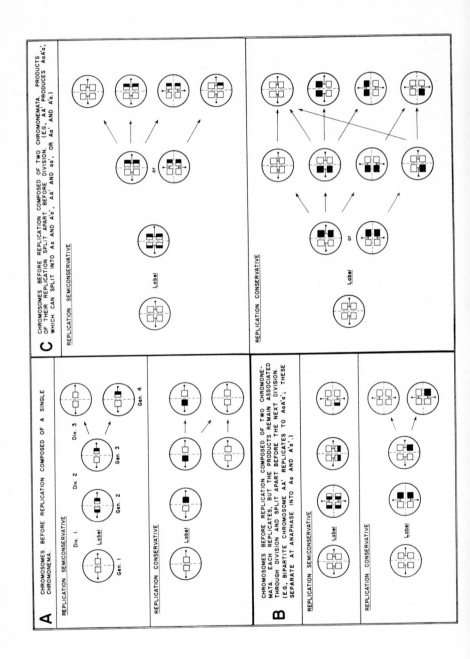

some multiplicity in the chromosomes, the possibilities are more numerous.

First, we must recognize that a semiconservative method of replication does not in any case permit inequality between the daughters of the first division, either between sister chromosomes or between daughter nuclei. If the observations of LaCour and Pelc on sister chromosomes and of Plaut and Mazia on sister nuclei have any validity, a conservative mechanism is mandatory. On the other hand, a conservative mechanism does allow all or most of the sisters at the first division to be equivalent, if it is imagined that the chromosomes are multiplex. We need only imagine that there is a lag between synthetic replication and splitting, so that the products of replication before a division have not yet split by the time of division. The preferred plane of splitting will then be between the units of the old generation.

Any variable affecting the time of splitting so that it came before division would tend to randomize the way in which the four-part (or more) chromosome at metaphase is physically divided into two at anaphase. This could vary with species, with conditions of growth, and from chromosome to chromosome and could be influenced by such agents as colchicine. The finding of LaCour and Pelc that the new DNA tended

---

FIG. 27.   The design of experiments on the distribution of parental and newly synthesized DNA in mitosis. The results to be expected under various hypothesis concerning the nature of the reproductive process and the multiplicity of the chromosomes. One chromosome is shown diagrammatically at the metaphase of each numbered generation. In all cases, the label (black) is introduced at the synthesis between the first and second generation.

A.   Chromosome composed of one unit. If replication is semiconservative, the label will always be distributed equally in the first division after introduction of the label and will always be distributed unequally at the second division. If replication is conservative, the distribution will always be unequal at the first division after labeling.

B.   Chromosome composed of two units, but splitting of new units from old follows one generation behind synthesis. That is, chromosome *AA* duplicates to produce *AA'AA'* but always splits into *AA'* and *AA'*. If the replication process is semiconservative, the label will be distributed equally for the first two divisions, and unequally at the third. If conservative, distribution will be equal at the first division, and unequal at the second.

C.   Chromosome composed of two units. Reproduction before division gives rise to four units, which may split at random. If replication is semiconservative, distribution will always be equal at the first division, with a variety of possibilities at the second and third. If replication is conservative, the distribution at the first division may be equal or unequal, with the probability depending on the relative frequency of splitting on one plane or the other.

to be equally distributed at the first division under normal conditions but frequently was unequally distributed after colchicine treatment, is entirely intelligible in terms of the way in which a multiplex chromosome is split—and the finding is so interpreted by them.

Thus, by considering the multiplicity of the chromosomes, the various and seemingly conflicting observations can be reconciled. To do so would seem to be a gratuitous gesture toward harmony were it not for the fact that the multiplex chromosome is the most acceptable model on other grounds, the most important one being that the units are so often seen at distances easily resolved by the ordinary microscope (Fig. 25).

If DNA itself replicates in a semiconservative way, it would be difficult to account for a seemingly conservative distribution between daughter chromosomes. One hypothetical possibility would be a multiplex chromosome in which only one DNA unit of each kind reproduced repeatedly until the number of daughter units equaled the number of units in the parent chromosome. However, the question of the mode of duplication of DNA has been reopened by Cavalieri and Rosenberg (1961) who conclude that the parental double helix is conserved. They suggest that the double helix does open up and generate another pair of strands, but their hypothesis calls for the reassociation of the parental strands and the association of the new strands.

Whatever the history of DNA may be, the student of mitosis is concerned with the multiplicity of the chromosomes, the time course of their total reproduction (and not merely the reproduction of DNA), and the problem of separating the products of their reproduction. The essential point being made here, and discussed more fully by Mazia, 1961), is that the actual distribution of the chromosome units produced in a given generation will depend on the time-relations between the completion of the material synthesis of new units and the physical splitting-apart of existing units.

iv. Summary. The preparation of chromosomes for mitotic separation involves the splitting and untwisting of the daughter strands. The considerable evidence that chromosomes are often duplex (and perhaps even more multiplex) implies that two equivalent and potentially separable units duplicate to give four and then split two-by-two. It is conceivable that this splitting follows one generation behind duplication, but there is evidence that it may occur with some randomness. As a consequence of their coiled structure, sister chromosomes may enter prophase wound around each other. They are observed to unwind during prophase, but the mechanism is not known.

c. Time course and magnitude of prophase "condensation." For practical purposes we often recognize the beginning of prophase when the contraction of the chromosomes has proceeded to the point at which we can resolve them as microscopic threads. It is sometimes implied in elementary descriptions of mitosis that the contraction process is completed during prophase, but this is not the typical case. It continues through metaphase and well into anaphase, as is illustrated in Fig. 28.

Many of the earlier data on the contraction of chromosomes and the problem of "packing" them in a more compact form by coiling are summarized by Darlington and Upcott (1939). In meiosis the magnitude of the contraction may be fiftyfold or more, varying greatly from one type of cell to another and in mitosis it tends to be less. The "true" value, the ratio of the length of the interphase chromosome to that at the most condensed stage during mitosis, can seldom be investigated. The "packing" will depend on the diameter of the unit strand, the number of coils, and the diameter of the whole coiled chromosome. Quantitative information on these data is summarized and discussed by Darlington and Upcott (1939).

There seems to be no rigid regulation between the degree of contraction of the chromosomes and their ability to join the mitotic apparatus. If metaphase comes abnormally early, the spindle will engage relatively long chromosomes; if it is delayed, the chromosomes will continue to contract and may be very compact compared to normal metaphase chromosomes (Swanson, 1943). It is well known that agents which block the operation of the spindle, such as colchicine (literature in Eigsti and Dustin, 1955) do not stop the condensation of the chromosomes, which may proceed to the extremes described in so-called "c-mitotic" figures.

It is interesting that all the chromosomes in a cell tend to shorten at the same relative rate, as though the process normally were driven by factors in the intracellular environment rather than those intrinsic to the chromosome itself. Even though the "contraction" attained by metaphase may vary, the lengths of the several chromosomes relative to each other will be constant from cell to cell (Marquardt, 1938). If one of the chromosomes tends to be out of phase with the others, as in the behavior of sex chromosomes in meiosis in certain organisms, its behavior will be consistent. A great deal of attention has been given *heterochromatic* regions of chromosomes, definite and reproducible regions whose state of condensation is different from that of the rest of the chromosome.

d. Chemical changes of chromosomes in prophase. Thanks to the power of the newer cytochemical methods, it is now certain that the mitotic behavior of the chromosomes is associated with changes in their

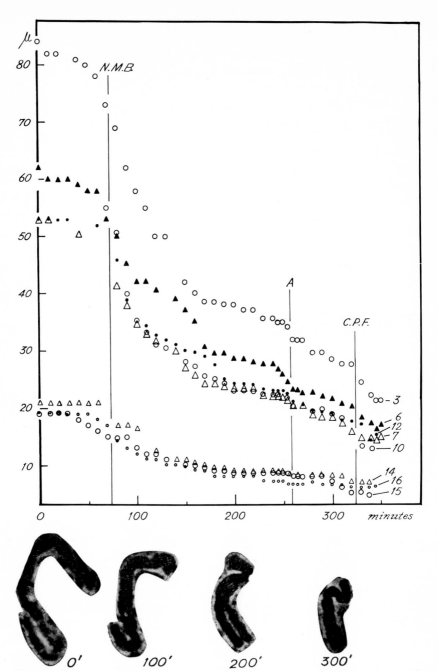

FIG. 28. The magnitude of the contraction of chromosomes in *Haemanthus* endosperm (Bajer, 1959). The lengths of several chromosomes, measured on motion picture records. *N.M.B.*, nuclear membrane breakdown; *A, anaphase; C.P.F.,* cell plate formation. The photographs below show chromosome number 6 (cf. Bajer, 1959).

chemical composition. The most striking of these changes is the apparent accumulation of RNA in prophase and the shedding of this RNA in anaphase or telophase; let us call this the "chromosomal RNA cycle." The meaning of chemical changes in chromosomes during mitosis has been discussed in the contexts of the spiralization mechanism, the breakdown and reconstruction of the nucleolus, and mitotic movements. A small but impressive body of facts has been accumulated, but the interpretation of these facts is still in the conjectural stage.

Undoubtedly, the earlier cytologists observed changes in the staining characteristics of chromosomes during mitosis, but a survey of the literature has not been attempted. The modern cytochemical investigation of this point—and of so many others—begins with the work of the pioneer Caspersson (1936, 1939).

The existence of a chromosomal RNA cycle was pointed out by Kaufmann *et al.* (1948), who found that the chromosomes of onion root tips going through prophase acquired a component which was stainable as RNA and could be removed by ribonuclease. This component was lost in telophase. They suggested that this cycle might be correlated with the breakdown and reconstitution of the nucleolus. Jacobson and Webb (1952) and Boss (1954) observed a similar cycle in animal cells. In this case, too, the chromosomal RNA was released during late anaphase or telophase, a phenomenon that will be discussed later (Section XI, A).

We cannot fail to be impressed with this change in the chemistry of the chromosome associated with the beginning of the mitotic period, and it opens up some important questions. Is it associated with the "condensation" process itself? It has been suggested in the past (e.g., by Serra 1947) that the contraction of the chromosomes involved the deposition of "peripheric" nucleoproteins in a matrix, although at the time Serra proposed that these were deoxyribonucleoproteins. Arguing against this, perhaps, is the observation that the RNA sometimes appears on the chromosomes later in prophase, when the contraction is far advanced (Jacobson and Webb, 1952). Does the chromosomal RNA derive from the nucleolus, the breakdown of which is an important event of prophase? This derivation has been suggested by S. W. Brown (1954), who correlated nucleolar breakdown in the plant *Luzula* with the appearance of a staining matrix, and by others. Some facts oppose such an interpretation. The ribonucleoprotein sometimes first appears in the nucleus in the form of very fine particles and deposits on chromosomes before the "erosion" of the nucleolus is evident (Jacobson and Webb, 1952; Boss, 1955). It is claimed by Love (1957) that staining properties of the chromosomal RNA suggest a cytoplasmic, but not a nucleolar, origin. Is the accumulation of RNA on the chromosomes related to the mitotic apparatus? It should be interesting to observe whether the chromosomal RNA cycle occurs in endomitotic situations, where a mitotic apparatus is not involved. It would also be important to evaluate the significance of chromosomal RNA in the production of mitotic abnormalities by ribonuclease, which has been demonstrated by Kaufmann and Das (1954), Firket *et al.* (1955), and others.

It may be misleading to describe the accumulation of RNA on the chromosomes during prophase as a "deposition." There is another and experimentally testable possibility. It has been found by Pelling (1959) and by Goldstein and Micou (1959) that the chromosome arms are the first site of synthesis of RNA, and that RNA is then rapidly transferred to the nucleolus and finally to the cytoplasm. We might imagine that the transfer of the chromosomal RNA to the nucleolus—which may be becoming nonfunctional—or to cytoplasm was blocked at some point in prophase and that the blockage resulted in its accumulation on the chromosomes. This possibility is quite the opposite of the hypothetical transfer of RNA from nucleolus to chromosomes.*

The recognized chemical changes in the chromosomes during prophase are not restricted to the RNA fraction. Recently LaCour and Chayen (1958) have described the reaction of mitotic and meiotic cells of a variety of plants to staining with a mixture of orange G and aniline blue. Particular attention was paid to orange G, which seems to be a specific stain for phospholipids after appropriate fixation (LaCour *et al.*, 1958). In both mitotic stages the euchromatic regions of the chromosomes tend to combine with orange G (staining yellow) during the period from about mid-prophase to telophase, but not during the intervening period, including interphase. The nucleoli consistently stain with orange G, but the authors note that the chromosomes of cells in mitosis begin to stain with this dye before the time of nucleolar breakdown. Thus there is a "chromosomal phospholipid cycle," if the interpretation of the orange G staining is correct, that corresponds in time to the RNA cycle. The possibility that RNA was responsible for the observations of LaCour and Chayen was excluded by experiments showing that the putative phospholipid was not affected by ribonuclease. The close parallelism between

---

* However, there is no detectable amount of RNA in chromosomes of amphibian eggs during cleavage, i.e., during the period when there is no visible nucleolus. RNA is clearly present in these chromosomes as soon as nucleoli become visible in resting cell nuclei (J. Brachet, personal communication).

the two cycles calls to mind the common association between ribonucleo-proteins and lipoproteins in cytoplasmic structures.

While the chromosomes are acquiring these substances during pro-phase, the nucleus may be losing others. In a study of endosperm cultures

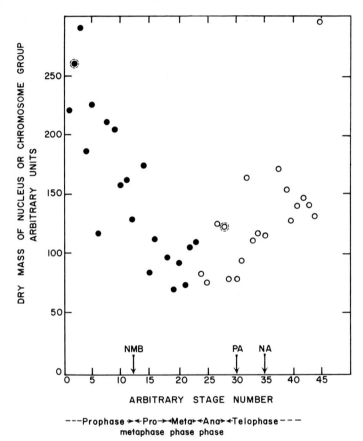

FIG. 29. Changes in dry mass of nucleus and chromosomes during the mitotic cycle in *Haemanthus* endosperm. Mass was measured by interference microscopy and is given in arbitrary units. Solid circles: chromosome group before anaphase. Open circles: sum of sister groups of chromosomes. *NMB*, nuclear membrane breakdown; *PA*, appearance of phragmoplast; *NA*, reappearance of nucleoli. Data of Richards and Bajer (1961).

of *Haemanthus* (Richards and Bajer, 1961) with the interference micro-scope, a sharp drop in the total mass of the nucleus was observed during prophase before the breakdown of the nuclear membrane (Fig. 29). Richards (1960) attributes the loss to proteins.

As yet the chemical changes in the chromosome in prophase cannot be interpreted in a definite way, but two orientations toward future work are possible. First, as we have mentioned, these changes may be related to the coiling of the chromosomes; they may relate also to the participation of the chromosomes in the formation of the mitotic apparatus. Second (and a matter of greater theoretical interest), we are led to realize that the chromosomes may be responsible for the distribution of substances other than the primary genetic material to the daughter nuclei. If so, we may yet find a basis for nuclear differentiation (Briggs and King, 1959) without challenging the invariability of the primary genetic material, as has been pointed out by Mazia (1958b).

e. *Conclusions.* Our knowledge of the coiling of the chromosomes in prophase still rests essentially on the conclusions of microscopic cytology. Ideas concerning the initiation of coiling are speculative. It is known that the contraction of chromosomes resulting from superimposed orders of coiling does not stop at metaphase, nor does it seem to be linked rigorously to the engagement of the chromosomes by the spindle. This may merely reflect the fact that the kinetochore becomes the controlling element of the chromosome once mitosis begins. An important discovery, whose significance is still not understood, is the fact that chromosomes acquire, during prophase, RNA and phospholipid components which they carry through mitosis and release before entering the next interphase.

3. Polarization of the Mitotic Figure

a. *Separation of centers.* In animal cells it is clear that mitosis is polarized by the centers. The poles are established by the separation of the centers, and we know the destinations of the chromosomes even before they take up their metaphase alignment. It is difficult to imagine how the chromosomes could be deployed to an equatorial plane unless that equator were defined by poles, but this perhaps is not adequately persuasive of the existence of material centers where they have not been seen.

In normal bipolar mitosis the axis connecting sister centers is a straight line, in tripolar mitosis the centers tend to be related as an equilateral triangle, in tetrapolar figures their relation is that of a square or of the edges of a symmetrical tetrahedron, etc. (Fig. 30). The geometric disposition of the poles tends to be very regular and could be described by the image of points which *repel* each other equally. This is purely descriptive; there is, unfortunately, no evidence that adequate repulsive forces exist. Although the normal polarization involves sister centers, this is not a necessary condition. In a number of situations we observe that centers of different parentage may establish the poles of a mitotic apparatus. Much of our information about this comes from studies of polyspermic eggs (e.g., Boveri, 1907), but we have also the detailed observations of Cleveland (1955) on *Barbulanympha*, in which it is shown that one condition of establishing a polarized mitotic figure is the proximity of two or more centers to a nucleus (Fig. 31).

It is likely that the separating centers are always connected. In the early stages of separation the connection was sometimes described as a "centrodesmose" (Heidenhain, 1907), but as the centers move farther apart a set of fibrous connections designated as the *central spindle* is

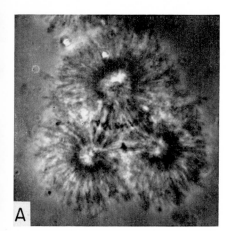
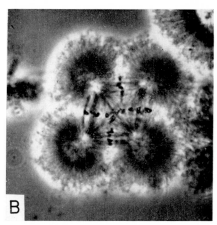

FIG. 30. Multipolar mitotic figures resulting from polyspermy in sea urchin eggs. Each spermatozoan introduces a centriole. If both centrioles reproduce, a tetrapolar figure (B) results; if one fails to reproduce, a tripolar figure (A) is formed. Note that in this case every center is connected by fibers to every other center.

observed. In forms where the separation of the centers takes place early in relation to prophase, it is clear that the formation of the central spindle does not depend on the participation of the chromosomes. This was already evident from the fact that such spindles could be observed in cells that did not contain chromosomes (Boveri, 1896; later observers cited by Wilson, 1925, p. 176). It is shown in Fig. 31,B, where a central spindle in *Barbulanympha* has formed at a distance from the nucleus, while the nucleus is going through endomitotic changes because it is too far from the centers to join the spindle.

Where material is favorable for observation, we are given the impression that the centers are being pushed apart by the growth of the connecting fibers, in which case the appearance of "repulsion" would be no more than an expression of the rigidity of the growing central spindle and would be subject to some variation. (But the fact that the "lines of force" are embodied physically in this way need not discourage reference to "repulsion," if it is helpful.)

In general, the fibrous connections between the separating centers can be seen by appropriate methods of observation: phase contrast (e.g., Fig. 31); stains for proteins (e.g., mercuric bromophenol blue, as used by Kawamura, 1957); and polarization microscopy (e.g., E. W. Taylor, 1959). K. Kawamura has made a careful study of the separation of the centers during spermatogenesis in various grasshoppers and during mitosis in grasshopper neuroblasts (1960a), and he consistently observed fibrous connections between the centers. In newt fibroblasts the separation of the centers, which takes place only in the latter part of prophase, can be measured as the increase in length of the birefringent central spindle (E. W. Taylor, 1959). Taylor observed that the rate of elongation is about 1.5 µ per minute and that the maximum distance attained from center to center is about 34 µ (Fig. 32). These numbers provide a realistic image of the time scale of this mitotic event. It is also evident from Fig. 32 that the rate of separation of the poles does not follow an inverse-square relationship, as might have been expected if we were dealing with a simple physical repulsion.

There is very little experimental information on the process of separa-

---

FIG. 31. Relations between centrioles, central spindle, chromosomal fibers, and chromosomes in the flagellate *Barbulanympha*. The nuclear membrane does not break down during division. Meiosis with abnormal number of centrioles and nuclei is not uncommon and reveals some interesting facts about the origin of the mitotic apparatus. (B, C, and D after Cleveland, 1955.)

A. Normal mitosis. The large, elongated centrioles (*C*) organize the flagella near the surface. At their inner ends are distinct "centrosomes" from which the fibers of the mitotic apparatus seem to derive. The central spindle (*CS*) lies outside the nucleus and depresses its surface. Some of the astral rays function as chromosomal fibers, connecting to the kinetochores (*K*) which are just inside the nuclear membrane (see also Figs. 36 and 45B). After Cleveland (1938).

B. A case of first meiotic division in which the nucleus was located at a distance from the centrioles. The astral rays do not reach the chromosomes. The mitotic apparatus forms and functions without chromosomes and the nucleus simultaneously goes through its chromosome cycle without movement of chromosomes to poles.

C. First meiotic division where one nucleus is associated with five centrioles, a second with none. The first forms the complex figure shown in D, the second simultaneously goes through cycle of chromosome condensation and splitting without poleward separation.

D. Enlargement of five-pole figure shown in C. It would appear that members of the same set of chromosomes can be engaged by different centers.

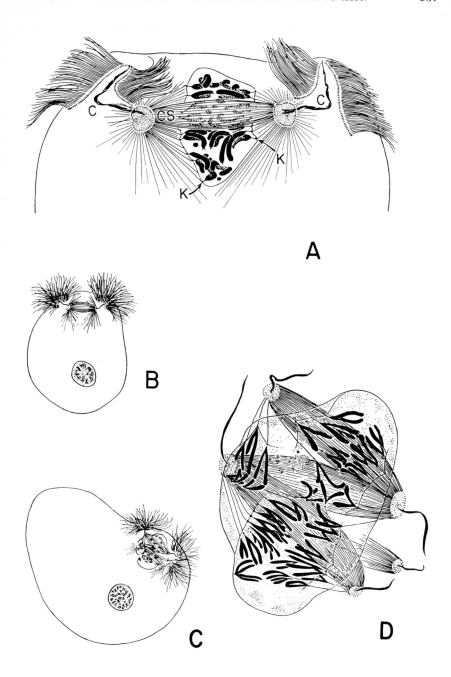

A

B

C

D

tion of the centers, although it is one of the remarkable mitotic movements. It is apparently not affected by mercaptoethanol (Fig. 14) and
occurs even while other mitotic movements in echinoderm eggs are
blocked by this agent. Chloramphenicol in high concentrations seems
to inhibit the elongation of the spindle in newt fibroblasts if it is applied
some time before the centers begin to separate, but it has no effect on it
once the separation has begun (E. W. Taylor, 1959).

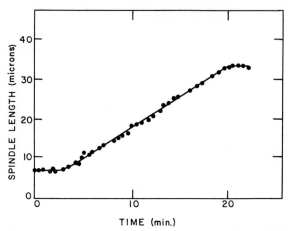

FIG. 32. The rate of separation of the centers in the newt fibroblast. In this
material, the birefingent spindle is laid down between the separating centers (cf.
Fig. 22,B) and accurate measurements can be made. After E. W. Taylor (1959).

b. Multipolar figures. The situation becomes more complicated
where we have more than two centers in a cell, a condition that may
result from the presence of several nuclei, each served by its associated
centers, from polyspermy in eggs, or from supernumerary divisions of the
centers. A well-studied case is that of the beetle *Popilius disjunctus* (Roberts and Johnson, 1956), in which the multinucleate condition is common
in spermatocytes. Each pair of sister centers gives rise to a spindle. When
two pairs of centers are present, the spindles may lie parallel, may join
at one pole to form a V-configuration, the diverging ends not being connected, or may lie across each other (Fig. 81). In the latter form there
are no spindles between centers that are not sisters. When three pairs of
centers form three spindles, they may join at the ends to form an equilateral triangle. There are many other combinations, but connections
between centers that are not sisters are doubtful in this case. Such a
result is in accord with the notion that central spindles are formed in
the course of the separation of sister centers.

At the other extreme, we have the classic case of the polyspermic egg, where there is a tendency for spindles to form between all or most of the centers present, whether or not they are sisters (Fig. 30). In the intermediate case of the flagellate *Barbulanympha* (Fig. 31) it would appear that centers of different parentage may connect, but they do not necessarily do so. In this organism the multipolar mitotic figures are observed in cells in which supernumerary divisions of the centrioles occur or in cases where more than two gametes fuse.

The information now available suggests that there are two ways of establishing pole-to-pole connections. One is by the elongation of a central spindle that is formed as sister centers separate. This elongation may be a driving force of the separation. The second is by the joining of fibers (astral rays) growing from the centers, not sisters, that are initially at some distance from each other. Here we may quote Cleveland's (1957b) description of the process in *Barbulanympha*: "In the early stages of achromatic figure development . . . astral rays grow out from each centriole. At first all the rays are free. Some, however, soon become long enough for those arising from one centriole to meet those arising from the other. As they meet, they grow along one another to form the central spindle."

c. Conclusions. In cases where centers can be recognized, mitosis is polarized by the separation of these centers, the form of which often suggests that centers repel each other. There is no physical basis for a repulsion mechanism, but there is a good bit of visual evidence that the separation usually involves a system of elongating fibers between the centers, termed the central spindle. The time of separation of centers for a given division may be as early as the anaphase of the previous division or as late as the prophase of the current division.

4. The Nucleolus at Prophase

Descriptively, the collapse or dispersion of the nucleolus during prophase is one of the most characteristic and most frequently encountered events of the mitotic cycle. We shall not expect to be able to interpret it until we have some real understanding of the role of the nucleolus in cell function. When we speak of its "breakdown" we are generally referring to the loss of the mass of staining substance, particularly nucleoprotein, which makes it conspicuous. As we shall see (Section XIV), there is some cytological evidence that another component of the nucleolus persists through mitosis.

There are cells in which the nucleolus does not break down. For example, a study made by Brown and Emery (1957), which contains a useful survey of older work on persistent nucleoli, leads to the conclusion that the breakdown or persistence of the nucleolus may be a species-specific character in the grasses with which they worked, and that this characteristic may provide a taxonomic aid.

The fate of the persistent nucleoli, where they do occur, is interesting. In some plant cells (Brown and Emery, 1957) the nucleolus may move into the equatorial plane at metaphase, in which case it is pinched into halves that are carried to the poles. If it is located toward one pole, it is carried to that pole at metakinesis or at anaphase without being divided.

Even where nucleolar breakdown is the normal expectation, it may fail in individual cases. This has been shown in studies by Bajer and Mole-Bajer (1956b, and personal communication from Dr. A. Bajer) on mitosis in cultures of plant endosperm. Persistent nucleoli may be caught up in the spindle and move toward one pole or may be left in the cytoplasm at the end of prophase. According to Dr. Bajer, they never are incorporated into daughter nuclei.

Persistent nucleoli are not ordinarily found in dividing animal cells. However, Heath (1954) has reported the extraordinary fact that low concentrations of cobalt salts suppress the breakdown of the nucleolus in cultured embryo cells, and that it is carried through mitosis apparently intact. The peculiar affinity of the nucleolus for heavy metals—cobalt, zinc (Fujii, 1955a, b), and silver—is one of the many mysteries concerning this body.

Speculations concerning the significance of the nucleolar breakdown at prophase emphasize three possibilities: (1) the nucleolar substance moves on to the chromosome threads, participates in their mitotic behavior, and is carried by them into the daughter nuclei; (2) part or all of the nucleolar substance makes a contribution to the forming spindle; or (3) there is an interchange of ribonucleoproteins and possibly other materials between nucleus and cytoplasm during mitosis.

The breakdown of the nucleolus is not an obligatory event of mitosis. But, even when the nucleoli persist, they are discarded by the chromosomes and enter the cytoplasm. Perhaps the most general conjecture that we can make is that the prophase changes in the chromosomes lead to the disassociation of the nucleoli from the "nucleolus-organizer" regions of the chromosomes and that once this has happened the nucleoli tend to be unstable. A more fanciful extrapolation of this view recalls that the nucleolus is active as "middle man" between the chromosome arms and the cytoplasm; it receives the products of the genetic sites, performs unknown further operations on them, and transfers them to the cytoplasm. Cut off from the source of supply, the nucleoli may wilt away.

When we consider the nucleolar substance, we are inclined to think first of RNA. This first thought may well be justified on functional grounds, for the notion that nucleolar RNA serves as mediator between the genetic material of the chromosomes and the synthetic systems of the cytoplasm has survived in its many versions ever since it was first invoked by Caspersson and Schultz (1940). Experience with cytochemical staining methods also leads to the impression that the concentration of RNA in the nucleolus is extremely high, for it stains strongly with appropriate dyes. This impression is not supported by the available chemical analyses of isolated nucleoli. Analyses of pea embryo nucleoli (H. Stern et al., 1959) and starfish oöcyte nucleoli (Vincent, 1955) give RNA contents in the neighborhood of 10% of nucleolar dry weight. It is possible, of course, that a readily soluble RNA-containing component is present which is lost in isolation procedures but preserved by cytological fixation.

The probable existence of a specific nucleolar substance has been discovered by Tandler (1955, 1959) and by Das and Alfert (1959), but at the time of writing we have no idea of its chemical nature. It is identified by a blackening of interphase nucleoli with silver under certain conditions. The chromosome arms are seen to be "stained" by the same method in early prophase and in late anaphase. During mitosis the substance is absent from nucleolar components, having been lost to the cytoplasm (Fig. 33). At the end of mitosis it is seen to concentrate in the chromosomes and in nucleoli as the nucleus is reconstituted. The substance is not RNA; it is more exclusively associated with chromosomes and nucleoli than RNA. For our present purpose, the important point is that this component of the nucleolus is not transferred to chromosomes as the nucleoli break down at prophase, but to the cytoplasm.

So far as nucleolar RNA is concerned, adequate tracer experiments should provide critical evidence of its fate in the course of nucleolar breakdown. As we have mentioned, it has been imagined that RNA is transferred to the chromosomes at prophase, but this hypothesis rests only on cytological inference, and there are other ways of dealing with the increase in the RNA concentrations in chromosomes at prophase.

We may anticipate that part of the story will be revealed by the electron microscope. A study by Lafontaine (1958) describes changes in nucleolar structure during prophase and the appearance of "prenucleolar" bodies (identifiable by the presence of characteristic dense particles about 140 A. in diameter) at late anaphase or telophase. The fate of the nucleolar material from prophase to the end of anaphase has not been traced.

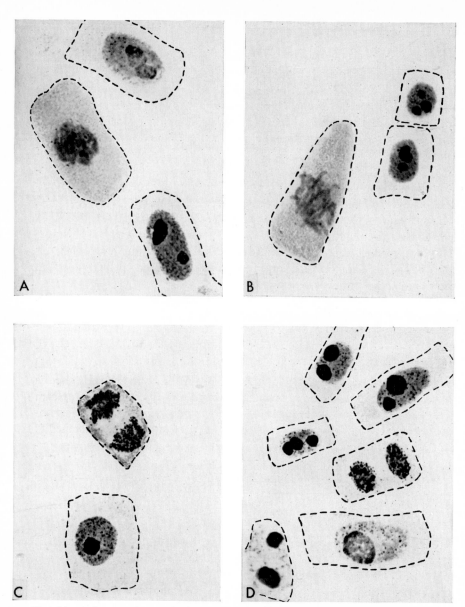

Fig. 33. Behavior of a nucleolar substance, characterized by its affinity for silver, during the mitotic cycle. A. Onion root tip cells in interphase and in prophase. Large nucleoli, very black, in interphase. Cytoplasm very light. In prophase, nucleoli have begun to break down, and the silver-staining component is seen in the cytoplasm. B. Metaphase. No silver-staining material associated with chromosomes. Cytoplasm stained. C. Anaphase. "Prenucleolar" particles collecting along chromosome arms. Cytoplasm lighter, but is still darkened by silver. D. Telophase. Numerous large "prenucleolar" bodies, staining with silver. Cytoplasm light. Compare with neighboring cells in interphase. Photographs by courtesy of Drs. Nirmal Das and Max Alfert. Cell outlines, unclear in preparations, have been marked with dotted lines.

A relation between the nucleolus and the progress of the cell toward division has now been demonstrated by Gaulden and Perry (1958). Direct irradiation of the nucleolus of grasshopper neuroblasts with ultraviolet microbeams permanently stopped mitosis if imposed at any stage from late telophase to mid-prophase. Comparable irradiation outside the nucleolus caused some delay of division, but did not stop it. But the irradiation of the nucleolus had less and less effect beginning at mid-prophase and none at all at late prophase. Apparently—and this is no surprise—the nucleolus plays a decisive role in the synthetic and other processes building up toward mitosis, but its job is done by prophase.

If the nucleolus played a direct and important part in the preparations for division, we should expect it always to be indispensable. In some cases, as in *Vicia faba* (McLeish, 1954), it has been found that cells cannot divide if they have lost their nucleoli. On the other hand, *Drosophila* eggs lacking the nucleolus-carrying chromosomes can, according to observations of Von Borstel and Rekemeyer (1958), carry out 10–12 divisions producing 1000–4000 nuclei before they die. If we may generalize from a few cases, it is suggested that the role of the nucleolus in the preparations for division is at the level of primary biosynthesis, and the nucleolus would be crucial only in cells that have to grow between divisions. The products of nucleolar activity may be stored in an egg to the extent that a series of divisions could proceed without further synthesis.

We shall return to the nucleolus when we consider how the new interphase cells are reconstituted.

a. Conclusions. The nucleolus is essential to the preparations for division, but its contributions have been completed by some point in prophase. Normally, it—or a major part of its substance—is discarded by the chromosomes with which it is associated at prophase. If it persists, as it does in some cases, it is not incorporated into the daughter nuclei.

5. The Nuclear Membrane

The breakdown of the nuclear membrane is a common but not universal feature of the end of prophase. The long history of microscopic observations is now supported by electron microscopic studies (Porter, 1961, p. 654). The structure of the nuclear membrane in electron microscopic preparations is so characteristic that its persistence surely would have been detected by Porter (1957), de Harven and Bernhard (1956), Amano (1957), and others in their studies of animal cells in metaphase and anaphase.

In plant cells detailed evidence of the disappearance of the nuclear membrane is given by the phase contrast observations of Bajer (1958a) and by electron microscopic observations of Porter and Machado (1960). There has been some discussion of the possible persistence of the nuclear membrane in plant cells as a boundary around the mitotic apparatus, especially in the publications of Wada (1950, 1955, 1957). Cytoplasmic membranes may aggregate around the nucleus and the spindle during mitosis, and this aggregation gives the impression, in light microscopy, of a persistent nuclear membrane or a membrane around the mitotic apparatus. Such a disposition of the endoplasmic reticulum has been described in detail in an electron microscopic study of spermatogenesis in *Drosophila virilis* by Ito (1960).

Among the Protozoa the nuclear membrane commonly persists through mitosis. Even here, there is evidence that it undergoes structural change and a functional "breakdown" in the sense that extrachromosomal material is lost to the cytoplasm. For example, Rabinovitch and Plaut (1956) observed the discharge of most of the nuclear RNA into the cytoplasm during division in *Amoeba proteus*. In this organism Cohen (1957) and Roth *et al.* (1960) have presented clear evidence of the persistence of one layer of the complex nuclear membrane, the thin outer layer, while the thicker inner layer breaks down (Fig. 34).

The most significant generalization we can make about the actual dissolution of the nuclear membrane is that there is no generalization. In cases where the spindle forms inside the nuclear membrane, in those where the chromosomes remain inside the membrane while the rest of the spindle lies outside (Fig. 31, A), and in the "typical" case where we are sure that the membrane has disappeared from sight, mitosis may be normal in every other respect. Nor can we attribute much weight to the hypothesis that the "typical" situation is significant because it permits direct contact between the genetic material and the cytoplasm. There are good reasons, summarized by C. Stern (1938), for thinking that action of the genetic material takes place when it is in the interphase condition,

---

Fig. 34. Changes of the nuclear membrane during mitosis in a cell, *Amoeba proteus,* in which a visible membrane persists throughout the cycle. A. Nucleus at prophase. The nuclear membrane still shows its interphase structure; it is composed of a thin outer layer and a thick perforated inner layer. At the stage shown, the membrane seems to be discharging substance into the cytoplasm by evagination (arrows). Chromosomal material (*CH*) is seen, as well as denser particles described as nucleolar material (*NO*). B. Nucleus at metaphase. Only the thin layer of the nuclear membrane remains. Chromosomes are condensed and aligned on a plate. A few of the masses identified as nucleolar material remain. Photographs by courtesy of Dr. Adolph I. Cohen (cf. A. Cohen, 1957).

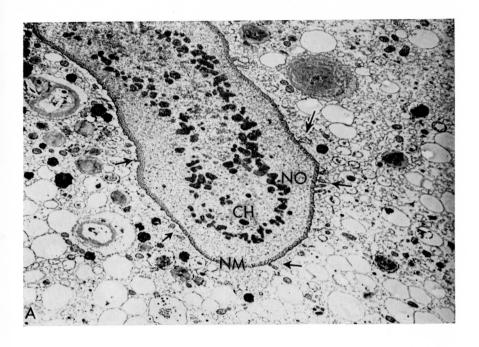

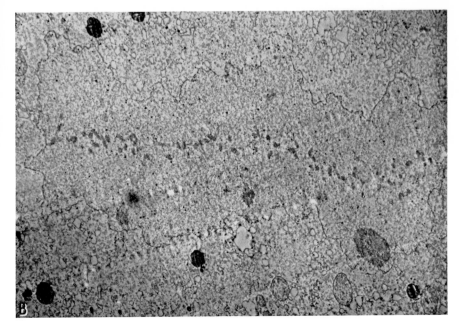

and, so far as we know, all the chemical changes in chromosomes during mitosis begin while the nuclear membrane is still present.

Practically nothing is known about the chemical mechanism of the breakdown of the nuclear membrane. In speculative discussions it is sometimes regarded as an enzymatic process. Barer and Joseph (1957) note that the breakdown is preceded by an accumulation of mitochondria around the nucleus in the case of the grasshopper spermatocyte, and they speculate on the possibility that the mitochondria may participate in an enzymatic disruption of the membrane. According to recent work on the "lysosomes" (de Duve, 1959) these particles might be a more likely source of lytic enzymes.

The transformations of the nuclear membrane in mitosis are bound to be linked to those of the endoplasmic reticulum, in view of the close relations between the two (e.g., Bernhard, 1959; Whaley et al., 1960; Porter, 1961). We shall have occasion to ask whether the breakdown of the nuclear membrane at prophase is a sign of the entrance of the cell into a period of depressed biosynthesis.

If the disappearance of the nuclear membrane is inhibited or delayed, the chromosomes continue to shorten inside the nucleus, yielding shorter chromosomes at metaphase or even metaphase-like chromosomes within an intact nucleus (Fig. 35). Evidently the changes of the nuclear membrane are not directly geared to the contraction of the chromosomes, although such a relationship has been suggested (e.g., Amano and Tanaka, 1957).

6. The Mitotic Apparatus in Prophase

In the flow of events toward the culminating phases of mitosis a good many of the essential steps leading to the formation of the mitotic apparatus are far advanced by the end of prophase. We have already discussed the synthesis of the protein components of the apparatus as an interphase event, and we have located the duplication and splitting of the centers in the time span of the previous division.

By the end of prophase the poles are clearly determined in those cells in which we can recognize them by the presence of visible centers. Where centers can be seen, they are often connected by a system of fibers usually called the *central spindle* or *primary spindle*, which lies outside the nucleus during prophase. As we have mentioned, the separation of the centers may be related to the growth of this central spindle. Older literature on this earliest visible phase of the formation of the mitotic apparatus is summarized by Wilson (1925, pp. 147-148) and by Schrader (1953, pp. 36-38). The central spindle is illustrated beautifully in cases such as *Barbulanympha*, where it remains separate from chromosome-to-pole fibers and can be seen in the living cell (Fig. 36). Quite comparable observations in the living have been made by K. Kawamura (1960a) on the grasshopper neuroblast. In this cell a core of cytoplasm passes through the peculiarly shaped nucleus, and the central spindle is seen to pass through this core at prophase.

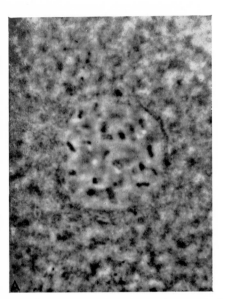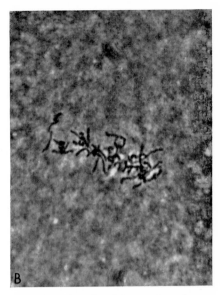

FIG. 35. Continued condensation of chromosomes when breakdown of nuclear membrane has been inhibited. A. Nucleus of a sea urchin egg which has been exposed to 0.75 M mercaptoethanol at 25 minutes before prophase. Chromosome condensation has continued, but the nuclear membrane has persisted. Some of the contracted chromosomes have clearly split. Such behavior is normal in forms in which endomitosis takes place. B. For comparison, sea urchin egg chromosomes in normal metakinesis, showing length of chromosomes shortly after breakdown of nuclear membrane.

It will be useful, for further discussion, to think of the completed mitotic apparatus as a dual structure: (1) a system of pole-to-pole connections, the central spindle, which is formed before the end of prophase and (2) a system of chromosome-to-pole connections, which seems to be established at the end of prophase. Later, we shall relate these two components to the apparent "pushing" and "pulling" movements that comprise anaphase.

There may be other visible signs of the assembly of the mitotic apparatus by the end of prophase. In many kinds of cells, a zone of relatively clear cytoplasm is seen to form near or around the nucleus.

Earlier descriptions of this behavior were summarized by Wasserman (1929), who interpreted it as the assembly of gelled material which would be embodied in the spindle. The advent of newer optical methods has added to our information about this phenomenon. The formation of a "clear zone" surrounding the nucleus and growing during prophase in *Haemanthus* endosperm has been described in detail by Bajer (1957), who interprets it as an early stage in the assembly of the spindle. The clear zone has been detected during prophase in a number of cell types by means of the interference microscope (Longwell and Mota, 1960). In the grasshopper spermatocyte, where centers are visible, it is seen that the clear material is collected between the centers, suggesting a loose central spindle. The adjective "clear" is highly meaningful here, for optical clarity signifies the absence of large particles such as mitochondria, and this is a general feature of the mitotic apparatus as a gel (Section IX, A, 1).

Where the mitotic spindle is formed initially inside the nucleus, as in the *Cyclops* egg (Stich, 1954), we should expect to observe the signs of its initial assembly as a growth of the nucleus or as an intra-nuclear increase in the concentration of the substances characteristic of the spindle. As we have seen, Stich and McIntyre (1958) have traced just such a development (Table VIII) in the *Cyclops* egg before and during prophase.

The fact that the formation of a central spindle and the assembly of material for the mitotic apparatus seems to be under the control of the centers in animal cells raises the question whether there is any evidence of a comparable polarization of these events in plant cells. As we have mentioned, the earliest indication of the assembly of the mitotic apparatus in plant cells, at least in endosperm, is the appearance of the "clear zone" around the nucleus during prophase. Polarization micro-

---

Fig. 36. The relations between the separation of the centers, the formation of the central spindle, and the engagement of the chromosomes, as seen in *Barbulanympha*. Compare Fig. 31, A. A. Mitotic prophase. The centers are separating above the nucleus, the central spindle is seen between the centers, and astral rays from the centers to the surface of the nucleus. B. Early anaphase. The centers have moved farther apart and the central spindle is longer. The condensed chromosomes are inside the nuclear membrane. At the lower right in the nucleus, a chromosome is seen clearly, with compact kinetochores at the nuclear surface, connected to the pole by visible fibers. Compare Fig. 45, B, where the relationships between the centriole, the central spindle, the chromosomal fibers, a kinetochore, and the nuclear membrane are shown in greater detail by electron microscopy. Phase contrast photographs of living material by courtesy of Dr. L. R. Cleveland (cf. Cleveland, 1953).

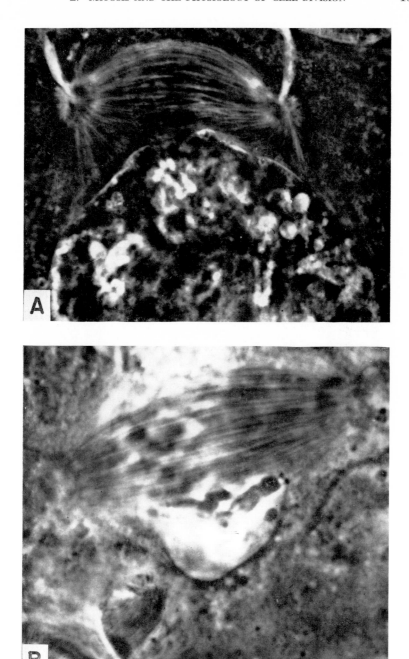

TABLE VIII

Composition of the Nucleus of *Cyclops strenuus* Eggs during the Formation of the Mitotic Apparatus[a,b]

Measurements	Interphase		Antephase		Prophase nuclear sap	Metaphase spindle
	Nuclear sap	Nucleolus	Nuclear sap	Nucleolus		
Volume in μ^3	55,067	4,578	57,114	3,407	56,607	41,088
Organic matter, gm. $10^{-12}/\mu^3$	0.247	0.568	0.272	0.531	0.418	0.593
Total organic matter in gm. 10^{-12} per subject	13,601	2,600	15,535	1,809	23,667	24,365
DNA in arbitrary units	5.42		5.25		5.28	5.51
RNA in arbitrary units (semiquantitative data)	0		62		85	88

[a] Data of Stich and McIntyre (1958).

[b] Total dry mass was determined by the X-ray absorption method. It was judged to be largely protein because extraction of lipids and digestion of RNA caused only small decreases in mass. Nucleic acids were determined by the cytophotometric method, with Feulgen staining of DNA and gallocyanin-chrome alum staining for RNA. The absolute relation of RNA and protein was estimated at 4–6% or less on the basis of loss of mass by RNAase digestion. It is seen that ribonucleoprotein begins to increase in the nucleus during antephase and culminates at prophase, and that the mass of protein in the nuclear sap at prophase corresponds to that in the metaphase spindle.

scopic evidence, illustrated in Fig. 37, now suggests that the material of the clear zone is indeed oriented with respect to the poles of the spindle that will be formed, and, furthermore, that there is an increasing and strong polar orientation of spindle material before metaphase. Indeed,

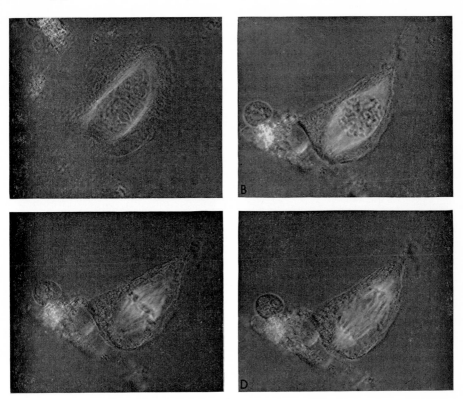

FIG. 37. Early stages in the assembly and orientation of the mitotic apparatus in *Haemanthus* endosperm, observed with polarized light. This cell is less flattened than those shown in Figs. 9 and 69. A. Prophase. Nucleolus is visible. Note material around the nucleus, oriented with respect to the poles. B. Late prophase. A well-oriented convergent spindle is seen, even though the chromosomes have not yet begun to move into their metaphase positions. C. Metaphase. D. Late anaphase. Note remaining orientation in the interzonal region. Photographs by courtesy of Drs. S. Inoué and A. Bajer.

the picture is not very different from what would be expected in animal cells and provides the strongest evidence that the destinations of the chromosomes are determined before they become oriented. Again we find in plant cells the activity associated with the mitotic centers, without any clue as to the structural incarnation of this activity.

a. Conclusions. There is good reason to think that substances of which the spindle will be composed not only are synthesized before division but are collected in the vicinity of the nucleus by the end of prophase and sometimes are organized into a *central spindle*. It is entirely conceivable that the whole task of mobilizing substance is completed by the end of prophase and that later development may involve only the organization of this material.

VII. Metakinesis: The First Movements of the Chromosomes

After the long and involved stages of preparation, the chromosomes begin to move in relation to the poles, and mitosis is under way. The first movements culminate in the establishment of the chromosomes in their metaphase position, and the stage in which this happens is termed *prometaphase* or *metakinesis*. It may be rather abrupt. In the grasshopper neuroblast, it occupies 4 minutes out of a mitotic time of 3 hours (Carlson and Hollaender, 1948). It may be much longer, as in *Haemanthus* endosperm (Bajer and Mole-Bajer, 1956b), and this longer duration is fortunate because it permits a closer analysis of the paths of the chromosomes. The earlier work, going back to Flemming, is reviewed admirably in a paper by Schneider (1933); some of the main cytological problems and paradoxes are summarized in Schrader's book (1953, pp. 64-70) and by Swanson (1957, pp. 218-231). We are required to explain (1) the movement of chromosomes typically to a point midway between the poles, (2) the alignment of the chromosomes on a well-defined equatorial plate, often with a rather consistent arrangement of individual chromosomes on that plate, and (3) most important of all, the fact that sister chromosomes are invariably attached to different poles at the termination of the process.

Anyone motivated to work on this challenging problem will find it necessary to explore the cytological literature in detail, but in the present chapter we restrict ourselves to selected examples.

A. Beginning of Metakinesis

The initiation of chromosome movement is not necessarily correlated with any definite stage in the contraction of the chromosomes; the evidence on this point has already been considered. It is not certain how exactly it is correlated with the behavior of the nuclear membrane.

Cytologists have long been impressed by visual evidence of the association of the chromosomes with the nuclear membrane; in so many cases the prophase chromosomes do seem to be arrayed at the nuclear periphery and to be in contact with the membrane. It is a fascinating possibility (discussed by Gay, 1956, 1960; and others) that the association between the chromosomes and the nuclear membrane is significant for chromosome activity in the cell.

It is a fact, as we have seen, that the complete disappearance of the nuclear membrane is not essential for the engagement of the chromosomes by the poles. Among the flagellates, for instance, we see clearly that connections are made through the nuclear surface (Fig. 31, A).

Evidence for interaction between the centers and the nuclear surface can also be found throughout the cytological literature. One reads of the changes in shape of the nucleus in relation to the positions of the centers (e.g., Policard and Bessis, 1953), of the indentation of the nuclear surface by fibers growing from the poles, of the penetration of the nuclear surface by such fibers, and of the stretching of the nucleus between the separating centers. Many of the examples have recently been discussed by Lettré and Lettré (1958).

The case of Loxa, described by Schrader (1947), is often cited (Fig. 38). In the grasshopper spermatocyte, Kawamura (1955) describes how the nuclear surface follows the separating centers: "The poles gradually separated away from each other and attached to the cell surface layer. At this time, the intact nuclear membrane near the cytoplasmic spindle and the chromosomes contained within it were drawn to each pole."

Finally, there is some evidence that the centers, acting through the nuclear membrane, move the chromosomes. In Cleveland's studies, already mentioned, there is no question about this. A well-documented case is that of the first meiotic division in Anisolabis (an earwig): Schrader finds (1953, p. 60) that "as the two centers separate and slide around the outside of the nucleus they are followed inside by the chromosomes which, as a consequence, separate into two groups."

Fell and Hughes (1949) observe a similar congregation of chromosomes at the poles of the prophase nucleus, adjacent to the centers, in their cinematographic study of mitosis in chick osteoblasts. Evidence of interaction between chromosomes and centers before the breakdown of the nuclear membranes is seen in those animal forms in which the chromosomes "polarize" toward the centers before the first meiotic division. A remarkable feature of this polarization is that it seems to involve the ends of the chromosomes, rather than the kinetochores.

This brief sketch of an interesting chapter in cytology is intended only to point out that the movements of chromosomes may begin before the breakdown of the nuclear membrane and that even under these circumstances they are apparently under control of the centers. In many cases such movements have not been seen, and in some, especially where cine-

matographic records are available (e.g., Bajer 1958b), they could not
have been missed if they did occur. The only conclusions required are
that the beginning of chromosome movement is not necessarily timed by
the breakdown of the nuclear membrane and, conversely, that the nuclear
membrane is not necessarily a barrier between the chromosomes and the
mitotic apparatus once the latter has become active.

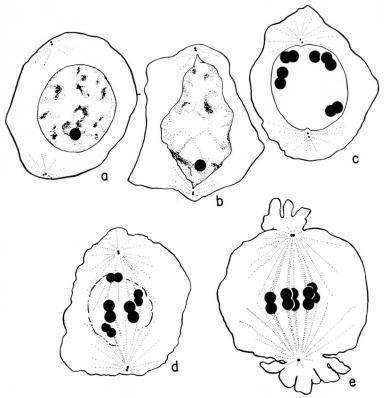

FIG. 38.   The apparent interaction of the centers and the nuclear membrane in
the preparatory stages of meiosis in *Loxa*. After Schrader (1947, 1953).

B. Paths of the Chromosomes in Metakinesis

In earlier descriptions of metakinetic movements of chromosomes
there are recurrent reports that they tend to move toward the poles before finally arriving at their metaphase position. Schneider (1933) deals
with this movement, and Schrader (1947) illustrates a simple form of it
in the case of *Homarus* (lobster) spermatocytes, where each chromosome pair appears to be pulled toward one pole or the other and then to

be drawn back toward the equator. A more complex example of the polar movement of chromosomes during metakinesis occurs in meiosis in some animals, where the members of synapsed pairs of homologous chromosomes seem to be pulled apart, toward the opposite poles, before moving to their metaphase position (Fig. 39). Here the poleward movement of

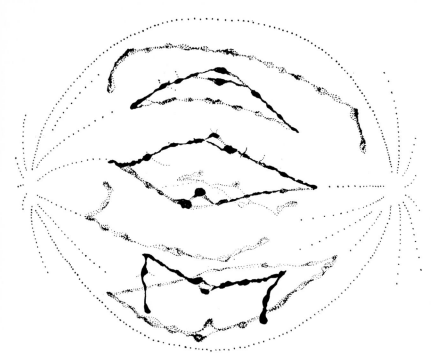

FIG. 39. The "premetaphase (or prometaphase) stretch." Chromosomes pair before the first meiotic division and then the homologous kinetochores move apart toward the poles, stretching the chromosome arms. The arms then pair again, as the kinetochores move into the equator. This phenomenon is observed only in certain groups of animals. The case illustrated is spermatogenesis of a mantid, *Angela guianensis*. After Hughes-Schrader (1943).

the kinetochores is expressed as a "premetaphase stretch" of the chromosome arms (e.g., Hughes-Schrader, 1947; Staiger, 1950).

The premetaphase stretch is one of those "exceptional" phenomena so disquieting to the seeker after generalizations. If we consider only the behavior of the individual chromosomes, apart from synapsis, their movement to one pole followed by their return to an equatorial position has its counterpart in mitosis; a possible explanation will be discussed below (pp. 210, 267). What is most difficult to explain is the restoration

of the synaptic association between the chromosomes, which may be
relegated to the still-unviolated mystery of meiotic pairing mechanisms.

We now have an adequate detailed description of the metakinetic
movements in one type of cell, thanks to the work of Bajer and Mole-
Bajer (1954b, 1956b). They have developed a method for culturing
living endosperm samples from many plant species, and these preparations, with the aid of phase contrast, yield superb cinematographic records of the behavior of the chromosomes through mitosis. The movements

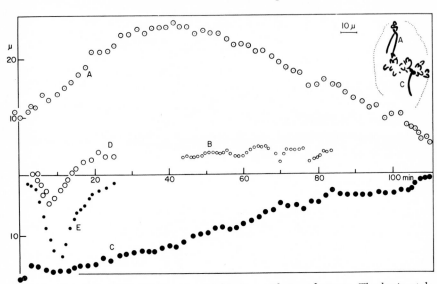

Fig. 40.   Paths of kinetochores in metakinesis in *Clivia* endosperm. The horizontal
line is approximately the position of the equator. Distances of the kinetochores *A,
B, C, D, E*, from this line are plotted as a function of time. In insert at upper right,
the actual paths of kinetochores *A* and *C* in relation to the whole spindle are shown.
After Bajer and Mole-Bajer (1956a).

of the kinetochores and the chromosome arms of individual chromosomes
have been plotted from these records.

The beginning of metakinesis in endosperm cells is signaled by a
contraction of the chromosome group at the time the nuclear membrane
breaks down. The chromosomes are still shortening at this time. In the
endosperm material the contraction stage sets in rather abruptly and
marks the beginning of metakinetic movements exactly. It is interpreted
(Bajer, 1958a) as signaling the engagement of the chromosomes by the
mitotic apparatus and the beginning of a process in which the mitotic
apparatus, previously a rather disoriented gel, achieves a higher degree
of fibrous orientation with respect to the poles.

After the "contraction stage," the chromosomes begin to move, but they do not necessarily move directly into their final metaphase configuration. Rather, a chromosome may follow a complex path, moving toward a pole, making a turn, and finally arriving at the equator. One of the plots given by Bajer and Mole-Bajer is shown in Fig. 40. The picture is most consistent with the idea that the kinetochores are the points by which the chromosomes are moved during metakinesis as well as during anaphase (Fig. 41).

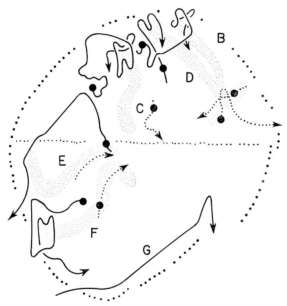

FIG. 41.   Paths of kinetochores and chromosome ends in metakinesis of *Haemanthus*. Dotted lines represent paths of kinetochores; solid lines represent ends of the same chromosomes. Within the limits of this static representation, it is seen that the kinetochores either move directly into the equator or first toward one pole and then to the equator, while the chromosome arms, following the kinetochores, swing and follow complex paths. After Bajer and Mole-Bajer (1956a).

Comparable cinematographic observations on metakinetic movements in animal cells come from extensive studies on newt fibroblasts carried out by a group of investigators in Chicago (reviewed by Zirkle, 1957). In this material a chromosome frequently will move to one center during metakinesis and remain there for some time, its kinetochore resting close to the visible centriole. The other chromosomes may lie in the equator, waiting for their "centrophilic" comrade to break away from the center and join the metaphase plate. Only when it does so will anaphase begin. These films give most vivid evidence of the interaction between the centers and the kinetochores before metaphase.

C. Possible Mechanisms of Metakinesis

At least four views of the means whereby metakinesis is accomplished can be defended. One is that the chromosomes function as free bodies, even though they may be sensitive to forces operating from the poles. Descriptively, we can go a long way with hypotheses involving attractive and repulsive forces between kinetochores and centers, as Darlington (1937), for instance, has shown. The ideal configuration of metaphase lends itself to such an interpretation, as do many other events of mitosis. The question is whether the "lines of force" express legitimate physical "fields" or whether, in this operation in a rather "macro" world, they have a physical embodiment in fibrous connections. If the concept of polarization is defined in a sufficiently abstract way, it can include not only the simplest consequences of polar forces but also the most complex mechanisms having the same general properties. To draw an analogy, we may imagine a recording potentiometer driven by a complex electronic circuit designed to keep the pen at a midpoint. If we did not understand it at all, we might deduce from observation that the pen was repelled by poles on either side of the midpoint. The discovery that the pen was moved by a string would change our point of view considerably, even though we still knew nothing about the electrical and mechanical system behind the string.

A second view of the mechanism of metakinesis is that the chromosomes remain contained in a nuclear gel and that their metaphase positions are determined by the form of this gel. This view, as developed by Duryee and Doherty (1954), is not entirely compatible with the observations already cited concerning the wanderings of chromosomes around the cell in the course of metakinesis. It also would be difficult to explain how, in multipolar figures, different chromosomes are oriented toward different poles. On the other hand, it does provide one explanation of the characteristic and moderately rigid spacings of the chromosomes on metaphase plates.

One very simple theory (Belar, 1929a, b; Wada, 1950) emphasizes a hypothetical pushing action of fibers that grow from the poles and sweep the chromosomes toward the equator. Apart from the fact that such a description does not tally with the complex paths of chromosomes that have been described in some cases, it is by no means clear why such an advancing front would push a body, rather than grow around it.

Finally, there is the hypothesis that the chromosomes in metakinesis are moved by the mitotic apparatus, employing essentially the same mechanism as in anaphase. Here the first question is whether the chromosome movements in metakinesis are determined by the paths of the kinetochores; this is the one aspect of the problem that is not largely speculative. An affirmative answer is given by the observations of Bajer and Mole-Bajer (1956a), as shown in Fig. 41. Experimental evidence is given by Carlson (1952) for the case of the grasshopper neuroblast. Here the chromosomes at prometaphase appear to be attached to the spindle by their kinetochores, while the arms of the chromosomes lie free in the cytoplasm. If the spindle is moved by a microneedle, the chromosomes follow as though they were rigidly attached.

Some of the best evidence for the role of the kinetochores in the movement of the chromosomes into the equator comes from studies employing point irradiation with ultraviolet or proton microbeams. In the newt fibroblast (Uretz et al., 1954; Zirkle, 1956, 1957) a particularly favorable situation is provided by frequently occurring "centrophilic" chromosomes: Any chromosome of the complex may, on occasion, migrate to one pole during metakinesis and tarry there for some time before going to the metaphase plane. If the kinetochore region is irradiated, such a chromosome never does move into the metaphase position, though it may drift poleward outside the main spindle at the time the other chromosomes go through anaphase. This inactivation of metakinetic movement requires irradiation of the kinetochore; if other parts of the chromosome are hit, it still makes its metakinetic movement, even though the irradiated region shows damage in the form of "paling." In a cytologically more favorable material, Haemanthus endosperm, it has been possible to pinpoint an ultraviolet beam on various parts of individual chromosomes during various stages (Bajer and Mole-Bajer, 1961). In no case did irradiation of the chromosome arms have a marked effect on chromosome movement, nor did irradiation of the kinetochores during prophase have any effect on their movement into the metaphase positions. Irradiation of the kinetochores during metakinesis did not permanently arrest them, as was the case in newt fibroblasts, but it did often bring about a reorientation of the paths of movement. In some cases, these paths were quite complex before the kinetochores arrived in the metaphase stations. The microbeam experiments make a strong case for the conclusion that the chromosomes move or are moved by kinetochores in establishing metaphase.

A second question is whether the kinetochores are attached to the poles by spindle fibers during metakinesis, by the same criteria that apply to putative fibrous attachments at anaphase. This often appears to be the case. An example from the cytological literature is metakinesis in lobster spermatocytes (Schrader, 1947) where chromosomal fibers are shown at all stages of the movements of chromosomes toward the poles and back to the equator. Zirkle (1956) notes that when the spindle axis is sometimes seen to shift in films of newt fibroblasts containing "centrophilic" chromosomes, the latter seem to be pulled along as though the kinetochores are attached to the poles.

The hypothesis that the chromosomes are engaged in the mitotic apparatus by their kinetochores during metakinesis, and are moved by mechanisms comparable to those operating during anaphase, is compatible with the complex paths of movement that have been described. We imagine that the still-inseparable pairs of kinetochores become attached to both poles, but if, in the early stages, one connection becomes active sooner than the other, the chromosome will move toward one pole, only to be drawn back to equilibrium at the equator (p. 227) as the action by the other pole develops.

It can now be shown that disorganization of the mitotic apparatus leads to a kind of "reversal" of metakinesis, after which the chromosomes may be brought back to their metaphase positions once more. These experiments grow out of a study of the effects of mercaptoethanol on the mitotic apparatus by Mazia and Zimmerman (1958). If sea urchin eggs which have just arrived at metaphase are exposed to mercaptoethanol, the mitotic apparatus becomes very disoriented but does not dissolve. If now the drug is removed, there is a rapid recovery for the fibrous orientation of the spindle, after which the scattered chromosomes are seemingly "drawn" back into a metaphase plate (Fig. 42). This suggests that the establishment and maintenance of the metaphase positions of the chromosomes does depend on the structural orientation of the mitotic apparatus and that metakinetic movements are the result of the activity of the apparatus. It excludes hypotheses that attribute metakinesis to the late-prophase condition of the nucleus or to the initial events in the growth of the mitotic apparatus. In the following section the role of the mitotic apparatus in metakinetic movements will be considered further.

D. Conclusions

Summarizing observations of metakinesis—the movement of the chromosomes from their positions at the end of prophase into their metaphase positions—it is concluded that these movements depend on chromosome-to-pole interactions and that they may be considered to be similar in essential ways to the later anaphase movements.

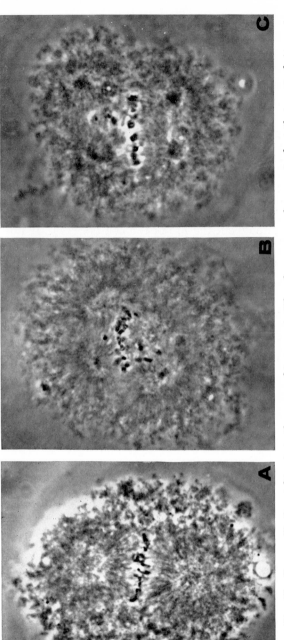

FIG. 42. The "reversal" of metakinesis in the sea urchin egg. A. The chromosomes have arrived at their metaphase positions. B. The cell at metaphase was exposed to mercaptoethanol. The mitotic apparatus disorients, seemingly "relaxes," and the chromosomes scatter. The photograph shows the condition of the mitotic apparatus after 3 hours in mercaptoethanol. C. Mercaptoethanol is removed. Within 15 minutes, the mitotic apparatus has regained its oriented form and the chromosomes have been drawn back into a metaphase configuration. Note that the centers have split and separated during the period of blockage. Phase contrast photographs of mitotic figures.

VIII. The Engagement of the Chromosomes: Metaphase

To carry out its ultimate function of separating the chromosomes, the mitotic apparatus must engage them in some way. Chromosome movement does not occur if the mitotic apparatus is not present, even though the complete cycle of chromosome coiling can proceed without the mitotic apparatus in the form of endomitosis. In fact, we can observe endomitosis and mitosis in the same cell at the same time, when one group of chromosomes is associated with a mitotic apparatus and the other is not (Fig. 31). As we have seen, it is possible that the engagement takes place at the beginning of metakinesis. Alternatively, it might take place at metaphase, leaving as an open question how the chromosomes find their way to the equator. It has also been proposed (Lettré and Lettré, 1957, 1958) that the connections between chromosomes and poles is one that persists throughout the life of the cell (p. 224). If this is so "engagement" would involve activation of existing connections rather than the formation of new ones.

A. Kinetochores (Centromeres)

No matter how we approach the activity of the chromosomes during mitosis, we are led to the conclusion that their movement depends on specialized regions, termed *kinetochores* or *centromeres*. We shall use the former term, rather than the equally popular "centromere," to avoid confusion and cacophony in many discussions where centers or centrioles are also involved. So far as terminology is concerned, Schrader's (1953, p. 25) list of twenty-seven synonyms for this little structure is an adequate commentary on liberties that have been possible.

The simplest conception of a kinetochore views it merely as the point of attachment of the chromosome to the mitotic apparatus, or, more literally, as the anchor point for a spindle fiber. We shall see, however, that it has also been viewed as a most active participant in mitotic events, and with reason.

In fact, we may consider the kinetochore to be the only essential part of the chromosome so far as mitosis is concerned. Chromosomes without kinetochores are incapable of mitotic movements, and chromosomes that have lost portions of their arms but retain their kinetochores perform normally. Indeed, the role in mitosis of the chromosome arms, which carry most of the genetic material, may be compared with that of a corpse at a funeral: they provide the reason for the proceedings but do not take an active part in them.

In the typical case the kinetochores are consistently located at a given point in a given chromosome. This point may be indicated by a constriction of the chromosome or by the presence of a distinct sphere or granule. As the chromosomes move to the poles, they give the impression of flexible bodies being dragged by the kinetochore region, and thus individual chromosomes will consistently have forms by which they can be identified: rods where the kinetochores are terminal, V-shapes where they are central, J-shapes, etc. In fact this is a practical basis for identifying individual chromosomes and karyotypes.

In gene-maps of chromosomes, the kinetochore regions of "typical" forms with compact kinetochores appear as genically inert segments, although mutational properties of loci seem to be affected by their proximity to the kinetochores. However, Lima-de-Faria (1958), in a review

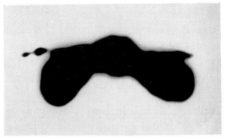

Fig. 43. Kinetochores of *Tradescantia paludosa* at metaphase of first meiotic division. (Cf. Lima-de-Faria, 1958.) Photograph by courtesy of Dr. A. Lima-de-Faria.

that includes much of the existing knowledge about kinetochores, presents evidence that the particles seen in favorable material do contain DNA, and therefore he considers their genetic activity to be a still-open question. He also notes that the kinetochores may have a complex structure, resolvable as several particles, even at the microscopic level (Fig. 43).

Even where the kinetochore is highly localized in the chromosome, a condition which we shall designate by the term "point kinetochore," it is not necessarily a unitary and indivisible body. If a chromosome is broken, e.g., by X-irradiation, at some distance from the kinetochore, the distal fragment can no longer engage in mitotic movement. But it has been shown (Schrader, 1939, who summarizes earlier evidence) that if the break is through the kinetochore region itself, both fragments are active, each having received part of the kinetochore.

The ultimate expression of the extended state or the multiplicity of the kinetochore is found in forms, both plant and animal, possessing *dif-*

fuse kinetochores (for plants; cf. Oestergren, 1949; S. W. Brown, 1954; for animals: Hughes-Schrader, 1948a; Piza, 1943). The presence of diffuse kinetochores is expressed in two ways. First, the chromosomes move at anaphase as though they were attached to the poles along most or all of their length (Fig. 44, A). Second, when they are broken, both fragments retain the ability to "attach" to the poles (Fig. 44, B).

The kinetochore has aspects both of a locus and of a function. As a locus, it is most commonly concentrated at a definite and reproducible region of a chromosome. It may be regarded as self-reproducing, for the loss of the region containing it results in the permanent inability of that chromosome to engage normally in mitotic movement; the chromosome becomes "acentric." Diffuse kinetochores appear consistently where they appear at all, and may be regarded as a special form of spatial extension of a kinetochore.

Most of what can be said about the structure and reproduction of kinetochores represents deductions from the forms of chromosomes in movement and from genetic mapping. Relatively little can be learned from light microscopy, for kinetochores are small and are not characterized by staining reactions.

They have been discerned by electron microscopy as bodies of definite form, relatively dense, in which the chromosomal fibers are inserted (Fig. 45), but the images do not as yet provide clues to their functioning. The requirements of intellectual symmetry would be satisfied by a structural correspondence between kinetochores and centrioles, in view of homologies already discussed (Section III, D, 2), but this is not yet sustained by the few available observations. We do not yet have the beginnings of a chemical description of the kinetochore, other than the suggestion that they stain for DNA.

We can ask a good many questions about the reproduction of kinetochores but cannot answer any of them. For example, we could imagine that it is the last step in the reproduction of a chromosome, and therefore important in deciding whether a cell is ready to enter division. In particular, the special features of meiosis in contrast with mitosis can be accounted for by hypotheses about the behavior of kinetochores (see Chapter I, this volume).

There is no basis for doubting that it is the kinetochores by which the chromosomes move or are moved in mitosis. The evidence that this is so is independent of opinions as to whether the chromosomes are pushed, pulled, moved by some motive forces of their own or by some combination of these. The image of the chromosome being dragged by its kinetochore region, the latter being viewed as the point of attachment of a

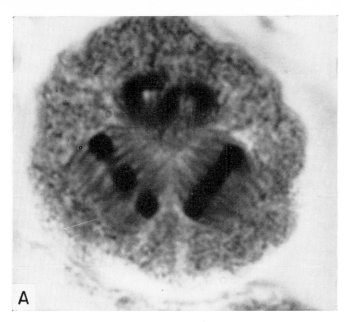

A

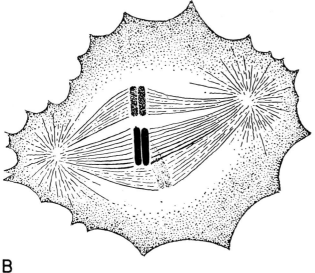

B

FIG. 44. Diffuse kinetochores. A. Mitosis in the plant *Luzula campestris* (wood rush). Three mitotic figures are seen in different orientation. At the lower right, a chromosome is seen at full length, with spindle fibers attached along its length. At the lower left, the chromosomes are seen in end view. At top, the metaphase chromosomes are seen in polar view. Photograph by Dr. Gunnar Oestergren (cf. Oestergren, 1949). B. Demonstration that a fragment of a chromosome possessing a diffuse kinetochore is capable of forming connections to the poles. Drawing shows a division figure of *Steatococcus* (an hemipteran insect) following X-irradiation. One of the two chromosomes has been broken by irradiation. The fragments as well as the intact chromosome form spindle connections. Drawn after Hughes-Schrader and Ris (1941).

traction fiber or the point at which some other poleward force is applied, is generally consistent with the shapes of the chromosomes at anaphase. Acentric fragments of chromosomes do not move in a normal way, although by some means they sometimes are translated poleward at the end of mitosis (e.g., Bajer, 1958b). One of the most dramatic visual demonstrations of the role of the kinetochore comes from cases where breakage and translocations produce chromosomes with two kinetochores. The two kinetochores tend to move to opposite poles, giving a "bridge" and resulting literally in the tearing of the chromosome by the opposed forces (Fig. 46). This is shown vividly in films of mitosis following irradiation.

Directed damage of chromosome regions has been made possible by the technique of microbeam irradiation with ultraviolet light or with protons (Uretz et al., 1954; Zirkle, 1957). If the beam is directed at the kinetochores of newt fibroblasts in metaphase or anaphase, the chromosomes are immobilized. Irradiation of other regions of the mitotic chromosome will produce visible structural effects, e.g., "paling" due to loss or modification of DNA, but such chromosomes will still participate normally in mitotic movement (e.g., Perry, 1957). Similar conclusions can be drawn from experiments by Takeda and Izutsu (1960) on the microbeam irradiation of grasshopper spermatocytes during meiotic divisions. Irradiation of the kinetochore of one chromosome at the end of metaphase I immobilizes it, and it remains at the equator during anaphase while its homolog moves to a pole. If the paired chromosome arms, rather than a kinetochore, are irradiated, they stick together and form a bridge at anaphase, as the kinetochores move apart. As has been mentioned, point-irradiation of kinetochores in *Haemanthus* endosperm does not inactivate them but does modify their behavior. Kinetochores exposed to the ultraviolet beam during prophase or during metakinesis do reach their metaphase positions, but can no longer split apart for anaphase. They remain in the equatorial regions, even though the motion pictures indicate attempts to "pull" them to the poles. The consequences

FIG. 45. Kinetochores as seen by the electron microscope. A. Fibroblast, mouse embryo. The dark regions in the middle of the photograph are chromosomes. Spindle filaments enter them and terminate in dense bodies, which appear to be their points of attachment. Photograph by courtesy of Dr. W. Bernhard. Magnification: × 10,000. B. *Barbulanympha*. Arrow indicates a kinetochore. This cup-shaped body is attached to the center by tubular filaments similar in structure to those of the central spindle below. The kinetochore is associated with the nuclear membrane, part of which is seen at upper right. Photograph by courtesy of Dr. Joan Erickson Cook. Magnification: × 9,440.

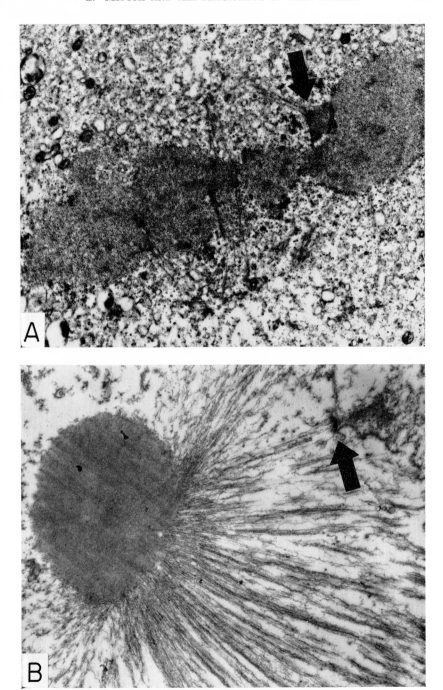

of point-irradiation of *Haemanthus* kinetochores at anaphase are curious: they tend to return to the equatorial region as though they had now come under the influence of both poles. Summing up, the ultraviolet microbeam has provided a uniquely direct method for experimentation on kinetochores, and thus far the results fully confirm the inference that

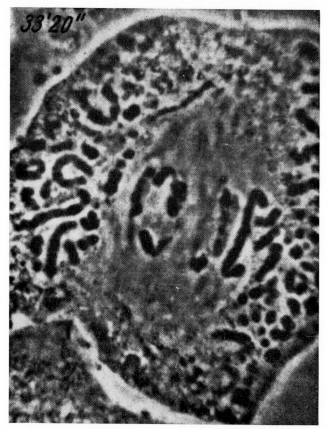

Fig. 46.   A chromosome "bridge" and other consequences of breakage of chromosomes by irradiation. Photograph (from a motion picture film) of *Haemanthus* endosperm cell in division following earlier heavy irradiation with beta particles. Chromosomes have been broken. In one case, broken end of chromosomes carrying kinetochores have joined, producing a chromosome with two kinetochores. These move to opposite poles producing a bridge. The bridge is ultimately broken, by the apparent pull from the two poles, but its resistance to breakage delays the completion of anaphase in this case. Other fragments that carry kinetochores are engaged by the mitotic apparatus, but the akinetic fragments are seen to collect outside the spindle and do not participate in normal anaphase movement. Photograph by Dr. A. Bajer (Bajer, 1958b).

this part of the chromosome is responsible for its participation in mitotic movements.

Some exceptions disturb these generalizations. The most celebrated is the case of meiotic divisions in the fly *Sciara* (Metz, 1933), where one set of chromosomes moves normally toward its pole, while the other appears to be "backing" toward the other pole, with the arms leading the kinetochores (Fig. 47).

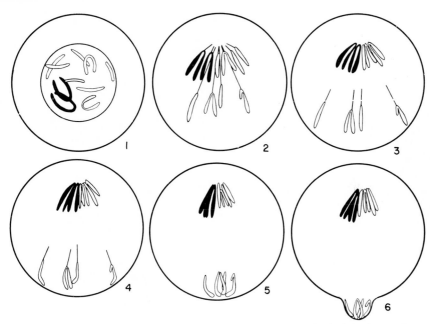

Fig. 47. Diagram of a celebrated exception to the principle that the kinetochores lead the movement of the chromosomes. First spermatocyte division of the dipteran *Sciara coprophila*. One group of chromosomes remains near the single apparent pole (top of cell) while another moves in divergent paths toward opposite end. Kinetochores of latter group apparently remain attached to the upper pole, chromosome arms lead, and chromosomes appear to "retreat." Another remarkable feature of this division is that it consistently separates maternal from paternal chromosomes. After Metz (1933).

There exist a number of examples of so-called "neocentric" activity, in which regions of the chromosome other than the recognized kinetochore are subjected to apparent "pull" by the poles. In certain strains of maize (Rhoades, 1952) the ends of chromosomes may be strongly "pulled" toward the poles in meiosis, at a time when the normal kinetochores are still in the metaphase plane (Fig. 48). So far as one can judge from microscopic observation, these ends are functioning at this time in a manner similar to kinetochores. Transient "neocentric" activity is believed by Oestergren and Bajer (1960) to be the cause of "abrupt bending movements" seen in ciné records of chromosomes in *Haemanthus* endosperm, described by them as follows: ". . . these movements are due to an active mobility on the spindle of small localized regions of the chromosome arms. The action of the spindle on these small regions is of a type that must be characterized as a pulling one. The chromosomes

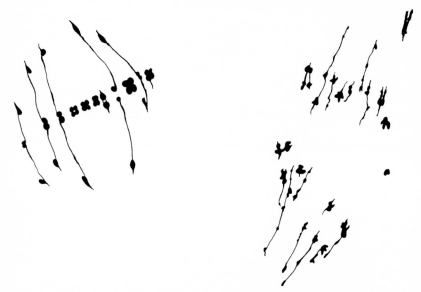

Fig. 48.   Neocentric behavior in a strain of maize. Metaphase I and anaphase I of meiosis, showing tendency of regions near the ends of some of the chromosomes to move to the poles in advance of the kinetochores. After Rhoades (1952).

are elastically deformed by the pulling action, small regions of them are drawn out to points during the movement and these points immediately disappear again when the pulling has stopped. The pulling force is capable of working in different directions on the spindle; usually, however, it works in the direction toward the metaphase plate." These authors also attribute to neocentric activity the fact that the chromosome arms in *Haemanthus* are bent so that they lie parallel to the spindle, rather than dangling as is so often the case. They note that neocentric activity is variable and subject to experimental variables, such as irradiation and exposure of the cells to methanol.

There is no reason to think that neocentric activity ordinarily plays an important part in mitosis. In all the cases cited, effective anaphase movement clearly centers on the normal kinetochores. In the case of maize, where precocious movement of the chromosome ends toward the poles may be obtained consistently in certain stocks, it depends somehow on the kinetochores and is not observed in acentric fragments. In the case of *Haemanthus*, where it is observed as transient and local bending movements, these movements apparently do take place even in acentric fragments but do not seem to be capable of translating the chromosomes. The significance of neocentric activity, in our present limited knowledge of kinetochore function, is to suggest that although this function is highly localized, it may yet spread to other regions of the chromosomes. Alternatively, we may simply imagine that any point on the chromosome has, under some conditions, the possibility of being engaged by the motive elements of the spindle. To hazard an extreme speculation, only to illustrate this point, we may imagine that a chromosome might move "backward" toward a pole with its arms leading the kinetochore (Fig. 47) because the ends were strongly neocentric and were "pulled" more strongly than the kinetochores.

Conclusions

The conclusion that movement of chromosomes in mitosis involves their "attachment" to the spindle by kinetochores is generally valid, regardless of any favored theory of the mechanism of movement. The kinetochores are reproducible regions that are reported to contain DNA, but whose purely genetic activity is not known.

B. Chromosome-to-Pole Connections

Perhaps the most rigorous rule of mitosis is that sister chromosomes move to different poles. In normal bipolar mitosis in animal cells we may state an even more definite rule: sister chromosomes go to sister centers.

Possible mechanisms by which the interaction between two sister kinetochores and one pole is forbidden have been discussed for a long time. These have been formulated at two levels: as expressions of attractions and repulsions involving kinetochores and poles and as evidence of the presence of physical connections, observed as fibers, which guide and determine the movements of kinetochores with respect to the poles. These are not conflicting views but represent different levels of abstraction. In general, the over-all events can always be formulated abstractly in terms of attraction and repulsion, and this is a useful device in cytogenetic research, for instance, where the end result may be more important than the mechanism. The questions of mechanism are (1)whether the attractions and repulsions are literally electrostatic or magnetic or whether they are accounted for by the literal pushing and pulling of the kinetochores by the connecting elements of the spindle and (2) whether, if the connections of chromosomes to poles are decisive, they are the agents of the movement itself or are merely the highways by which the movement is guided. An interesting general discussion of the implications of attractions and repulsions for metakinetic and anaphase movements is given by Oestergren (1950).

A theory of chromosome movement based entirely on attraction and repulsion, interpreted as physical forces and not involving chromosome-to-pole connections, has been developed by Darlington (1937, 1939). Anaphase separation of sister chromosomes is described in terms of repulsions between sister kinetochores. Since such a scheme would work only if the chromosomes were properly aligned at metaphase, metakinesis is described as the result of repulsion between kinetochores and poles before anaphase.

Apart from considerations of the nature of the forces, it does not seem realistic to regard chromosome movement as the result of the repulsion of sister chromosomes. The realities are concisely summarized in Oestergren's remark that "the movement of the anaphase chromosomes is definitely directed toward the poles and not away from each other." This becomes especially clear if we consider multipolar figures, divergent figures, monopolar figures, curved figures, etc. Some form of chromosome-to-pole interaction is required, and it must involve the interaction of sister chromosomes with different poles. There is no basic objection to a formulation in terms of attractions and repulsions if this condition can be met. The idea that the chromosome-to-pole interactions are embodied as physical connections, *chromosomal fibers,* is not the result of theorizing. On the contrary, the connections have been observed from the earliest days of the study of mitosis, and, as we shall see, their existence has been confirmed by all the modern methods of observation. The long history of contention about their "reality" actually had to do with the underlying molecular basis of the fibers so clearly seen by conventional microscopy and with questions about their role in the chromosome movements themselves. At the moment we need not consider these questions, to which we shall return, but need only note the general equivalence between the observed fibers and the "lines of force" that would be postulated if we dealt with the problem more abstractly.

However, in describing the chromosome-to-pole interactions, we are confronted with a difficult problem in explaining how sister kinetochores invariably associate with different poles. One approach has been through the hypothesis that the kinetochores are polarized and have "faces," so that when one sister faces one way, the other faces in the opposite direction. This idea was stated by Boveri (1904, p. 24). Freely translated, he says: "[The] points of attachment of the chromosomes are so arranged that they are located on two opposite sides, which will be the 'polar sides' of the daughter elements; the regular distribution of the daughter elements depends on this arrangement." On the basis of this hypothesis he states the following as probably being general laws: "(1) The chromosomes are attached to the centers only on their 'polar sides.' (2) When the first fiber from a pole combines with the 'polar side' of a chromosome, then other fibers from the same pole can attach only to this side, even though the other side may still be free. (3) If a chromosome has become attached to one pole, the fibers from the other pole can attach only to the other 'polar side.' This third rule implies that once a chromosome has made attachments to two poles, all other attachments are excluded."

The hypothesis of a polarized chromosome each of whose kinetochores can associate with only one pole, the pole toward which it "faces," has been developed most fully by Oestergren (1950, 1951), who generalizes it to include metakinesis. In principle the hypothesis says that the polarization principle applies even before metaphase. Wherever the chromosome may be initially, there will be a time when each sister kinetochore faces a pole and, by definition, no time when both face the same pole. The principles expressed by Boveri would thus permit the sister kinetochores to become associated with (or attracted toward) the two poles at a time when they are still inseparable. If the poles are acting on the chromosome, the latter will move into an equilibrium position, and if the "force" varies directly with the distance (a crucial part of the hypothesis), the equilibrium position will be on the equator. Once the chromosomes, and especially the kinetochores, have split, the same forces would account for anaphase movement, and this simplification is one of the most attractive features of the hypothesis.

The heart of the problem of the establishment of kinetochore-to-pole associations is to be found in what may be called the "exclusion principle" as stated by Boveri; once a kinetochore comes under the influence of one pole, that pole cannot engage its sister. If we grant this principle and assume that the duplication of the chromosomes before division included the provision of the sisters with distinct kinetochores, the system cannot fail to make correct connections. We cannot pretend to have a concrete picture of mechanisms by which the "exclusion principle" would operate. We might invent schemes whereby a kinetochore, once engaged, can no longer react to a second pole, but how does the first pole "know" that it cannot react with the sister kinetochore of the same chromosome?

A simple way of solving the problem of the connection of sister kinetochores to different poles is given by the hypothesis of Lettré and Lettré (1957, 1958, 1960). According to this hypothesis, the connections are permanent, persisting through interphase. Instead of seeing the reproductive event of mitosis as the separate duplication of centers and chromosomes, followed later by the establishment of connections between them, Lettré and Lettré propose that the reproducing unit is, in effect, a center and a kinetochore connected by a fiber. The reproductive event is the production of a new center-fiber-kinetochore unit from an old one. In support of their view they marshall a variety of cases from the cytological literature in which the persistence of fibrous connections from the centers to the interphase nucleus is described. The possibility that the nuclear membrane may be penetrated by chromosomal fibers has already been mentioned (Section VII, A).

This is logically a most attractive hypothesis. In its simple form it encounters a number of objections; for instance, the fact that in cells containing abnormal numbers of centers (e.g., polyspermic eggs, abnormal individuals in *Barbulanympha;* Cleveland, 1954, 1957b) the chromosomes appear to be capable of attaching to foreign centers. In Cleveland's work the formation of kinetochore-to-center connections is observed microscopically as an outgrowth of fibers from a nearby center to a nucleus, with no evidence of a pre-existing connection. The numbers of nuclei and centers in *Barbulanympha* zygotes may not correspond, mitotic figures may be established by different combinations of nuclei and centers (e.g., Fig. 31), and the engagement of chromosomes seems to depend chiefly on the proximity of a nucleus to at least two centers. To meet some other objections, refinements of the Lettré hypothesis are possible, as its authors have kindly pointed out in personal communications. In any event, the hypothesis does call attention to possible new facets of the kinetochore-center relationship and should have a stimulating effect on experimentation in this field.

Exceptional cases, where sister chromosomes attach to or move to the same pole are uncommon. In *Tradescantia*, the establishment of such forbidden associations has been observed after the disorganization of the mitotic figure by high hydrostatic pressures (Pease, 1946). In that sensitive detector of chromosomal disturbances, *Drosophila*, mosaic individuals are found in which the characteristics of various regions suggest the presence of cells with one X chromosome and with three X chromosomes (C. Stern, 1960). As Stern points out, these results can be explained simply if mitotic non-disjunction, which is a violation of the rule that sister chromosomes go to different poles, takes place in the division of a nucleus early in development. Normally, the XX cells will give rise to XX progeny. But if the daughters of the replication of one of the X chromosomes happen to go to one pole, one daughter cell will contain one X chromosome and the other will contain three X chromosomes. The regions of the individual diagnosed as X and XXX would be the progeny of these cells. Since the evidence is purely genetic, it cannot be decided, assuming the hypothesis of mitotic non-disjunction to be correct, whether the sister X chromosomes actually formed attachments to the same pole or whether one failed to be engaged by a pole and was carried along by its sister.

The engagement of the chromosomes by the mitotic apparatus implies not only the establishment of connections to guide them to the poles, but also the activation of whatever mechanism is involved in their movement.

Conclusions

There are various approaches to the explanation of how sister chromosomes invariably come under the influence of different poles. The problem can be solved formally by postulation of attractive and repulsive forces between kinetochores and pole, or by hypotheses involving polarization of the sister kinetochores such that when one is "attracted" to one pole, the other must be "attracted" to a second pole. If attractions are viewed more concretely as physical connections, the essential requirements for a successful hypothesis are (1) the presence of a discrete kinetochore on each of the chromosome elements that are to be separated and (2) an "exclusion principle" whereby a given kinetochore is forbidden to attach to more than one pole, and a given pole can attach to only one of a pair of sister kinetochores. It is suggested that the attractions or attachments according to these rules are established at the beginning of metakinesis, and, as a consequence, the same chromosome-to-pole interactions may account for metakinesis, metaphase, and anaphase, the latter being merely a consequence of splitting sister chromosomes. This conception is developed in the sections that follow.

C. The Metaphase Configuration

1. Metaphase Plate

Generalizing, we may say that the distinctive feature of metaphase is the confinement of the kinetochores to a single plane exactly midway between the poles, with considerable precision. It is not clear why it has to be so. The significant requirement is that sister chromosomes be connected to sister poles and, when they separate, move all the way to their respective poles. There is no logical reason why the chromosomes should be deployed to the poles by way of the equator, and the meaning of metaphase must lie at the level of mechanics. It may simply be an inevitable consequence of the fact that the chromosomes come under the influence of two poles some time before they are ready to split apart. The omission of a metaphase plate is the common finding in those cells, especially among the Protozoa (Belar, 1926), in which the nuclear membrane does not break down, although the cells may go through all the other stages typical of mitosis. Even in other kinds of cells the metaphase plate may fail to form when the mitotic apparatus is disturbed, yet an anaphase resulting in the correct separation of sister chromosomes may follow. An example is mitosis in onion root tips exposed to excessive concentrations of phosphate ions (Galinsky, 1949). Perhaps the most general and functional definition of metaphase is that it is the stage at which the chromosomes are engaged in a fully polarized mitotic apparatus but have not yet split apart.

   a. The equatorial position of the chromosomes. The "equatorial" position refers only to the spindle axis and to its polar ends, and need bear no direct relations to any axis of the cell as a whole. Even in figures containing three, four, or more poles, the chromosomes tend to lie equidistant from them at metaphase (Fig. 30). We have every reason to think —especially when visible centers are present—that the poles alone determine the positions of the chromosomes at metaphase, and little reason to think that the chromosomes determine the positions of the poles. The simplest interpretation of the facts, and a reasonable basis for a mechanism, is the idea that the equatorial position signifies equal action of the two poles on the chromosomes.

   This may be formulated as (1) repulsion of the chromosomes by the poles (Darlington, 1937), (2) attraction of polarized kinetochores to the poles, and (3) the "pulling" of the kinetochores by specific connection to the poles. The latter two are equivalent; the third postulates a physical model for the attraction.

   There have been various theories concerning the metaphase ordering of the chromosomes, and the background of cytological literature on the subject has been reviewed thoroughly by Schrader (1947) as well as by Hughes (1952a) and others. The "equilibrium" theory, developed most fully by Oestergren (1950, 1951), probably has the highest content of testable assumptions, although this does not necessarily mean that it will prove to be true. As we have mentioned, this theory states that the chromosomes come under the influence of the poles at the beginning of metakinesis. Each kinetochore is attracted (or pulled) toward a pole by a force whose strength is proportional to the initial kinetochore-to-pole distance. The equilibrium of the opposed forces on the still-paired sister kinetochores would place the chromosomes midway between the poles. It is further implied that the chromosomes are held in equilibrium position at the equator by the continued operation of the opposed forces until the chromosomes split, at which time the same forces will separate the sisters toward the poles.

We might expect that the equilibrium at metaphase would not be absolutely stable if it were governed by active fibers, and in fact it is not. Both in animal cells (e.g., observations of Lewis, 1939; Hughes and Swann, 1948; Makino and Nakahara, 1953a) and plant cells (*Haemanthus* endosperm, observed by Bajer and Mole-Bajer, 1956b) the chromosomes are shown to oscillate in an irregular way. The latter authors have measured and plotted the oscillations (Fig. 49).

A number of cytological situations afford a test of the "equilibrium theory." For instance, we might expect to find that a chromosome would not settle midway between the poles at metaphase if the polar "attractions" were unbalanced. Oestergren (1945a) finds this to be so when a meiotic spindle contains "trivalent" chromosomes. In such cases two kinetochores are connected with one pole and a third kinetochore to the other. The metaphase position is toward the pole confronted with two kinetochores, as though two are pulled more strongly than one.

Monopolar mitotic figures might provide an additional test of the "equilibrium theory," since it would be predicted that the chromosomes would move directly to one pole at the stage equivalent to metakinesis or metaphase, there being no opposed force. We have already cited, in another context, a case where this prediction is not supported. In monopolar figures produced after quadripartition of echinoderm eggs, illustrated in Figs. 10, B and 15, we see chromosome-to-pole fibers and even a tendency of the chromosomes to line up in a quasi-metaphase, but they go through a complete cycle of condensation followed by restoration of an interphase nucleus without moving close to the one pole that is present. Belar and Huth (1933) observed monopolar figures produced by parthenogenetic activation of *Urechis* eggs and even noted a tendency of the chromosomes to move apart at a stage equivalent to anaphase, but they did not observe a poleward movement. These observations are not in accord with predictions from the equilibrium theory, but a small possibility of escape is provided by some observations of Cleveland (1957b) on *Barbulanympha* containing only one centriole. It appeared that the fibers grew from the centriole toward the chromosomes, but did not attach to them, as though one kinetochore could not attach to a pole unless its sister attached to a second pole. We could imagine that the same rule applied to monopolar figures in other cells, such as the sand

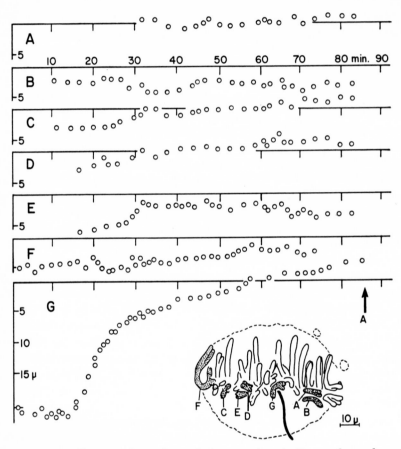

FIG. 49. Oscillations of kinetochores during metaphase in *Haemanthus* endosperm. Horizontal lines represent equator. Each row of points represents successive positions of one kinetochore, plotted from motion picture records. Chromosome G was delayed near one pole, and finally moves into equator while others "wait," oscillating as shown. After Bajer and Mole-Bajer (1956b).

dollar eggs shown in Fig. 15, and that the fibers observed in this less favorable material were not equivalent to normal kinetochore-to-pole attachments. This weak argument is given a modicum of value by the expectation that we shall be able to check the presence or absence of actual connections of kinetochores to the poles in the near future by advanced microscopic methods (cf. Fig. 45).

The simplest question we can ask about the position of the chromosomes at metaphase is whether it does represent a sustained activity of the mitotic apparatus.

Some relevant experiments have been mentioned in connection with the question of the reversibility of metakinesis (p. 210 and Fig. 42). Briefly, it has been found that the mitotic apparatus may be disorganized drastically if mercaptoethanol is introduced at the beginning of metaphase in sea urchin eggs (Mazia and Zimmerman, 1958; and more recent experiments by the author). There is no reason to assume that mercaptoethanol is specific here; similar results might be obtained with many agents affecting the spindle. The highly oriented metaphase figure seems to be converted to an amorphous gel and the chromosomes appear to be scattered about this gel. But when the mercaptoethanol is removed, the orientation returns and the chromosomes find their way back to the metaphase plate (Fig. 42). One interpretation of this experiment is that mercaptoethanol has merely "relaxed" the active structure responsible for the microscopic order of the mitotic apparatus at metaphase. The "tightening up" of the structure upon removal of mercaptoethanol not only restores the fibrous orientation, but also pulls the chromosomes back into an equilibrium position at the equator. If the metaphase configuration is the consequence of *activity* of the mitotic apparatus, it should be lost when the apparatus is "anesthetized" and be restored when it recovers; this figure of speech does cover the experimental facts.

The hypothesis of a metaphase equilibrium could be tested by experiments in which the supposed attractive action of one pole was reduced or eliminated in some manner. It would be predicted that the chromosome would be shifted toward the unaffected pole. Such experiments have been done by Izutsu (1959b) and by Takeda and Izutsu (1960) on grasshopper spermatocytes in first meiotic metaphase. Individual kinetochores of bivalents (paired homologous chromosomes) could be irradiated with an ultraviolet microbeam. When this was done it was observed that "the bivalent shifted to the pole toward which the other unirradiated kinetochore was orientated." If the spindle region adjacent to such a kinetochore, but not the kinetochore, was irradiated, a similar shift in the position of the bivalent was observed, but after a short time it returned to the equator. These observations do fit the above predictions and suggest, as well, that radiation damage in the spindle may weaken the kinetochore-pole interaction during metaphase in a reversible way.

b. Chromosome arrangement on the plate. The form of the "metaphase plate" is variable from one kind of cell to another but consistent for any one kind. Sometimes only the kinetochores seem to be confined in the plate, the chromosome arms dangling free. This arrangement is often conspicuous in plants and occurs commonly also in animal cells. Carlson (1952) has shown that the reality corresponds to appearance; when the spindle of a grasshopper neuroblast is moved by a microneedle, the kinetochore regions move with the spindle body but chromosome arms bend as would be expected of free threads being dragged in a fluid medium. In some cells, especially where the chromosomes are short, the whole chromosome seems to be confined to the metaphase plate. The arrangements of the chromosomes are characteristic. Very often, they are arrayed around the circumference of the equatorial plate, the spindle appearing "hollow" in cross section. In other cells, certain chromosomes are found in the central region, others around the circumference. It is sometimes remarked that the smaller chromosomes tend to lie closer to the central axis, the larger to the periphery. The location and spacing of chromosomes on the metaphase plate may be influenced by various experimental conditions; for example, by low temperature or by colchicine (Barber and Callan, 1943). The extreme deviation is the collapse of the chromosomes into clumps. This collapse has been reported as a natural occurrence in the first meiotic division in certain lobes of the testis of some Hemiptera (Schrader, 1946, 1947). It is encountered as an expression of mitotic pathology (Politzer, 1934) and appears in descriptions of effects of antimitotic agents such as aminopterin (e.g., Jacobson, 1954), of irradiation (e.g., Smith, 1959), of hydrostatic pressure (e.g., Guyot *et al.*, 1960), etc.

Attempting to interpret the regular arrangements of chromosomes on the metaphase plate, we must first answer a much simpler question: Why do the chromosomes not touch each other? In answering this question, we are, of course, permitted to appeal to "repulsion" as a kind of conceptual shorthand (cf. Darlington, 1937); but we are bound to inquire into its physical meaning. One consequence of the repulsion concept is that it leads to an examination of the surface properties of the chromosomes themselves, and the clumping of chromosomes is frequently related to the more general phenomenon of "stickiness." The various mitotic aberrations resulting from stickiness must convince us that the surface properties of chromosome are important in maintaining a discreteness necessary for normal behavior, but it does not necessarily follow that they are responsible for repulsions operating over long distances, as would be necessary if these were to account for the metaphase configurations.

We may also consider the spacing of the chromosomes in terms of the properties of the spindle. One of the most interesting viewpoints is that of Oestergren (1945a, b). His hypothesis assumes the validity of the "equilibrium" theory, ascribing the tendency of chromosomes to lie equidistant from the two poles to a continuous longitudinal action of both poles. In addition, it postulates that the chromosomes tend to be ejected from the spindle by virtue of properties of the latter as a *tactoid* body. We shall have occasion to discuss the tactoid concept later; for the present, the relevant point is that a tactoid body tends to eject "foreign" particles contained within it. Thus, according to Oestergren, a chromosome at metaphase is subjected to two sets of forces, the longitudinal or centripetal forces that tend to hold it midway between the poles and the centrifugal or lateral forces that tend to throw it out of the spindle. The centripetal force depends only on the kinetochores; the centrifugal depends on the mass of the chromosomes. It is postulated that the "transverse" equilibrium represents the resultant of the two tendencies, and it is predicted that large chromosomes will tend to come to equilibrium closer to the periphery of the metaphase plate, small chromosomes closer to the axis. We can imagine that the centrifugal tendency could be expressed only in the equatorial plane, since the equilibrium hypothesis postulated that the action of the poles was proportional to the distance of the kinetochores from the poles, thus holding the chromosome on the equatorial plane.

Whether or not the mitotic apparatus meets the description of a "tactoid body," we are reasonably sure that it does, in its formation as a gel, tend to exclude large particles from its domain (p. 234). Thus we are permitted to predict that a chromosome which is not attached to a pole will be excluded from the metaphase figure. Such an occurrence is described by Hughes-Schrader (1948b) for divisions in spermatogenesis of the mantid *Humbertiella*. Here the X chromosome appears to be ejected from the main spindle at metaphase, and only then to form visible attachments to the poles, making a separate small spindle. In general, acentric fragments do lie outside the spindle (Fig. 46). On the other hand, it would be predicted that inactivation of a kinetochore at metaphase would be followed by immediate exclusion of that chromosome from the mitotic apparatus, and this has not been confirmed by microbeam irradiation experiments.

The problem of the spacing of the chromosomes may be formulated in structural terms. We have good reasons for viewing the mitotic spindle as a *dual* structure, consisting of a central spindle comprising pole-to-pole connections and a system of chromosome-to-pole connections. In some cases, as in *Barbulanympha* (Fig. 36) the two are completely separate spatially and in the mode of their formation, and one can understand Cleveland's (1953) wry remark: "Most biologists—cytologists included—use the word 'spindle' in the same way that the layman uses the word 'stomach' . . . ." Structurally, the spacing of the chromosomes at metaphase may reflect only the relations between the pole-to-pole fibers (to use the term only descriptively) and the chromosome-to-pole fibers. Where the nuclear membrane does not break down, the chromosomal fibers may lie completely outside the central spindle as in *Barbulanympha*. If the chromosome-to-pole connections are formed initially outside the central spindle, which, as we have seen, is formed well before metaphase, then the equilibrium theory of metakinesis and metaphase would predict that they would be drawn to the equatorial surface of the central spindle. Whether they would penetrate it would depend on the forces upon the kinetochores and the resistance of the central spindle. The "hollow" spindle with chromosomes arrayed around the equatorial periphery should be found, and it is indeed very common. Where the chromosomes are arrayed across the equatorial plane at metaphase, their spacing would be described by the image of each chromosomal fiber being surrounded by a group of pole-to-pole fibers of the central spindle. If the latter were destroyed or weakened, the chromsomes would tend to shift toward the center of the metaphase plane, and in extreme cases might even clump there. The whole range of metaphase arrangements, from "star figures" in which the kinetochores are arrayed around the periphery of the spindle equator to figures in which they are solidly clumped in the center, can be induced experimentally. Such a spectrum of metaphase figures has been described in a study by Siebs (1960) on the action of a number of drugs on mitosis in cultures of mammalian fibroblasts and of a mouse mammary carcinoma. In interpreting the results of this and earlier studies, Siebs invokes an interpretation similar to that outlined above, viewing the metaphase positions of the chromosomes as a resultant of the action of the two poles on the unsplit chromosome and of variable development of the central spindle.

The proposition that the central spindle and the chromosomal-fiber system are functionally different does not represent a mere idle speculation, for it will reappear in an important way when we consider the role of the two in anaphase movement. Nevertheless, this discussion is not an attempt to explain the metaphase arrangements, but only a reconnaissance of known features of the structure of the mitotic apparatus. We cannot pretend that we know what are the forces involved in maintaining the arrangements.

2. Conclusions

In constructing a functional image of the metaphase configuration of the chromosomes, we may appeal to two operations. First, the facts enable us to imagine that the "pull" of the poles on the chromosomes is active and operative at metaphase; thus we can derive an "equilibrium theory" of the equatorial position of the metaphase plate. Second, the spacing of the chromosomes on the equator may be a consequence of the relations between the chromosome-to-pole connections and the continuous pole-to-pole central spindle.

Obviously metaphase is the turning point in the history of the mitotic apparatus. The preceding events create an apparatus in which polarization is complete, a logical alignment of the chromosomes has been achieved in metakinesis, and the chromosomes are correctly connected with (or at least oriented toward) the poles to which they will travel. The lines along which they will travel are clearly indicated by the chromosomal fibers. The duration of metaphase is variable from cell to cell. But we cannot make any definite statement as to what is happening during metaphase, as we can for all other periods of the mitotic cycle. On the contrary, it strikes us as an interruption of the flow of events during which the mitotic apparatus is waiting for something to happen! That visible event it is waiting for is the parting of the sister chromosomes. Much else may be happening.

IX. THE MITOTIC APPARATUS

The mitotic apparatus has been defined (Mazia and Dan, 1952) as "the ensemble of structures constituting the 'chromatic' and 'achromatic' figures in the classical descriptions of mitosis. It includes spindles, asters, centrioles, nuclei (before breakdown) and chromosomal structures (after breakdown of the nuclear membrane)." It is a useful concept because the sense of the mitotic process is embodied in the coordinated interplay of recognizable structures and because these structures are in fact associated physically in a body that may be isolated as a unit. It would be a misleading concept if it implied that the rest of the cell was not involved in its function, but no intelligent biologist would make such an inference about any part of the cell.

In the sections that follow, the abbreviation MA will sometimes be used for the mitotic apparatus.

A. The Mitotic Apparatus as a Physical Body

1. A General View. The Mitotic Apparatus as a Gel

The mitotic apparatus occupies a large part of the volume of the dividing cell and accounts for a considerable proportion of its total substance. The finding by Mazia and Roslansky (1956) that the mitotic apparatus of a sea urchin egg involved at least 10% of the cell's protein content must be considered minimal. In some cells the volume of the MA is obviously large, perhaps 50% of the cell volume. We now know from the results of interference microscopy that its relative water content is not conspicuously greater than that of the surrounding cytoplasm (Mitchison and Swann, 1953; Barer and Joseph, 1957).

Visually, the mitotic apparatus displays itself as an unbounded region within the cell. It has been argued that a boundary layer exists in some cases (e.g., Wada, 1950), but usually there is no sign of one even where it might have been detected by the electron microscope. As a domain within the cell, the MA is characterized by the absence of large particles such as mitochondria (Fig. 50). The latter may, in some cells (notably insect spermatocytes: e.g., Makino and Nakahara, 1953b; Kawamura, 1955; Barer and Joseph, 1957), cluster around the mitotic apparatus and provide a useful outline, but they do not penetrate it (Fig. 95). When we turn to isolation methods we find that the region of the mitotic apparatus is a coherent body whose molecular units are associated in a distinctive way. There have long been reasons to characterize it as a *gel*.

The formation of the basic gel may precede its consolidation and the imposition of fibrous orientation upon it. The appearance of a definitive spindle is foreshadowed by a general augmentation in cytoplasmic viscosity which Heilbrunn terms the "mitotic gelation." We would imagine that the polymerization of the structural units takes place throughout the cell, after which the aggregates progressively interact and draw together into a compact and more orderly mass. If this is the correct picture, we still have to explain how larger particles, e.g., mitochondria, are excluded from the domain of the gel, although sometimes even larger bodies, such as persistent nucleoli, may be trapped. About this important question we can only speculate. One line of speculation draws upon the superficial analogies between the structure of the spindle and of "tactoid" bodies—spindle-shaped, liquid-crystalline aggregates of elongated particles that are observed to form spontaneously in solutions of such particles. The hypothesis that the spindle was a tactoid body has fascinated cytologists ever since it was set forth by Bernal (1940) although very little of it survives serious critical analysis, such as was given by Swann (in Hughes, 1952a). Apparently, a tactoid body does tend to exclude foreign particles. If the exclusion of particles by a tactoid depends on the mutual orientation of its structural units—and the latter would seem to be a defining property—we would predict that particles would penetrate its domain when the orientation is lost. This is not the case; in experiments with mercaptoethanol, for instance, the region of

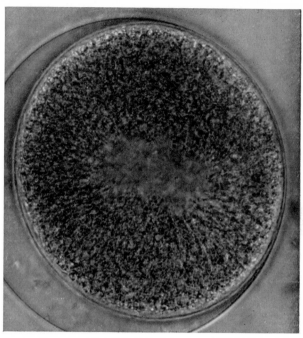

FIG. 50. A living sea urchin egg in division, somewhat flattened. Note that the spindle region appears clear, reflecting the absence of large particles such as mitochondria. The astral rays pass through regions of the cell containing large particles, and are outlined by them.

the mitotic apparatus remains clear and free from large particles even when disordered.

The tendency of a gel to exclude particles from its domain should depend mainly on the strength of the interactions by which it is formed. If the mitotic apparatus as a gel is not a loose network, but a compact mass of interacting subunits, its assembly could well squeeze out "foreign" particles. For example, regions of cells where elements of endoplasmic reticulum are densely associated contain no mitochondria (cf. Porter, 1961, Fig. 15). Recent work on the mitotic apparatus suggests that the mitotic gel may be composed of a compact mass of vesicular and tubular elements (p. 262).

It may seem to be mere verbalism to remind ourselves that the mitotic apparatus is both a *region* and a *body,* but it is not trivial. In viewing the apparatus as a body, we are equipped to handle only that part of it which is structured and coherent. As a domain it also may involve important small molecules and special physical-chemical conditions, such as may affect ion distributions, diffusion gradients, etc., and these cannot be discovered in structural studies alone. To illustrate from experience: if we have isolated the mitotic apparatus in what may be a "native" form, what steps are needed to reconstruct around it the conditions under which it will move chromosomes? The question of the unstructured "internal environment" becomes the critical one.

Let us consider some of the properties of the mitotic apparatus in its aspect as a region that is relatively free from microscopic particles and has the physical features of a gel. Its domain is larger than that occupied by the oriented portion of the spindle. Both within and around the oriented fibrous structure we see less well oriented regions. The fibrous order may be abolished reversibly by various chemicals, such as colchicine (Inoué, 1952a), ether (Swann, 1954b), or mercaptoethanol (Mazia, 1958a; Mazia and Zimmerman, 1958). It is also sensitive to physical variables, such as high temperature (Inoué, 1952b) or high pressure (Pease, 1946). In many of these cases, the MA remains as a coherent mass and reorganizes quickly when restored to normal conditions. For example, treatment of grasshopper neuroblasts with colchicine converts the MA into what appears to be a liquid sphere (Gaulden and Carlson, 1951). One might receive the same impression from sea urchin eggs blocked by mercaptoethanol, where the MA is converted to a somewhat spherical clear space; but isolation shows that it is preserved as an amorphous mass of gel (Fig. 51). This point is made because the loss of orientation is so often described as a dissolution or disappearance of the mitotic apparatus, whereas it may sometimes merely be the modification of that one property, such as birefringence, on which we are relying to "see" it. In brief, we may look upon the MA as a gel which may be ordered locally to various degrees and may suspect that such phenomena as the growth of the spindle or of an aster may represent a transformation of some of its substance from a disordered to an ordered condition.

Such an image of the mitotic apparatus has been given a more precise formulation by Inoué (1959). He observes that the birefringence of spindles in eggs of the annelid *Chaetopterus* increases with temperature within the range of 10 to 40°C. (Fig. 52, A). The temperature effect is reversible and leads to the conception of the spindle as a gel in temper-

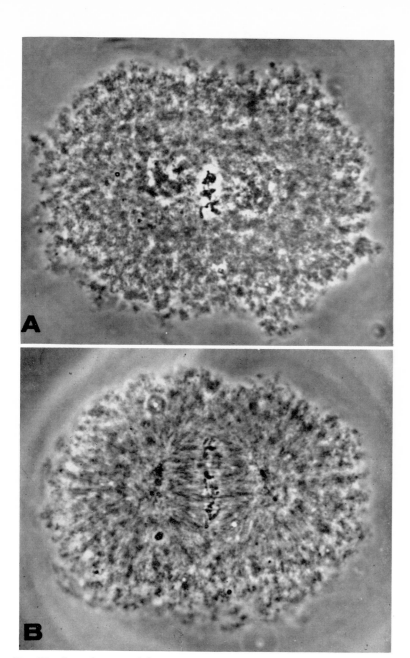

Fig. 51. Some features of the mitotic apparatus as a gel containing regions of high orientation. A. Mitotic apparatus of sea urchin egg isolated 14 minutes after immersion in 0.075 M mercaptoethanol at metaphase. The fibrous orientation has been destroyed, but the apparatus retains its character as a coherent gelled region of the cell. B. Recovery from disorientation by mercaptoethanol. Mitotic apparatus 10 minutes after removal of mercaptoethanol. Comparing this figure with A, one can see that the orientation may be readily restored.

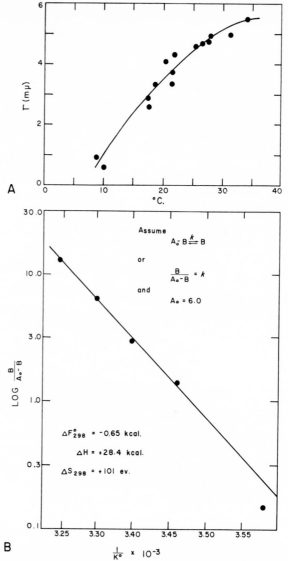

FIG. 52. An interpretation of the mitotic spindle as a gel in which the oriented and unoriented materials are in a temperature-sensitive equilibrium (Inoué, 1959). A. Orientation in the mitotic apparatus as a function of temperature. Relation between birefringence of the spindle and temperature in living eggs of *Chaetopterus*. As the temperature is shifted up or down, the birefringence values reach an equilibrium characteristic of each temperature. B. Thermodynamic analysis of the data given in Fig. 52, A. The equation at the upper right represents the temperature-sensitive equilibrium. A_0, the total amount of orientable material, is assumed to remain constant. B is the amount of oriented material. A_0 is measured as the asymptote of the curve given in Fig. 52, A, B is measured as the retardation at a given temperature. The ordinate is the equilibrium constant, the abscissa the reciprocal of the absolute temperature. Data and interpretation by Inoué (1959). Recalculation of $\Delta F°_{298}$ given by Inoué (1960).

ature-sensitive equilibrium; the temperature affects the equilibrium constant that describes the reaction

$$A_0 - B \overset{k}{\rightleftarrows} B$$

where A_0 is the total amount of material in the gel, assumed to be constant under the conditions of the experiments, and B is the amount of oriented material. A thermodynamic analysis of the relationship between the equilibrium constant and temperature (Fig. 52, B) yields a value for the free-energy change which is consistent with the idea that the orientation depends on very weak bonding, expressing in quantitative form the experimental evidence of the structural instability of the mitotic apparatus.

The statement that the mitotic apparatus is a gel is probably a truth, but a limited and not entirely satisfying one. It provides a physical description of the apparatus as a cohering mass of substance, as a system of unspecified macromolecules interacting in vaguely specified ways, and it gives a reasonable basis for the orientation that we observe as "fibers" while providing for their evanescence. But the concept provides only the substrate for the polarization of fibers and for the specific relations between chromosomes and poles, and it does not move chromosomes except to the degree that faith moves mountains. The fault lies, perhaps, in the relatively small conceptual content of the term "gel," which, after all, is only a loose if useful description of very wet and weakly associated solids or of liquids with peculiar flow properties.

Often the size of the mitotic apparatus is regulated to the size of the cell. For example, nucleated fragments of sea urchin eggs produce a correspondingly smaller MA. This may seem a trivial point, but it does suggest that the amount of material mobilized depends on some factor such as the distance between the centers, and not so much on the nucleus or chromosomes. Experimental conditions may influence the size of the MA; the production of "reduced" spindles is often described. For example, Inoué (1952a) describes the diminution of the spindle in *Chaetopterus* eggs under the influence of colchicine and, in another study (1952b), the appearance of reduced spindles, which then grow, after exposure of these cells to abnormal high or low temperatures.

2. Micromanipulation Studies

The view of the mitotic apparatus as a discrete mass of gel is generally supported by its behavior under micromanipulation. The pioneering studies were those of Chambers (summarized by Chambers and Chambers, 1961). Perhaps the most complete works on the subject are those of Wada (1935) on *Tradescantia* stamen hair cells and of Carlson (1952) on grasshopper neuroblasts. Both observers affirm the image of the MA as a semisolid body. Wada was able to pull the mitotic apparatus out of the cell at metaphase and anaphase. Carlson describes how it may be distorted by the needle or pushed about in the cell. (As we have mentioned, the chromosomes move with the MA.) Carlson also finds that the needle moves through the MA more easily along the spindle axis than across it, suggesting the presence of oriented fibers. The mitotic apparatus may actually be sucked out of the cell (Lorch, 1952; Hiramoto, 1956). The consequences of this operation for cell division will be discussed in Section XII, B.

3. Centrifugation Studies

Of the various methods of studying the physical properties of bodies inside the cell, none is more free from the hazards of artifact than the use of centrifugal force. We need cite here only a few of the experiments on the mitotic apparatus; an extensive literature has been reviewed by Shimamura (1940) and by Beams (1951). All the evidence affirms the conclusion that the mitotic apparatus is a discrete body. Its movement in a centrifugal field in relation to other cell components provides evidence concerning its relative density, and the distortions observed at high forces are a source of information on orientation and on the attachment of chromosomes. In the sea urchin egg (Harvey, 1934) the mitotic apparatus shifts toward the centripetal pole on centrifugation; it is less dense than the cytoplasmic particles. Lipid drops, also moving to the centripetal pole adhere to its surface but do not penetrate it, demonstrating, in Harvey's words, that the "mitotic figure is a very definite structure consisting of more rigid or gelated material than the surrounding medium." In the cytoplasm of meristem cells of the pea root the MA is slightly more dense than the surrounding cytoplasm (Němec, 1929). By treating the roots with nicotine solutions, Němec obtained an interesting situation in which the chromosomes completed mitosis and formed interphase-type nuclei while the spindle persisted; thus he could study the properties of the "pure" spindle. In pollen mother cells of the lily (Shimamura, 1940) the MA also moved to the centrifugal pole, though it was bent and distorted in various ways by the centrifugal field. The stretching of a spindle by centrifugal force increases its birefringence [experiments of Pfeiffer (1938) on the eggs of the *Phynchelmis*], an observation that is fully consistent with the expected behavior of an oriented gel. Within the spindle, chromosomes may be displaced by high forces. At very high forces (in the neighborhood of 150,000 g) chromosomes can be pulled out of the spindle, sometimes breaking in the process (Beams and King, 1936: experiments on chick embryo cells; Beams and King, 1938: experiments on wheat root tips).

Summarizing the literature, Beams (1951) says: "In general, the evidence from the centrifuging of the spindle seems for the most part to support the view that it is a gelled region composed of fibers which are highly elastic."

4. Optical Studies

The polarizing microscope is the best tool available for the analysis of the orientation of the molecular elements of the mitotic apparatus. [We may also add that its applications to cell division have stimulated the most important advances in the technique of biological polarization microscopy, among which may be mentioned the Swann and Mitchison (1950) analysis of the technical problems, Inoué's (1953) development of a microscope of radically advanced design, and, finally, the elaboration by Inoué and Hyde (1957) of the rectification principle in polarization microscopy.] A substantial literature on the polarization microscopy of the mitotic apparatus exists. Earlier literature is reviewed by the pioneer W. J. Schmidt (1939), and later studies include those of Monné (1944), Hughes and Swann (1948), Swann (1952), Pfeiffer (1952), Inoué (1953), E. W. Taylor (1959), and Inoué and Bajer (1961).

Most of the findings concerning the polarization-optical properties of the MA in the living cell harmonize. The mitotic apparatus is a birefringent structure, hence contains oriented units, and the birefringence is positive in sign with respect to the spindle axis. The positive sign is consistent with the view that asymmetric protein molecules are oriented parallel to the axis. In addition to the predominant *positive form* birefringence a residual positive *intrinsic* birefringence can be demonstrated (Pfeiffer, 1952). With the more advanced methods introduced by Inoué (1952a; Inoué and Hyde, 1957), the classic spindle fibers, both those running from pole-to-pole and those joining kinetocheres to poles, are resolved as definite strands or bundles of strands having a higher birefringence than the background material (Fig. 53).

A possible source of misinterpretation of observations with the polarization microscope should be recalled. It is only a device for studying the orientation of structures and has no advantages over any other method for "seeing" unoriented material. It is sometimes implied, when the birefringence disappears under certain experimental conditions, that the object being observed has dissolved. This need not be the case, for the

MA can exist as a coherent body without its normal structural regularity (Fig. 51).

We have already mentioned some of the applications of the interference microscope and allied methods for measuring refractive index *in vivo* to the study of the mitotic apparatus.

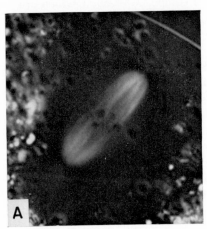 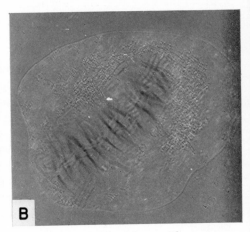

Fig. 53. Birefringence of spindles. A. Meiotic spindle of living *Chaetopterus* oöcyte at first metaphase (Inoué, 1952, 1953). B. Mitotic figure of living *Haemanthus* endosperm at metaphase. In this photograph, the individual chromosomal fibers are seen, running poleward from the kinetochores. The optics are so oriented that the birefringent fibers appear dark. From Inoué and Bajer (1961); photograph by courtesy of Drs. Inoué and Bajer.

5. Conclusions

The general view that the mitotic apparatus is describable physically as a *gel* is supported from many sides, and this loose characterization is a useful though limited basis for a molecular analysis.

B. Chemistry of the Mitotic Apparatus

In the following discussion the results of the chemical studies of the isolated mitotic apparatus will serve as a frame of reference. The results obtained by microscopic cytochemical methods will be woven into the discussion. The field is so new that all conclusions should be taken as tentative simplifications.

1. Isolation of the Mitotic Apparatus

As a structure, the mitotic apparatus is not a permanent organ of the cell. Much as we hesitate to make statements smacking of teleology, we must say that it appears when it is "needed" and disappears when its work is done. It is a highly unstable structure and disappears all too easily when the dividing cell is abused. For example, the structure of the mitotic apparatus of a dividing newt fibroblast is as badly damaged by point irradiation of the surrounding cytoplasm as by direct irradiation of the spindle itself (Zirkle, 1957). The still-unknown conditions of its stability during division not only affect our ability to isolate it, but also raise provocative questions about the peculiarities of the internal environment of the cell during the period of division.

The first successful mass isolation of the MA was achieved by Mazia and Dan (1952), who used sea urchin eggs as material. If further work has been largely restricted to material of this type, it is because there is no other in which large quantities of dividing cells are available. Gram quantities of cells are needed to obtain small amounts of MA. Successful isolation of MA from grasshopper spermatocytes by the first method of Mazia and Dan has been reported by Pfeiffer (1954). In the original work considerations of the "native" condition had to be sacrificed for the sake of stability, even though methods as gentle as possible were sought. The principle employed was that of "selective solubilization." In brief, the dividing cells were first stabilized by exposure to 30–40% ethanol at —10°C., after which the cytoplasm, but not the mitotic apparatus, could be dispersed by means of detergents. In the earliest work the MA had to be further stabilized by hydrogen peroxide before being isolated with the aid of synthetic detergents. In later experience it was found that this step could be omitted if gentler dispersing agents, such as digitonin (Mazia, 1955) or adenosine triphosphate (ATP) (Mazia, 1957) were used. The preparations obtained by these methods retained all the morphological features of the mitotic apparatus at all stages of division in a coherent MA and were free from other cell constituents (Fig. 54, A). They provided a reasonable basis for straightforward chemical analysis and an assurance that the mitotic apparatus was a discrete and structurally coherent assembly. The very fact of its isolation on the basis of its reactions with both the stabilizing and dispersing agents demonstrated that it had a chemical individuality distinct from that of the rest of the cell.

Only recently have we been able to isolate the MA *directly* from the living dividing cell without use of either alcohol or dispersing agents. The problem was viewed as one of mimicking some stabilizing condition existing in the cell. On the basis of various experiences (discussed by Mazia, 1959a,b) it was guessed—and this is the appropriate word—that chemical bonds in the MA having some properties of S—S bonds must be "protected" and that they could be protected by an excess of an S—S

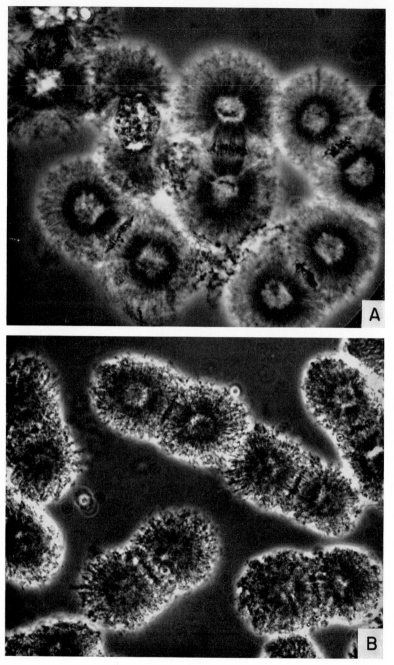

Fig. 54. Isolated mitotic apparatus from sea urchin eggs (*Strongylocentrotus purpuratus*). A. Isolated by alcohol-digitonin method. B. Isolated directly from dividing cells by "DTDG" method (see text).

compound. The latter had to penetrate the cell rapidly and must not be excessively toxic. The substance chosen was dithiodiglycol ($OHCH_2CH_2SSCH_2CH_2OH$). The guess was successful. When dividing sea urchin eggs, after removal of various extraneous membranes, were placed in a 1 M solution of dextrose (or sucrose) containing 0.15 M dithiodiglycol (at pH 6.2–6.3), and the flask was merely shaken by hand, the cells dispersed and a structurally intact mitotic apparatus was set free (Fig. 54,B). The rest of the procedure involved the separation of the free MA from the suspension of cytoplasmic particles, which happened to be more difficult in practice than in principle. However, reasonably "clean" preparations of MA can be prepared in this way for further study (Mazia et al., 1961b).

The MA isolated by the new method (which we may call the DTDG method) were less stable than those prepared by the older procedures, and their stability depended on the presence of dithiodiglycol (DTDG). Some of the stability of the MA prepared by the older methods was, therefore, the result of artifact; this is not entirely surprising in retrospect, since artificial stabilization was part of the procedure. Whether or not the less drastic and reversible stabilization by DTDG is entirely artificial remains an important question, for if it is not we may consider that we are now isolating essentially "native" mitotic apparatus. We can yet hope that the DTDG is mimicking a comparable, though of course not identical, condition within the dividing cell. It is certainly a reasonable hypothesis that such conditions exist, for any chemical picture of the cell in division must explain the temporary stability of the MA and the fact that it breaks down rapidly after telophase.

One fact must be emphasized in thinking about the isolated mitotic apparatus. We can know that it is structurally complete, but, until we have reconstructed all its functional requirements, we cannot know what important small or labile constituents have been lost in the isolation procedure.

2. Chemical Description of the Mitotic Apparatus

a. Proteins. It is certain that proteins are a major component of the mitotic apparatus. As has been mentioned, the mitotic apparatus may account for 10% or more of all the protein in the cell. Analyses of MA isolated from sea urchin eggs by methods involving detergents give a protein content of more than 90% (Mazia and Dan, 1952; Mazia, 1955; Zimmerman, 1960) and values in the same range have been estimated from X-ray absorption analyses of *Cyclops* eggs (Stich and McIntyre, 1958).

The amino acid composition of the isolated MA has been determined by Roslansky (Mazia, 1955; Roslansky, 1957). The relative abundance of the several amino acids in the mitotic apparatus proves to be strikingly similar to that in actin from mammalian muscle, and even more similar to that of the protein of isolated flagella of the flagellate *Chlamydomonas* (Jones and Lewin, 1960).

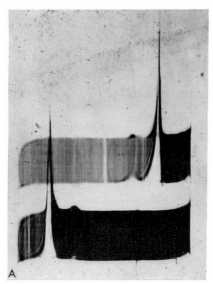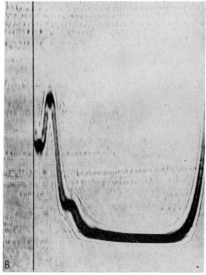

Fig. 55. A. Electrophoretic pattern of dissolved mitotic apparatus. Mitotic apparatus isolated by the alcohol-digitonin method were dissolved in 0.1 M Salyrgan at pH 9.0. Run in phosphate buffer pH 7.5, ionic strength 0.2. Ascending boundary above. Mobilities: major peak = 5.4 × 10^{-5} cm.^{2} volt-sec.; minor peak = 10.7 × 10^{-4} cm.^{2} volt-sec. Data of Zimmerman (1960). B. Ultracentrifuge pattern of dissolved mitotic apparatus, prepared by the alcohol-digitonin method and dissolved in 0.1 M Salyrgan at pH 9.0. Concentration 4.2 mg./ml. Bar angle 50°. S_{20} for lighter major component = 3.67; for heavier component S_{20} = 8.56. Data of Zimmerman (1960).

The average molecular weight of the proteins obtained by dissolving the mitotic apparatus after isolation by the alcohol-digitonin method is 315,000 ± 20,000 (Zimmerman, 1958, 1960). They are not basic proteins. The amino acid composition, electrophoretic mobilities, and pH-solubility relationships (Mazia, 1955, Zimmerman, 1960) all point to a protein or proteins whose isoelectric points are in the neighborhood of pH 4.5.

From the complex structure of the mitotic apparatus, we would predict a corresponding complexity of molecular composition. By electrophoretic (Fig. 55, A) and ultracentrifugal (Fig. 55, B) criteria, the proteins of the mitotic apparatus prepared by the alcohol-digitonin method, show a surprising degree of homogeneity. This would only mean that a few proteins predominate quantitatively and are present in sufficient concentration to yield detectable boundaries. As is seen in Fig. 55, the electrophoretic and ultracentrifugal patterns suggest that most of the protein is one component, but that enough of a minor component is present to give a small peak which has the higher negative charge and sedimentation constant. Zimmerman (1960) gives the calculations (see tabulation) from the patterns shown in Fig. 55:

	Major component	Minor component
Electrophoretic mobility (cm.^{2}/volt sec. at pH 7.5)	5.4×10^{-5}	10.7×10^{-4}
Sedimentation constant (S_{20})	3.7	8.6

The study of the isolated mitotic apparatus by the more sensitive immunochemical methods confirms and supplements the results just discussed. In studies by Went (1959a, b) two antigenic components were detected, one of which appeared to be present in higher concentration than the other (Fig. 17, A). In more recent unpublished studies by H. Sauaia, at least two additional components have been found in mitotic apparatus isolated by both the alcohol-digitonin methods and the newer DTDG method (Fig. 17, B).

The simplest conclusion to be drawn is that there is one protein which is a major structural building-block and numerous others which may or may not have structural significance and some of which may emerge as the enzymes associated with mitotic action.

b. Nucleic acids. There can be no doubt of the presence of RNA in the region of the mitotic apparatus; the question is whether it is related to the mitotic process. The staining of the mitotic spindle relative to the rest of the cell may be variable, and this consideration tends to influence judgments as to whether the "achromatic figure" is rich or poor in RNA. Results obtained by staining methods have been compiled by Shimamura and Ōta (1956), who cite some 15 references to positive staining for RNA in the mitotic apparatus in plant and animal cells. Ultraviolet microscopy (e.g., Pollister and Ris, 1947; Davies, 1952) confirms the presence of nucleic acids in the spindle. In the *Cyclops* egg, the mass of the mitotic spindle, measured by X-ray absorption, is reduced by 5% by digestion with ribonuclease (Stich and McIntyre, 1958).

Analyses of the isolated mitotic apparatus consistently show the presence of RNA. Zimmerman (1960) has analyzed the mitotic apparatus of the sea urchin egg, after isolation by the digitonin method. It contained 6% RNA and the molar ratios of the ribonucleotides were not consistently different from those obtained with the RNA of the whole cell. An earlier report of the predominance of adenylic nucleotides (Mazia, 1957) must be retracted as being the result of inadequate technique. The major protein components discussed in the previous section have consistently proved to be ribonucleoproteins (Mazia, 1955).

Assuming that RNA is built into the structure of the mitotic apparatus, what could its significance be? We tend to associate RNA with protein synthesis, but there is no reason to suppose that the mitotic apparatus is engaged in such synthesis. The idea that polynucleotides can be regarded as energy-storing molecules has a reasonable basis, although there is no evidence justifying a further discussion of it in relation to the energetics of mitosis. Still another line of speculation considers RNA in structural role. A simple and testable hypothesis is that RNA-to-RNA interactions, perhaps through ionic bridges, are important in the assembly of the mitotic apparatus. A more tenuous version invokes the specificity of RNA in assigning it a structural task. The argument would run as follows. Genetic information clearly determines cell architecture as well as enzyme specificity. The assembly of a structure composed of molecules of a given kind will, in a sense, involve the mutual "recognition" of these molecules. The factors involved in recognition may be built into protein structure itself, as in the well-studied case of the reconstitution of collagen fibrils, but it is also possible to imagine that the genetic determination of the molecular association may be imposed directly by attaching an RNA "message." If an RNA "message" can determine the structure of a protein, could it not also recognize such a structure, and could not this recognition play a part in the associations of ribonucleoprotein macromolecules?

The facts are that the mitotic apparatus seems to be built up of ribonucleoprotein molecules and that we do not know the significance of the presence of RNA.

c. *Polysaccharides.* The association of polysaccharides with the mitotic apparatus has been inferred from its positive reaction under the PAS (periodic acid-Schiff) staining method. There is a considerable literature in which the significance of the apparent presence of polysaccharides in the mitotic apparatus is discussed (e.g., Stich, 1951, 1954; Immers, 1957). In the sea urchin egg it is especially noteworthy that the reaction is concentrated toward the poles and in the asters and is weak in the spindle itself. The isolated mitotic apparatus gives a positive PAS reaction (Mazia, 1955), but polysaccharide has not yet been isolated by chemical means.

d. *Lipids.* The lipid components of the mitotic apparatus have drawn little attention, lacking the attractions provided by simple and facile methods of observation or by simple and facile prejudices about the nature of mitotic functions. But a very strong stimulus to take them into account comes from results of electron microscopy in which affinities between structure in the mitotic apparatus and in the endoplasmic reticulum appear in many forms. A picture of the lipids in the mitotic apparatus could not very well have been drawn from studies on material isolated by methods involving detergents, for the latter would be expected to disperse lipids. With the new DTDG method, the presence of a large lipid fraction in the mitotic apparatus as a whole and in the solution obtained after dissolving it in KCl solutions and sedimenting out the particulate components has been established by J. Engelberg and the author. At the time this is being written, the lipid component has not been characterized, but all the evidence points to its association with ribonucleoprotein. On the basis of electron microscopy and of these preliminary chemical findings, it becomes entirely possible that the structure of the mitotic apparatus is fundamentally related to that of the intracellular lipoprotein system expressing itself variously as membranes, vesicles, and tubular filaments.

e. *Enzymes.* The complex character of mitosis would lead us to suppose that many enzymes are involved, but it is not easy to decide what enzymes should be searched for. On the basis of generalized hypotheses about the role of ATP-splitting in various forms of cell movement, a search for an ATPase is a natural starting point. In studies with the isolated mitotic apparatus, no reaction with ATP was found as long as methods of isolation employing alcohol and digitonin were used. Recently, the MA isolated by the DTDG method has been examined (Mazia *et al.*, 1961a) and an active and specific ATPase has been found in association with the fraction soluble in 0.5 M KCl, which is presumed to include the "fibrous" components of the MA and to exclude contaminating cytoplasmic particles. The striking feature of this Mg^{++}-activated ATPase is its specificity; it splits ATP, inosine triphosphate to a lesser extent, but does not split ADP, CTP, UTP, or GTP. No alkaline phosphatase has been found in the isolated sea urchin mitotic apparatus, although Pfeiffer (1954) has reported a positive cytochemical reaction for this enzyme in grasshopper spermatocytes isolated by the original method of Mazia and Dan (1952), employing alcohol, hydrogen peroxide, and the detergent Dupnol.

The finding of an ATPase does conform to the prediction from the fertile hypothesis that biological systems carrying out movement possess this enzyme activity.

f. Zinc. An interesting, if still uninterpreted, cytochemical finding on the mitotic apparatus is Fujii's (1954, 1955a, b) report of the presence of something that stains strongly with the dithizone reaction. This is interpreted as an indicator of the presence of zinc. According to Fujii, the dithizone-staining substance deposits in the spindle when the MA forms, and leaves it at anaphase.

g. Thiol groups. If the role of thiol groups in mitosis now occupies the attention of more workers than do many other problems that might seem equally important, it is a consequence of the pioneering imagination of Louis Rapkine. His 1931 paper especially may be considered to be the first effort to come to grips with the chemistry of cell division. Rapkine's basic chemical finding was that a "glutathione cycle" operated during cell division (Fig. 56). The "soluble" SH groups, interpreted as glutathione, decreased in quantity up to about metaphase and then reappeared as division proceeded. He translated these changes in terms of complementary changes in the protein SH. These were interpreted in terms of a reversible denaturation of the proteins, which would, in the denatured state, be unfolded and in a favorable configuration for forming fibers. A detailed critique of Rapkine's views has been given by Stern (1959b).

In the course of the investigations on the isolated mitotic apparatus, the idea that it was held together by S—S bonds (without excluding bonds of other kinds) has been an influential guide. The original method of isolation employed hydrogen peroxide because it might stabilize the MA by oxidizing sites of potential S—S bonds. Later, when H_2O_2 was no longer necessary, it was found that the solubility of the MA prepared by the digitonin method depended on —SH groups. In the latest method dithiodiglycol was introduced because it might "protect" S—S bonds, and this approach has made the direct isolation possible.

Yet direct evidence that S—S bonds as such are the main links holding the mitotic apparatus together is not strong. Although it seemed necessary at first to use strong disulfide-splitting agents such as alkaline thioglycolate to dissolve the isolated mitotic apparatus, this requirement has become less important as more attention has been given to technical details such as working rapidly with freshly isolated material and extreme care in the maintenance of low temperature. With such precautions, mitotic apparatus isolated by the alcohol-digitonin method may be dissolved at mildly alkaline pH with the acid of Salyrgan or *p*-chloromercuribenzoate (Zimmerman, 1960) or merely under mildly alkaline conditions

(Went, 1959b). The mitotic apparatus isolated directly with the aid of dithiodiglycol dissolves when the latter reagent is removed, especially in such solvents as 0.5 M KCl.

The present picture is not clear. The mitotic apparatus seems to contain many potential S—S groups. Merely on standing at refrigerator temperatures after isolation by the alcohol-digitonin method, it becomes stabilized, after which it can be dissolved only by splitting S—S bonds. This stabilization proceeds very rapidly if oxidizing agents are intro-

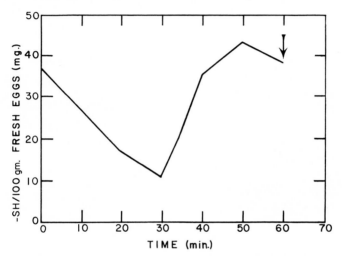

FIG. 56. The "Rapkine cycle." Original data of Rapkine (1931) on sea urchin eggs. The TCA-soluble SH decreases during the preparatory stages of the first division, then increases at the time the mitotic apparatus is forming and growing, and possibly begins to decrease at the time of cytokinesis (arrow). The TCA-soluble SH was interpreted as glutathione. Later work (Fig. 59) throws doubt on the fluctuations of glutathione as such, but it does indicate the presence of a similar cycle involving a TCA-soluble polypeptide.

duced. All this suggests the presence of —SH groups in propinquity in the mitotic apparatus.

There have been also some convincing demonstrations of the role of protein SH groups in the mitotic apparatus. The observation that p-chloromercuribenzoate and similar SH agents help to solubilize the isolated mitotic apparatus would point to a structural involvement of SH, although it still could be interpreted as an effect on S—S groups. In the beautiful cytochemical experiments of Kawamura and Dan (1958) and N. Kawamura (1960), the formation of the mitotic apparatus in sea urchin eggs is evidenced as the assembly of proteins having a higher SH concentration

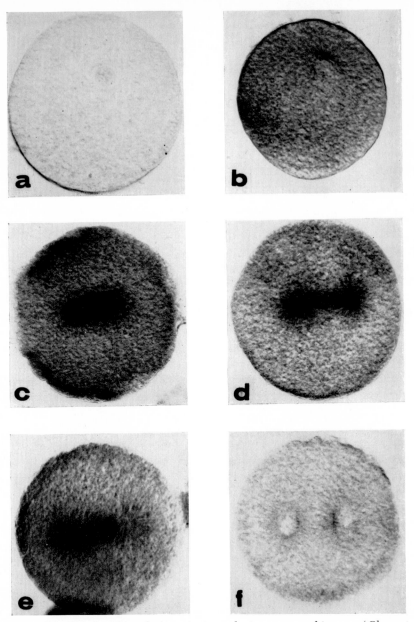

F<small>IG</small>. 57. Protein SH and the mitotic cycle in a sea urchin egg (*Clypeaster japonicus*). The eggs are stained for protein SH groups by the method of Bennett (1951). a. Unfertilized. b. Fertilized showing increase in stainable groups. c. Prophase showing concentration of proteins high in SH as the spindle is assembling. d. Metaphase. Proteins of spindle and asters high in SH. e. Anaphase. f. Telophase; the SH-staining is no longer conspicuous. Photographs by courtesy of Drs. N. Kawamura and K. Dan (cf. N. Kawamura and K. Dan, 1958).

than the other proteins of the cytoplasm. This is best shown by the photographs of Fig. 57. According to N. Kawamura (1960) the changes in protein SH in the dividing sea urchin egg are more significant than those of S—S, although the latter are also present. Other workers (Shimamura et al., 1957; Sandritter and Krygier, 1959) also observe significant fluctuations of protein SH in the course of mitosis and in the mitotic apparatus.

In an interpretation of the role of thiol groups in the formation of the mitotic apparatus by the dividing cell, the "Rapkine cycle" has been incorporated into a cycle involving the protein SH (Fig. 58). Briefly, the hypothesis (Mazia, 1954, 1955) proposed that the lowering of the soluble SH level during the period before metaphase was mirrored,

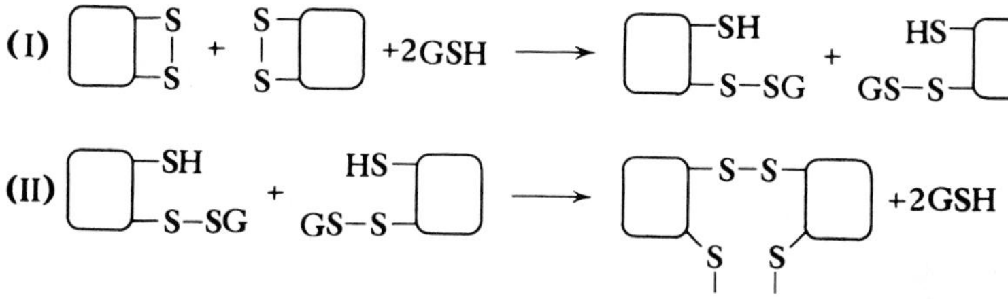

FIG. 58. An interpretation of the significance of the "Rapkine cycle" for the formation of the mitotic apparatus. The hypothesis implies that the decrease in soluble SH before the formation of the mitotic apparatus is reflected in reduction of intramolecular S—S in the structural proteins out of which the apparatus will be assembled. After the turning-point in the "Rapkine cycle," the increase in soluble SH reflects the formation of intermolecular S—S bonds in the later phases of mitosis.

and in a causal way, by the reduction of *intramolecular* S—S bonds in the macromolecular "monomer," whereas the reverse phase of the cycle after metaphase was reflected in the formation of *intermolecular* S—S *bonds*. In the light of Fig. 57, it could be said that the initial assembly of the mitotic apparatus involves the appearance of protein SH groups which disappear during the anaphase functioning of the MA. This differs from earlier interpretations which stressed S—S in the formation of the MA.

Such a stoichiometric cycle is not the only way in which an S—S bonded gel can be formed. An alternative system can be derived from one proposed by Huggins et al. (1951): a small amount of soluble SH catalyzes a chain reaction in which intramolecular S—S is transformed into intermolecular S—S. Reactions of this type have been reviewed by E. V. Jensen (1959). The proposal did, however, stimulate a reinvestigation of the Rapkine cycle.

Neither Neufeld and Mazia (1957) nor Sakai and Dan (1959) were able to confirm the Rapkine glutathione cycle as such in sea urchin eggs when more modern methods were used to separate glutathione from proteins. But Sakai and Dan demonstrated that Rapkine's description of a cyclic fluctuation of trichloroacetic acid-soluble SH was fundamentally correct, except that the fluctuating substance was not glutathione, but a

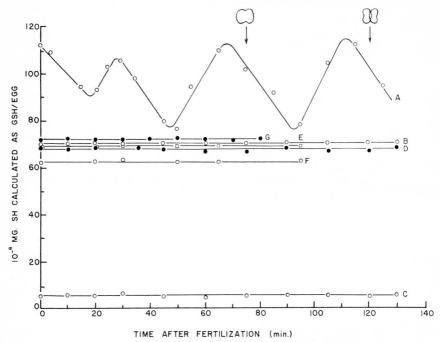

FIG. 59. The newer evidence on the nature of the "Rapkine cycle" in cell division. SH determinations on eggs of the sea urchin *Pseudocentrotus depressus*. Curve *A*: Total TCA-soluble SH, showing a fluctuation very similar to that in Fig. 56. Curve *B*: Extract after precipitation of TCA-soluble protein with ammonium sulfate. Curve *C*: TCA-soluble S—S after deproteinization by ammonia sulfate. Curve *D*: Similar to *B*, except that SH was determined by nitroprusside method instead of iodimetry. Curve *E*: Further deproteination by ammonium sulfate. Curve *F*: Dialyzable SH in TCA extracts. Curve *G*: SH extractable through fertilization membrane. The conclusions from these findings are: (1) some SH-containing, TCA-soluble substance does follow the "Rapkine cycle," (2) the substance has the properties of a protein, not of glutathione (after Sakai and Dan, 1959).

protein or polypeptide which was soluble in trichloroacetic acid but could be salted-out with concentrated ammonium sulfate (Fig. 59). It would be most important to know the nature of this interesting substance, which may be playing an essential part in the regulation of the dividing cell.

The most detailed chemical data on the protein SH of dividing cells—the cell as a whole and not just the mitotic apparatus—have been provided by Stern (1958, 1959b), who followed sporogenous tissue of lily and *Trillium* through its meiotic and mitotic divisions. The striking changes he observes (e.g., Fig. 60) can, as he says, be harmonized with the picture we have been discussing, but it is hardly certain that only

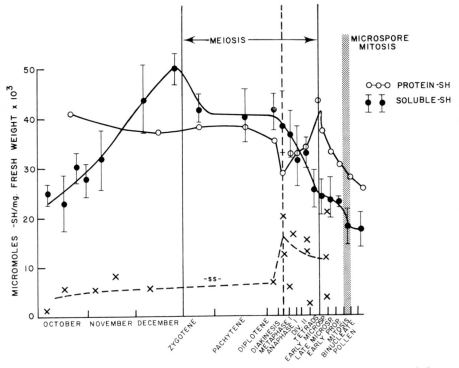

FIG. 60.   Changes in protein and nonprotein SH during the development of the *Trillium* anther. During the divisions there are striking changes suggesting an important role of protein SH in the division process, but they do not confirm the hypothesis illustrated in Fig. 58. From H. Stern (1958).

the mitotic apparatus is concerned with them. The most we can say is that the protein SH does tend to decline before the formation of the MA. On the other hand, the soluble thiols do not follow the Rapkine picture in this plant material, and Stern stresses the probable multiplicity of functions of soluble SH compounds in these cells.

Comparable data on HeLa cells by Sandritter and Krygier (1959) also follow the prediction that the protein-bound SH should increase in the preliminary stage of preparation of the mitotic apparatus, decrease as the mitotic apparatus forms, and increase again at the end of division.

h. Other intermolecular bonds. Rather than assess the relative importance of thiol bonds in the assembly of the MA, it is more prudent to assert that they are merely the first type of intermolecular linkage to have come under substantial experimental investigation—and with interesting results. It is a safe hypothesis that other types of intermolecular links are important. Heilbrunn has stressed the involvement of cations in the formation of the mitotic gel, and Gross (1957) has dealt with the physical chemistry of such ion-induced gelation reactions on the basis of experiments with extracted cytoplasmic proteins. Anderson (1956a, b) has proposed that organic polycations be investigated as the agents of ion bonding mechanisms in the gelation process. The hydrogen bond has played such a prominent part in the theory of protein-to-protein interactions (Waugh, 1954, 1959) that it must inevitably enter into our thinking about intermolecular linkages in the mitotic apparatus. On the basis of the behavior of the isolated mitotic apparatus toward urea solutions, it was proposed (Mazia, 1955) that the macromolecules of the mitotic apparatus formed linear polymers by sulfur bonding, and these chains were condensed and oriented into fibrous bundles by hydrogen bonds. As we have seen, more recent experience with the isolated mitotic apparatus emphasizes its instability and directs attention to bonds weaker than disulfide bonds. It is by no means excluded that the bonding of the mitotic apparatus involves weak bonding through SH groups. Such bonds are not well-understood, but evidence for their existence is summarized by E. V. Jensen (1959). This would be consistent with the conspicuous levels of protein SH in the mitotic apparatus (Fig. 57) and with the finding (Zimmerman, 1958, 1960) that SH agents such as *p*-chloromercuribenzoate dissolve the mitotic apparatus even after isolation by the alcohol-digitonin method. Above all, the action of such a great variety of agents in reversibly disorganizing the mitotic apparatus *in vivo* would suggest that weak and sensitive interactions between macromolecules are crucial. The vast literature on "spindle poisons" (summarized by Dustin, 1956; Biesele, 1958) requires that we find a common point of attack for colchicine, a great array of narcotics, elevated temperatures, elevated pressures, and a multitude of seemingly unrelated chemicals.

The blockage of mitosis, or the production of mitotic abnormalities, by heavy water has been interpreted in terms of the participation of deuterium in H—bonds (Gross and Spindel, 1960) and may be an important tool for further analysis.

i. Conclusions. Chemically, the mitotic apparatus is describable as a gel created by the polymerization of protein macromolecules with which RNA and lipids are associated. A few kinds of proteins account for most of its mass, and these few proteins account for a considerable fraction of all the protein in the cell as it enters division. At the intermolecular level, there is evidence of participation of intermolecular S-S links, or other links involving sulfur, in the polymerization leading to the formation of the gel. Certainly other types of bonds must be involved. If what has been said about these questions seems pathetically oversimplified, the difficulty lies not so much in lack of information as in lack of knowledge as to what information is required. At one end of the spectrum we have the chief structural molecules of the mitotic apparatus, which are becoming reasonably well defined. At the other we have a large body, the mitotic apparatus, whose structure is describable in microscopic dimensions. But the realm between the molecular and the microscopic, the physics of the transitions from the former to the latter, has been explored very poorly, and if we are unable to say very much about the organization of the mitotic apparatus, we cannot do much better in accounting for any other cellular structure at the level of chemical bonding.

C. *The Electron Microscopic Image*

The mitotic apparatus was rather recalcitrant toward electron microscopic study until quite recently; in some of the pioneer studies either it was not found at all or it yielded an image too coarse to add much to the evidence from light microscopy. Significantly new facts have emerged only in recent years. Some of the contributions that record the progress of the field are those of Rosza and Wyckoff (1951), Beams *et al.* (1950), Schultz-Larsen (1953), Selby (1953), Bretschneider (1950a, b), de Harven and Bernhard (1956), K. R. Porter (1955, 1957), Bessis *et al.* (1958), Gross *et al.* (1958), Amano (1957), Ruthmann (1958), Kurosumi (1958), Sato (1958), Roth *et al.* (1960), and Yasuzumi *et al.* (1961). Even now, we may be sure that there is a great deal more to be seen than has been seen. Let us consider here only a few findings that extend the already-rich lore of light microscopy and bear directly on our functional image of the mitotic apparatus.

The elucidation of the structure of the centrioles, which has already been discussed (Section III, D, 2), is one of the important advances.

The "existence" of chromosome-to-pole fibers has been confirmed, and we now have some opinions as to the inner structure of the microscopic fibers. A new concept is that of the *spindle filaments*, submicroscopic elements which, according to K. R. Porter (1955, 1957) and de Harven

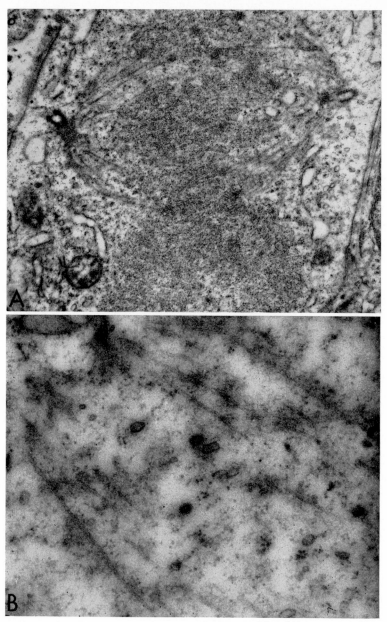

Fig. 61. The electron microscopic image of the mitotic apparatus. A. Vertebrate (chick) cells. Thin section passing through both poles. Note centrioles, and spindle filaments passing from vicinity of centrioles to the kinetochores (seen here as dark areas near the equator). Small particles are seen inside the spindle area, but no mitochondria. Magnification: × 15,000. B. Higher magnification, showing the filaments as distinctly bounded paired units. Magnification: × 45,000. Photographs A and B by courtesy of Dr. W. Bernhard. C. Part of the mitotic apparatus of a sea urchin embryo (*Strongylocentrotus purpuratus*) at anaphase. In this section, chromosomal fibers stand out as groups of oriented tubulelike filaments. Chromosomes (above) ap-

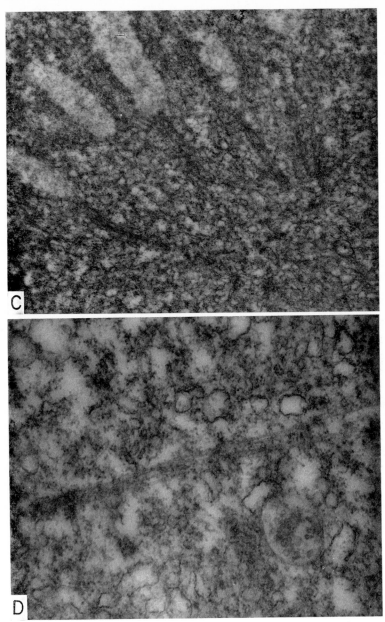

pear light. The gel structure in the aster (lower right) and between the oriented chromosomal fibers is seen as a dense aggregate of filaments and vesicles, free of large particles. Centrioles not seen in this section. Magnification: × 15,000. D. A portion of the interzonal region of the mitotic apparatus in the sea urchin embryo at anaphase. The structure appears to be more granular and amorphous than the region between chromosomes and poles, as seen above, but a group of filaments is seen. These are oriented along the polar axis. Magnification: × 43,000. Photographs C and D by Patricia Harris.

and Bernhard (1956), are about 200 A. in diameter, tend to occur in pairs, and are described as "tubular" (Fig. 61). As Porter describes them, the filaments characterize the chromosome-to-pole connections and are found elsewhere in the spindle and in astral rays (Bessis *et al.*, 1958). They are seen in the interzonal region at the end of mitosis. The similarity between these paired filaments in the spindle and those observed in cilia is, of course, provocative in view of the corresponding homologies between centrioles in basal granules of cilia and flagella. Around the spindle filament, less definitely organized fibrous material is collected. Porter defines the *spindle fiber* as the "combination of paired filaments and associated fibrous materials." This would be the microscopic spindle fiber seen so well with polarized light (Fig. 53).

At this time, it may be more advantageous to outline the points that have emerged from the electron microscopic studies of the mitotic apparatus thus far than to attempt a definitive picture: almost any statement is likely to be out of date in a short time.

1. *Chromosomal fibers.* In most cases the core of the chromosomal fiber consists of spindle filaments. In some cases a single chromosome seems to be associated with a single pair of these filaments. In others the fiber seems to involve a bundle of them.

2. *Insertion into chromosomes.* The spindle filaments seem to be attached to the kinetochores, and the points of attachment are characterized as regions of high density and perhaps by a more definite structure (cf. Fig. 45).

3. *Pole-to-pole fibers.* Filaments having the basic structure described above have been seen in the "interzonal" region between chromosome groups that have separated at anaphase, and presumably they may be related to the "continuous" pole-to-pole fibers discerned by light microscopy. These filaments do not appear to be very numerous in thin sections. Amano (1957) describes 9 fibers, 0.2 μ in diameter, running from pole to pole in mitotic spindles of lymphoblasts and reticulocytes. He interprets them as being operative in the elongation of the spindle at anaphase, but such fibers have not been seen by others. On the whole the structure of the central spindle in relation to the chromosomal fiber system is not well worked out, although it is important in relation to the formation of the mitotic apparatus and to the apparent "pushing" and "pulling" movements in anaphase (Section X, B). All we can say is that the spindle filament seems to be present in both chromosome-to-pole connections and pole-to-pole connections.

4. *Connections of fibers to centrioles.* In some cases (cf. Bernhard, and de Harven, 1960), the spindle filaments approach the centrioles but

do not touch them. In others (cf. Ruthmann's 1958 study on crayfish meiosis) the fibers may touch the wall of the cylindrical centriole. The question of the exact relations of fibers and centrioles is obviously important in the consideration of the origin of fibers and of mitotic mechanics. If, as seems to be the case in the classic cytological literature, the centriole itself may or may not be part of a larger "centrosome," it would not be surprising to find consistent variations in the appearance of the attachments of fibers at the poles.

5. *Background structure of the mitotic apparatus.* The pole-fiber-chromosome systems of the mitotic apparatus do not reside in a vacuum. We could imagine, at one extreme, that the interstitial material is merely cytoplasm having the same structure as that surrounding the region of the mitotic apparatus. At the other extreme, we could suppose that the entire volume of the mitotic apparatus is distinctive in structure. The truth of the matter is intermediate between these possibilities. The region of the mitotic spindle ordinarily contains no large particles, mitochondria being excluded. In some cases and at some stages (e.g., *Drosophila* spermatocytes; Ito, 1960) it contains no ergastoplasmic structures in its interior, but in others (crayfish spermatocytes: Ruthmann, 1958; onion root tips: Porter and Machado, 1960) ergastoplasmic material is seen as vesicles oriented along the spindle axis. In all cases small particles, having the character of the so-called "Palade granules," are found; sometimes they are scattered at random or in clusters (K. R. Porter, 1955), and sometimes they are more oriented as though they were part of the spindle fibers (Gross *et al.*, 1958). It is possible that these particles are related to the "minor" nucleoprotein fraction consistently recovered from the isolated mitotic apparatus. The function of the normal cytoplasmic components that appear in the mitotic apparatus is not clear. On the one hand, they may be concerned with the essential structure and operation of the apparatus. On the other, they may represent a "trapping" of particulate material in the formation of the gel. If the image of gel formation does describe the initial stages of the formation of the mitotic apparatus, it is, as we have seen, more difficult to account for the exclusion of particles such as mitochondria than to suppose that the consolidation of fibrous material into a mitotic apparatus would include various cytoplasmic components in the interstitial volume of the gel. Cytological tradition prepares us to assign to the filaments and fibers an intelligible role both in the structural organization and in the functions of the mitotic apparatus. Whether the particles that are present also play a significant part in mitosis remains to be discovered.

In attempting a synthesis of the results obtained thus far in the electron microscopic study of mitosis, we may assume that all of the observations are meaningful but that none is complete. It is most impressive that the fine structure of the "fibers" associated with chromosome movement seems to be based on elements that appear to be tubular. It is not evident what "tubular" means in a literal sense, but the images suggest that the filaments derive from sheets of molecules tightly arrayed around a long axis, rather than from end-to-end arrays with cross-linking. This view is not easy to harmonize with other evidence, such as the positive birefringence of chromosomal fibers. With fortunate fixation, it is also possible to vizualize the less specifically oriented parts of the mitotic apparatus, its over-all gel structure. As is seen in Fig. 61, C and D, this can be a very dense mass of sheets, tubules, and vesicles, whose basic structure can be related to that of the internal membrane system, particularly some forms of endoplasmic reticulum. The gel as a whole gives a very different impression from what was expected from such models as a fibrin clot. It might be described as a "micellar gel" rather than a "molecular gel," which implies that the gelatin involves the following steps: association of molecules into essentially two-dimensional micelles, association of micelles into larger sheets, disposition of the sheets into tubules, vesicles, etc., and association of these larger units into a compact mass in microscopic dimensions. In such a process, we would expect to find that lipoproteins were a major molecular component and that the weak attractions between nonpolar groups would be an important factor in the "bonding" of the system. This is anything but a conventional picture of an intracellular gel or of intracellular fibers, and if it proves to have any validity it will be a case where the electron microscope has compelled a total reconsideration of a biochemical problem.

D. A Crisis at Metaphase

It has been convenient to view the formation of the mitotic apparatus as involving two steps not necessarily separated in time: the gathering together of macromolecular precursors into a gel and the imposition of order and orientation upon the gel. A striking "tightening up" of the structure takes place as the MA goes into metaphase. This is seen readily in work with the isolated MA; as the metaphase figure is established, the fibers of the spindle and asters become much sharper. It is expressed quantitatively in birefringence measurements (Swann, 1951a) in which the retardation of the spindle rises very abruptly as the chromosomes move rapidly into their metaphase configuration (Fig. 62). It is seen as a "point of no return" for the blockage of mitosis by agents such as mer-

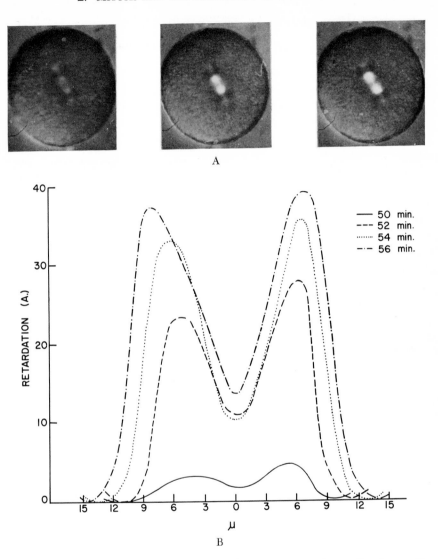

FIG. 62. Development of orientation in the mitotic apparatus as it enters metaphase. Data of Swann (1951a) on sea urchin eggs (*Psammechinus miliaris*).

A. Appearance in polarized light. From left to right: Early prophase, later prophase (4 minutes later), and metaphase. Photographs by courtesy of Dr. M. M. Swann.

B. Birefringence, measured as retardation along the axis of the spindle as it passes from prophase (50 minutes) to metaphase (56 minutes). The zero point on the abscissa is the equator. The birefringence increases at all points, but is focused on the centers.

captoethanol (Mazia, 1958a; Mazia and Zimmerman, 1958), as though the structure "locks" and is no longer susceptible to the same agent which could disorganize it a few minutes earlier.

Whatever the agent of the enhanced orientation may be, the birefringence data (Fig. 62, B) suggest that it is focused in the centers in the sea urchin egg at least.

E. Recapitulation: The Establishment of the Mitotic Apparatus

1. Review of Facts

Let us pause—with the cell—at metaphase, and review the essential events leading up to this climax at which the plot of mitosis is fully determined and needs only to be played out. Some of the essential facts are listed below:

1. The mitotic apparatus "grows" by a gathering together of preformed macromolecular components—including one quantitatively predominant protein which has been partially characterized—into a compact body having the properties of a gel.

2. The organized mitotic apparatus may be viewed as a dual structure consisting of a "central spindle" that accounts for pole-to-pole connections and a "chromosomal spindle" that accounts for chromosome-to-pole connections. The structural duality could conceivably correspond to a biochemical and functional duality.

3. The two components may have different relationships in the time and in the sites of their formation. In animals the central spindle may begin to form as soon as the centers begin to separate during the preceding division and may polarize the cell for mitosis before the nuclear membrane breaks down. In some flagellates the chromosome-to-pole connections may lie completely outside the central spindle. In others the chromosome-to-pole connection may be arrayed around the circumference of the central spindle or may be distributed through its equatorial cross section.

4. The chromosomal fibers and perhaps all the fibers of the spindle may be dual structures consisting of a core of submicroscopic filaments surrounded by a layer of oriented fibrous material.

5. Not all the mitotic apparatus at metaphase is fibrous and oriented. A good deal of its mass may be a less well organized "matrix," but there is no basis for thinking of this as differing chemically from the fibers. If the orientation at the microscopic level is destroyed, it may be regained rapidly. The orientated portion could increase merely by the ordering of the background material.

6. Chromosome movement may begin before or at the time of the

breakdown of the nuclear membrane, and there are cases where the latter does not break down at all.

7. Even during metakinesis the chromosomes move as though guided by kinetochores and are under the influence of the poles. In many cases metakinesis is describable as a "searching" by the chromosomes for the equatorial position.

8. There are reasons for considering that the kinetochores are "attracted" to the poles at metaphase or before, and that the metaphase configuration represents the resultant equilibrium of these attractions.

9. Metaphase is a period during which the structure of the mitotic apparatus becomes visibly more highly oriented, and the "tightening" corresponds to a "point of no return" at which division may no longer be blocked by means which did block it earlier.

2. Some Traditional Controversies

At this point we may dispose quickly of questions that were argued with some vigor, and even acerbity, in earlier times. The question of the "existence" of spindle fibers has been settled by observation of living cells (especially with polarized light), by experimental manipulation, by isolation of the mitotic apparatus, and by electron microscopy. In particular, the polarization microscopic evidence of Inoué (1952a) left no doubt of the "reality" of both chromosomal fibers and pole-to-pole fibers in the mitotic apparatus of the living, dividing cell. This does not mean that we now think of these fine and evanescent structures as ropes or wires.

The question of the nuclear versus the cytoplasmic origin of the spindle has lost its meaning. Undoubtedly the *immediate* source of the substance of the MA may be the nucleus or the cytoplasm in one case or another, and the question of its *ultimate* source, the site of its actual synthesis, has not yet been properly investigated.

3. Speculations on the Engagement of the Chromosomes

These, then, are some of the generalizations we may make concerning the over-all morphogenesis of the mitotic apparatus. The paramount functional questions are: How are the chromosomes engaged and how are they moved into the metaphase plate? Concerning the establishment of chromosome-to-pole connections, we may imagine that (a) there are persistent and, in an operational sense, self-reproducing connections, (b) the connections are formed at the beginning of metakinesis and are responsible for moving the chromosomes to the equator, and (c) the connections form at metaphase, after the chromosomes have attained a proper orientation by some yet unknown means.

From the first two of these alternatives it might follow that the chromosomes are moved into the equator by essentially the same forces as later move them to the poles. The metakinetic movement would lead to a metaphase equilibrium only because the sister chromosomes were not yet separable, the pause at metaphase would merely measure the delay in this separation, and anaphase movement would follow smoothly as a realization of forces already operating. During the whole period from the first engagement of the chromosomes, the MA would be active. We do have evidence that it is active in relation to the cell as a whole; in some cases [for example, the grasshopper neuroblast (McGrath, 1959) and the *Spisula* egg (Rebhun, 1959)] it is seen to oscillate or rock most actively during the period before metaphase.

If, as is proposed by Lettré and Lettré (1957, 1958, 1960), the basic connections of kinetochores to centers persist through interphase, the problem of the engagement of the chromosomes is not so much one of forming connections as of activating them. The hypothesis of dual character of the spindle *fiber* suggests one means of doing so. If, as Lettré and Lettré suggest, the permanent connections corresponded to the submicroscopic *filaments*, the movement of chromosomes could begin only after the filaments had added additional material to form complete microscopic *fibers*, and this might happen at the time when the macromolecular "precursors" of the MA were being gathered together to form the voluminous gel.

If kinetochore-to-center connections form anew at the beginning of metakinesis, we are, of course, faced with the traditional problem of how the two "find" each other. The literature includes accounts of fibers "growing" from centrioles (e.g., Cleveland, 1953, 1957b) and of fibers growing from chromosomes (e.g., McMahon, 1956). The logic of the situation demands that both kinetochores and centers (where present) be active. It is not, however, necessary to assume that the actual substance of the fibers is spun out of one or the other particle. For example, we may imagine (Mazia, 1956b) that a bonding agent [a "structure agent," as formulated by Swann (1952)] diffuses from centers and kinetochores into the already-forming gel and condenses and orients the molecular chains into fibrous bundles. These fibers would tend to radiate from the centers (and kinetochores). The theory of formation of fibers *parallel* to the path of diffusion is not obvious, but the phenomenon is seen in various inanimate models (e.g., Theile, 1948) and was invoked in the past (Fischer, 1899) as a demonstration of how the spindle and asters could arise as artifacts!

If both the kinetochores and centers were radiating such fibers, they would be bound to join wherever their advancing fronts meet. Where the fronts growing from the two poles meet each other, continuous fibers of the central spindle would be formed. Fibers growing toward the surface would remain as astral rays. Cleveland (1957b) has observed the formation of the various fibers in *Barbulanympha* and concludes: "No method of study so far employed has revealed any difference between the astral rays that join one another to produce the central spindle and those which become chromosomal fibers. Nor can the free ones which appear to perform no function be differentiated from chromosomal fibers or those of the central spindle." The conclusion tends to be confirmed by electron microscopy, for comparable filaments are found in chromosomal fibers, in the central part of the spindle, and in astral rays (K. R. Porter, 1955).

If the connection of a chromosome to one pole became active first, the chromosome would move in that direction before being pulled back when the other connection was activated. The hypothesis contains a hidden assumption that the strength of the "pull" from a pole is proportional to the distance from that pole to the chromosome; only thus will the equilibrium position of a chromosome be midway between the poles. Such an assumption would be consistent with the finding (Fig. 42) that chromosomes return to the equator even after they are disarranged at metaphase. Considering the known properties of contractile systems such as muscle fibers, it is an awkward hypothesis, for we would expect the tension developed to be a function of the diameter and not of the length of the fibers.

X. ANAPHASE

The sense and purpose of the mitotic process is revealed in its climax at anaphase. While no biologist can harden himself against a slightly despairing sense of mystery as he watches the swift precise movements of the mitotic apparatus, especially in the beautiful films now available, nevertheless it is here that mitosis is most amenable to experimental analysis. Not only can we subject the anaphase movements to precise measurements, but we can, if only as an act of faith in biological unity, attempt to assimilate them into our thinking about cellular movement in general. The ingenuity of past attempts to explain anaphase movements is recorded critically in Franz Schrader's book (1953).

A. The "Parting" of the Sister Chromosomes

The dividing cell spends a longer or shorter time in metaphase (cf. Table V), but we are required to explain why it is delayed at that stage at all. There are two obvious possibilities. If the mitotic apparatus be-

comes functional only at anaphase, then the pause at metaphase might
represent the time required for the engagement of the chromosomes and
the completion of the motor mechanisms. If, on the other hand, the
chromosomes at metaphase are already subject to pull from both poles,
the process of physical separation of sister chromosomes (or kinetochores) may determine the time when they can move apart.

We know practically nothing about what happens *during* the usual
pause at metaphase except that something is happening! At least, the
duration of this period is temperature sensitive in a conventional way
(Table VII).

We may view the splitting apart of the sister chromosomes as an
event timed by a "signal" given by the cell, and one that does not depend
on the mitotic apparatus. This is seen most vividly in the many cases of
endomitosis in which the chromosomes go through a complete cycle—
duplication, condensation, parting of the sisters, and uncoiling—without
benefit of a mitotic apparatus, and thus become polyploid in number.
If a cell has two nuclei, one going through mitosis and the other through
endomitosis, the chromosome cycles proceed synchronously (Fig. 31, C).

There is other evidence that the notions of "completion of metaphase"
or "initiation of anaphase" have objective meaning. In several cases—
this type of information can best be obtained from ciné records—it has
been observed that one or more chromosomes are delayed in metakinesis.
They may be delayed near one pole (Zirkle, 1957; Bajer and Mole-Bajer,
1956b). The others, which have already reached the equator, may "wait"
for them for some time, and only when the metaphase plate contains all
the chromosomes does anaphase begin. This is not a universal rule. For
example, Hughes-Schrader (1948b) describes a situation in meiosis in a
mantid where an X chromosome, which has no homolog, moves to one
pole before the other chromosomes enter anaphase. But in this meiotic
situation the splitting of sister chromosomes is not involved.

The initial "parting" of the sister chromosomes is a visible event, and
observation tells us that it involves the arms of the chromosomes as well
as the kinetochores. This is most vividly seen in chromosomes that have
been broken by irradiation. Those fragments of arms which are dissociated from their kinetochores are not engaged in the mitotic apparatus
and may lie outside it. Yet the sister fragments are clearly seen to move
apart at the same time as those that remain in the spindle. In time lapse
films, they seem to jump a short distance away from each other, although
they remain associated while the others separate completely as anaphase
proceeds.

This "parting" of akinetic arms has been recorded by Carlson (1938,

1956) in grasshopper neuroblasts and by Zirkle (1956) in newt fibroblast. It had probably been seen also by Belar and Huth (1933), who described the clear separation of chromosomes in monopolar figures in parthenogenetically activated *Urechis* eggs, where normal anaphase movements did not occur in the absence of a second pole. The striking separation of arms in chromosomes blocked by colchicine ("c-mitosis") may be a related phenomenon; here the block seems to prevent the parting of the kinetochores. In films of c-mitosis (Mole-Bajer, 1958), the arms seem to leap apart, forming X-shaped chromosome pairs.

Conclusions

The "parting" of sister chromosomes is a distinct event marking the transition from metaphase to anaphase. It does not seem to depend on the mitotic apparatus, but it does seem to proceed upon a "signal" that affects all the chromosomes within a cell at the same time. It involves the chromosome arms, and not merely the kinetochores. Visually, it is describable in terms of a "repulsion" between sister chromosomes.

B. Anaphase Movement: Descriptive

1. Quantitive Data

We now have an abundance of accurate measurements of chromosome movement and of dimensional changes in the mitotic apparatus and of the cell during anaphase. Further analysis of these data might be productive, and some of the sources are tabulated for the benefit of pencil-and-paper researchers.

Reference	Type of cell
Barber (1939)	*Tradescantia* stamen hairs
Ris (1943)	*Tamalia* spermatocytes
Ris (1949)	*Chorthophaga* (grasshopper) spermatocytes
Hughes and Swann (1948)	Chick osteoblasts in culture
Swann (1951b)	Sea urchin eggs (*Psammechinus*)
K. Kawamura (1955)	*Graphosoma* (shield bug) spermatocytes
Makino and Nakanishi (1955)	*Podisma* and *Acrydium* (grasshopper) spermatocytes
Bajer and Mole-Bajer (1954a, b, 1956b)	Endosperm cultures, numerous species
Jacquez and Biesele (1954)	*Psophus* (grasshopper) spermatocytes
Boss (1954)	*Triturus* (newt) fibroblasts
Duncan and Persidsky (1958)	Maize endosperm
Bucciante (1927)	Chick fibroblasts, in culture
Izutsu (1959a)	Grasshopper spermatocytes (5 species)
Hsu (1955)	Human and other mammalian cell strains in culture

The curves in Fig. 63 illustrate some of the patterns and give an impression of a fundamental similarity of the anaphase proceedings in a variety of cells.

2. Velocity

The reported speeds of chromosome movement in anaphase are somewhat variable, the range being from about 0.2 μ per minute to about 5 μ per minute at temperatures that are normal for the cells being measured (Tables IX and X). As Barber (1939) has pointed out, this is quite slow compared to some other kinds of biological movement; for example, particles carried by cytoplasmic streaming in plant cells move at a rate of 250–300 microns per minute (Table XI).

The temperature dependence of chromosome movement has been studied in a number of cases (Fig. 64 and Table X).

3. Movement of Individual Chromosomes

In most cases the members of a set of chromosomes appear to move in almost perfect synchrony, as an "anaphase plate," to use a descriptive term that is encountered in the older literature. Detailed measurements of the movements of individual kinetochores in a normal anaphase (*Haemanthus* endosperm, Bajer and Mole-Bajer, 1956b) showed some variability within a chromosome set, but the near-uniformity was very striking. However, the cytological literature contains very many deviations from this generalization. In some cases one chromosome of the complement is precocious or consistently lags. Disturbance of the spindle by various experimental treatments may upset the synchrony of the chromosomes in anaphase to various degrees (discussed by Mota, 1952). Even more impressive is the evidence of a genetic influence on the synchrony (Darlington, 1937; Upcott, 1939) expressed in the fact

---

FIG. 63. Plots of anaphase chromosome movement in various types of cells. These plots are representative of the accurate data now available on the velocity of chromosome movement and on the relations between the two movements responsible for the separation of the chromosomes: the kinetochore-to-pole movement and the increase in pole-to-pole distance (spindle elongation).

A. *Tamalia*, an aphid. Spermatocytes in second meiotic division. The initial separation of the chromosomes is entirely the result of their movement to the poles. At about 9 minutes, the spindle begins to elongate and further separation of the chromosomes is the result of the movement of the poles. Spindle elongation is the result of the movement of the poles. Spindle elongation is paralleled by an increase in the cell length. Observations of living material by Ris (1943).

B. *Haemanthus* endosperm. Measurements of movements of the two chromosome groups (*Ch*) and of a pair of sister kinetochores (*K*). Data from A. Bajer.

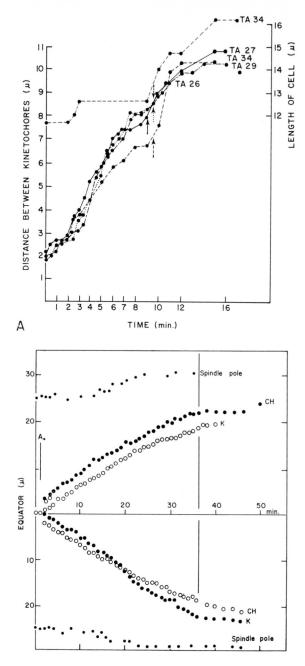

that it may be disturbed as a result of polyploidization, hybridization, etc. Among the variables involved there may be a variation in the timing of the initial separation of individual chromosomes, as Upcott has demonstrated.

With reference to the mitotic mechanism, the normal synchrony of anaphase movement reflects the uniformity of the several kinetochores, and of the forces moving them, whether internal or external. The fact that they *may* move asynchronously leads to the important, if seemingly self-evident, conclusion that the chromosomes *are* moved individually, and not as a group. In dealing with the mechanism of movement we shall not be satisfied with liquid currents or expanding masses of gel; we must have a specific kinetochore-to-pole motor for each chromosome.

It is interesting to note that the rate of movement of a chromosome does not depend on its size when we compare members of the same set, nor does there seem to be much correlation between velocity and size if we compare chromosomes of various kinds of cells.

The sister chromosome sets move toward their respective poles at similar velocities, but the velocities need not be identical. This has been shown in a large series of measurements by Bajer and Mole-Bajer (1954b). This observation bears on the hypothesis, calling for the pushing of the chromosomes by an elongating interzonal body, which would predict that the two groups move at the same speed.

4. Two Types of Movement

An important result of our increasing knowledge of anaphase events has been their resolution into two movements, especially since the work of Ris (1943, 1949). One is an elongation of the spindle, moving the

---

Fig. 63. C. Spermatocytes of *Popilius disjunctus,* a beetle. Some spindle elongation follows the initial period during which the separation of the chromosomes is largely accounted for by the chromosome-to-pole movement. Unpublished data supplied by Professor Henry S. Roberts, Duke University.

D. Newt (*Triturus cristatus*) fibroblasts. Note rapid separation of chromosomes during first few minutes. After this initial chromosome-to-pole movement, further separation involves both a slower movement to the poles and the elongation of the spindle.

E. *Psophus stridulus* (grasshopper) spermatocyte, shown over a time scale beginning at prometaphase. Simultaneous chromosome movement and spindle elongation. Measurements on whole cell show an increase in volume at anaphase, and the course of furrowing in relation to chromosome movement. Curve A, cell length along spindle axis; curve B, cell width at equator; curve C, spindle length; curve D, spindle width; curve E, chromosome separation. Measurements of Jacquez and Biesele (1954) from a film by Dr. K. Michel.

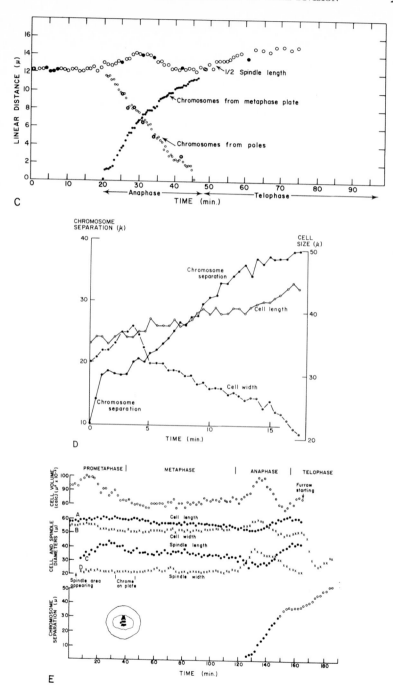

chromosome sets apart by expanding the "interzonal" region between them. The other is the movement of the chromosomes toward the poles. Various earlier workers had tended to stress one or the other of these movements (loosely contrasted as "pushing" versus "pulling"), but it now seems clear that both must be invoked in any general theory of anaphase.

TABLE IX

REPRESENTATIVE DATA ON VELOCITIES OF CHROMOSOME MOVEMENT
(CHROMOSOME-TO-POLE MOVEMENT)

Cell type	Chromosome movement (μ/min.)	References
Tamalia (aphid) embryonic cell (26°C.)	0.7–2.0	Ris (1943)
Chortophaga (grasshopper) spermatocyte (30°C.)	1.5	Ris (1949)
Chick osteoblast	4	Hughes and Swann (1948)
Psammechinus miliaris (sea urchin) egg	2.2	Swann (1951b)
Newt fibroblast (26°C.)	1–8	Boss (1954)
Chick fibroblast (41°C.)	3.7	Bucciante (1927)
Pea endosperm	4	Bajer and Mole-Bajer (1954b)
Iris endosperm	2	Bajer and Mole-Bajer (1954b)
Tradescantia staminal hairs (20°C.)	0.7	Barber (1939)

The relations between the two movements that separate the chromosomes vary. At one extreme, we find that elongation of the spindle is predominant; in fact the chromosomes may not move perceptibly closer to the poles. Examples are the giant ameba *Chaos* or *Pelomyxa* (Short, 1946; Berkeley, 1948), some of the flagellates studied by Cleveland, and the secondary spermatocytes of the aphid *Tamalia* (Ris, 1943). The latter is interesting because other kinds of cells in the same organism do show a movement of chromosomes to the poles. At the other extreme (Fig. 63 B, C) elongation may be slight, and this must be the case in many plant cells. Where both movements take place, they may, in some cases, be simultaneous and so give smooth time curves of chromosome movement or, in others, be separated in time (Fig. 63 D, E). Ris (1943) ob-

FIG. 63. F. Maize endosperm. Abscissa represents a relative time scale, estimated from frequencies of the successive stages, diagrammed below, in fixed material (Duncan and Persidsky, 1958).

G. Chick osteoblasts. Measurements from ciné records. Data on anaphase movement in eight cells are averaged. In this case, spindle elongation and the shortening of the chromosome-to-pole fibers proceed simultaneously (Hughes and Swann, 1948).

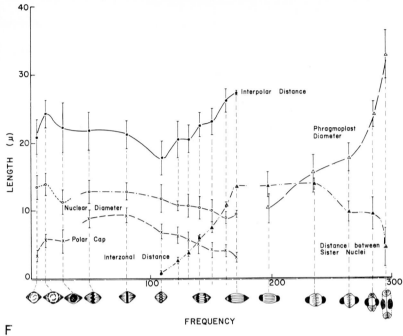

F

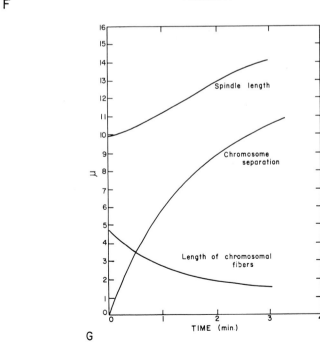

G

TABLE X

CHROMOSOME VELOCITIES IN DIFFERENT ORGANISMS

Organism	Movement at	Temp. (°C.)	Mean distance traveled (μ)	Mean velocity (μ/min.)	Maximum velocity (μ/min.)	Source
Tradescantia virginiana	Mitosis, congression	10	10	0.19	—	Barber (1939)
Tradescantia virginiana	Mitosis, congression	20	10	0.50	—	Barber (1939)
Tradescantia virginiana	Mitosis, anaphase	10	16.5	0.25	0.30	Barber (1939)
Tradescantia virginiana	Mitosis, anaphase	20	16.5	0.70	1.20	Barber (1939)
Tradescantia virginiana	Mitosis, anaphase	35	16.5	0.74	1.20	Barber (1939)
Gallus domesticus	Mitosis, anaphase	21	6.5	0.28	—	Bucciante (1927)
Gallus domesticus	Mitosis, anaphase	41	6.5	3.68	—	Bucciante (1927)
Gallus domesticus	Mitosis, anaphase	45	6.5	3.25	—	Bucciante (1927)
Stenobothrus lineatus	Meiosis I, anaphase	ca.20	15	0.14	0.24	Belar (1929a)
Stenobothrus lineatus	Meiosis II, anaphase	ca.20	14	0.21	0.43	Belar (1929a)

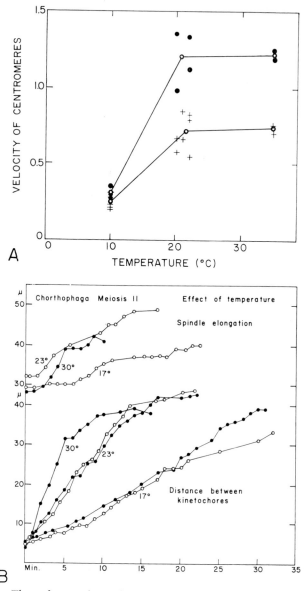

FIG. 64. The velocity of anaphase movement as a function of temperature. A. Data of Barber (1939) on *Tradescantia* staminal hairs. Dots represent maximum velocity and crosses represent mean velocity.

B. Data of Ris (1949) on *Chorthophaga* spermatocytes in second meiotic division. Points represent maximum velocities. Chromosome-to-pole movement is distinguished from spindle elongation.

served that the movement of the chromosomes to the poles preceded spindle elongation in cells of various aphids, and Boss (1954) has observed a similar relationship in cultured newt cells.

In our discussion of the origin of the mitotic apparatus the diverse histories of the center-to-center connections (sometimes seen as a central spindle) and chromosome-to-center connections has already been considered. A great many of the facts concerning anaphase movement—as well as preceding events—can be subsumed under the generalization that the pole-to-pole connections tend to lengthen and the chromosome-to-pole connections tend to shorten.

TABLE XI

RATES OF MOVEMENT OF CELLS AND CELL ORGANS[a]

Organism	Type of movement	Size of body moved (μ)	Velocity of movement (μ/min.)
Tradescantia	Chromosome at anaphase	$18 \times 0.8 \times 0.8$	0.7
Avena	Growth in length of cell in coleoptile	—	Less than 1
Datura	Growth in length of pollen tube	—	32–55
Amoeba	Ameboid movement of whole cell	—	150
Elodea	Chloroplast in cytoplasmic stream	$4.5 \times 4.5 \times 1.5$	250
Tradescantia	Granule in cytoplasmic stream	0.4^3	300
Mytilus	End of cilium	$10 \times 0.1 \times 0.1$	22,500

[a] From Barber (1939).

All the observations support the image of the spindle elongation as an active movement of a relatively rigid body. The most striking evidence is the elongation of the cell as a whole that often parallels the extension of the spindle at anaphase (e.g., Fig. 63 A, D). If we are not deceived by visual evidence, we are seeing the spindle push the ends of the cell.

The properties of the spindle-elongation mechanism have been distinguished in a number of ways, especially by Ris (1949). It has already been mentioned that it may operate at a different time and at a different velocity from the shortening of the chromosomal fibers. Ris has shown that the elongation may be inhibited by chloral hydrate in concentrations that do not affect the movements of the chromosomes to the poles. He has also shown that if the separation of the chromosomes is impeded, by rendering them sticky with X-irradiation, the tendency of the spindle to expand is expressed as a lateral growth which, in grasshopper spermatocytes, may cause the cell surface to bulge in the equatorial region.

Some of the physical factors underlying the elongation of the spindle were visualized in the celebrated experiments of Belar (1929a) on living grasshopper spermatocytes. Exposing the cells to strongly hypertonic solutions, he noted that the spindle tended to elongate as the rest of the cell was dehydrated. The spindle sometimes split along its axis as this occurred. At the extreme, the ends of the spindle pushed out the poles of the cell. His observations suggest very strongly that an anisodiametric dehydration may be a factor in the normal spindle-elongation mechanism, but the implications have not been pursued by modern techniques.

There is every reason to think that the spindle has sufficient rigidity to move the chromosomes apart as it elongates, whether we regard them as being attached to the poles or, as Belar proposed at one time, they are attached to an equatorial region of the pole-to-pole elements (his *Stemmkörper*) whose elongation separates them. In addition to Belar's observations, we can cite various micromanipulation data (Carlson, 1952; K. Kawamura, 1960b) and the observation by Cleveland (1958) that the central spindle in *Barbulanympha*, the elongation of which is the major factor in the separation of the chromosomes in this cell, behaves as a rigid body even if it is cut away from one of the centers.

One long-standing criticism of the theory that contractile fibers pull chromosomes toward the poles was that the poles would have to be anchored, else the contraction might move them closer together rather than move the chromosomes poleward. This ceases to be a problem if the poles tend to be pushed apart by a relatively rigid central spindle. Our picture of metaphase, according to the equilibrium theory, would require the forces that keep the poles apart to be stronger than those between chromosomes and poles. If the former were ever weaker, we would expect the mitotic apparatus to *shorten* at metaphase. Sometimes this actually does happen. A shortening at metaphase is seen in spindles of newt fibroblasts, which have been carefully measured by E. W. Taylor (1959) with the aid of the polarization microscope. Here the shortening amounts to as much as 50–60% between the end of metakinesis and the beginning of anaphase (Fig. 65). Such observations (also cf. Fig. 63 E, F) lend credibility to the idea of a balance between forces that tend to keep the poles apart and those that tend to decrease the chromosome-to-pole distance. If the former are weaker than the latter, and if the chromosomes cannot go to the poles, the poles come to the chromosomes.

5. Conclusions

The anaphase events may be described in terms of two movements: (1) an elongation of the central spindle, describable as a pushing apart of the poles, and (2) a movement of the chromosomes toward the poles. The relative contributions of these in the separation of sister chromosomes varies from one type of cell to another, as do their time relations.

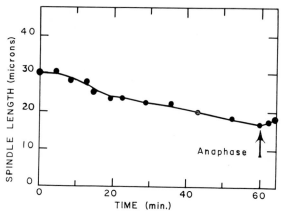

Fig. 65.   Shortening of the spindle during metaphase in newt fibroblasts. From E. W. Taylor (1959).

C. Paths of the Chromosomes in Anaphase

General Features of Chromosome Movement

At the descriptive level, the movement of the chromosomes to the poles is observed as a shortening of the visible kinetochore-to-pole fibers. This is clear and definite, whether it is observed in fixed material by optical or electron microscopy or in living cells by polarization microscopy. To dismiss it, is to ignore the facts. On the other hand, it does not follow automatically that the chromosomes are being pulled *passively* by contractile fibers. The kinetochore is so indispensable a part of the picture that we are bound to seek for it a role more active than that of a mere anchor point for a fiber.

Let us summarize a few of the regularities of kinetochore-to-pole movement:

(1) It tends to follow a straight line (Bajer and Mole-Bajer, 1954b).

(2) The relative "contraction" may be large. In the cases assembled by Hughes (1952b, p. 128) the kinetochore-to-pole connections are seen to contract to as little as one-fifth the original length.

(3) The movement proceeds at a linear or decelerating rate, never at an accelerating rate (Fig. 63). This excludes a mechanism of "attraction" involving an inverse-square relationship and is consistent with the image of a contractile mechanism. These problems of mechanics are discussed in detail by Hughes and Swann (1948) and Jacquez and Biesele (1954).

(4) Commonly, all the chromosomes begin anaphase movement at the same time and move at the same speed, regardless of size. Sometimes, this uniformity is very striking; in cells with small chromosomes, such as a sea urchin egg, we observe the moving chromosomes as "anaphase plates." But exceptions are very numerous: "lagging" chromosomes are frequently described in accounts of mitotic perturbations and are not rare in descriptions of normal mitosis in some forms.

Observing the individual chromosomes, we see that the kinetochores lead the way to the poles. The most famous "exception" is the first spermatocyte division in the fly *Sciara*, where one set of chromosomes seems to "back" away from the other (Fig. 47).

Chromosome movement can take place in the face of rather drastic distortions of the spindle. For example, Bajer and Mole-Bajer (1956b) describe anaphase movements in exceedingly flattened cells in which spindles may split into two, chromosomes may appear to move in tandem, polarity may be virtually absent, and the only apparent determiner of the direction of travel of a given chromosome is the position of its kinetochore and the chromosomal fiber connected to it. Similar "diffuse anaphases" have been induced in onion root tips by treatments with seed extracts (Mota, 1952). These observations, as Dr. Bajer has pointed out (personal communication), provide strong evidence against the necessity of a compact center for chromosome movement in plant cells.

Chromosome movements other than the normal deployment of the kinetochores along the spindle are observed in pathological situations. Fragments without kinetochores may be trapped in the spindle and carried to one pole or the other. If the akinetic fragments find themselves outside the spindle they may be swept poleward, perhaps by cytoplasmic currents, during anaphase or telophase. If the spindle is damaged by irradiation (Zirkle, 1957) or by chemicals (e.g., Hyppio *et al.*, 1955) a "false anaphase" is sometimes observed. Here the sister chromosomes do not separate but are carried to one pole or the other in groups that cluster around the center in the so-called "rosette" formation (Fig. 82). Superficially, these several abnormal chromosome movements add to the impression of an "attraction" between chromosomes and poles.

D. Mechanism of Chromosome Movement at Anaphase

We do not know the mechanism of chromosome movement. With this preamble we may review various hypothesis with the aim of excluding the improbable and of discovering variables that must be accommodated by a successful hypothesis. The efforts range from peaks of ingenuity to irresponsible shibboleths, and often they suffer from two of the more melancholy weaknesses of the biology of the past: gullibility toward physical scientists who happen to be playing at biology and the tendency to believe one's own theories.

1. Some Earlier Theories

Certain approaches to chromosome movement will be summarized very briefly. Some of them are discussed in more detail by Milovidov (1949) and by Schrader (1953).

a. Chromosome autonomy (e.g., Metz, 1936). It is imaginable that the chromosomes possess independent powers of locomotion and could find their way to the poles independently. No one has seriously proposed this extreme view, but the activity of the chromosomes has been invoked when it seemed improbable that they were being pulled passively by the kinetochores, as in the famous case of *Sciara* (Fig. 47).

The view that the chromosomes, and especially the kinetochores, play an active part in anaphase movement is very much alive today, and we shall return to it.

b. Electrical and magnetic theories (e.g., Lillie, 1911; Bernstein, 1912; Kuwada, 1929; Darlington, 1937). An extraordinary number of the events of mitosis can be described very well in terms of attractions and repulsions involving chromosomes and centers.

Some attempts have been made to test this approach by exposing dividing cells to magnetic fields. Milovidov (1949, pp. 316-320; 1954, p. 112) describes experiments of his own in which fields of 28,000–35,000 gauss were applied to bean and onion root tips for several hours, without evidence of mitotic abnormalities, and experiments of Perakis (1947), who exposed sea urchin eggs to fields up to 43,000 gauss with negative results. There have been a few claims that magnetic fields do cause mitotic abnormalities. It remains an interesting question whether the really strong magnets now in use by physicists might affect mitosis and, if they do, whether the results would give any support to the notion that the chromosome-pole interaction involves attractive or repulsive electromagnetic forces.

c. Diffusion (Rashevsky, 1940; Buchsbaum and Williamson, 1943).

Rashevsky has drawn attention to the fact that diffusion forces can bring about movements of particles and has speculated on the possible applications of these of mitotic movements.

d. Currents (Schaede, 1929, 1930; Burton and Haynes, 1955). Cytoplasmic streaming is, of course, one of the basic forms of biological movement, and we can imagine that currents that are oriented and directed by the mitotic apparatus might be involved in chromosome movement. Such a scheme has been worked out in detail by Schaede. More recently, Burton and Haynes have speculated on the existence of a "vortex" at the equator, set up by currents from the poles, which would account for the oscillations of the chromosomes at metaphase and their transport to the poles when they separate.

e. Tactoids (Bernal, 1940; Oestergren, 1950). Tactoids are liquid-crystalline aggregates of asymmetric macromolecules which often form spontaneously in solutions of such molecules. Sometimes they have pointed ends, like some mitotic spindles. As we have mentioned, the hypothesis that the mitotic spindle is a tactoid body has had some attractive features as a means of explaining the metaphase equilibrium, but it has not contributed interesting or plausible speculations concerning anaphase movement. There would be no serious objection to the use of the term "tactoid" to describe a molecular aggregation in which the units are oriented, but neither is there any obvious profit in doing so. Correspondences between the shapes of tactoid bodies and those of spindle would be trivial, even if spindles were always spindle shaped. It is most difficult to see how the tactoid body could provide for any specific relations between individual chromosomes and the poles to which they move. In short, the tactoid concept does not seem to lead to a viable hypothesis of chromosome movement, although it may yet enlighten us concerning macromolecular interactions of importance to our understanding of the mitotic apparatus.

f. Swelling, gelation, and related colloidal phenomena (Wassermann, 1929; Kupka and Seelich, 1948; Duryee and Doherty, 1954; von Möllendorf, 1939; and others). This class of hypothesis invokes viscosity changes, local solation and gelation, changes in the hydration of gels, and other familiar colloidal phenomena in attempting to account for chromosome movements. As we have seen, it is legitimate to describe the mitotic apparatus as a gel. It is realistic to imagine the spread of fronts of gelation from the centrioles and the reverse. A wave of gelation will not necessarily propel particles; in a conventional gel such as gelatin or fibrin it is more likely to trap them. But we have seen that the mitotic apparatus is a different kind of gel, a highly compact one which does in fact exclude large particles from the region in which it forms (p. 235), and could be imagined to push chromosomes. We could not in any case expect to build a complete explanation of chromosome movement around gross colloidal changes, although we might hope to find some of the motive forces among these changes. Anaphase involves an elongation of the spindles as well as a decrease in chromosome-to-pole distance, and these may or may not proceed simultaneously. Some specific chromosome-to-pole interaction is essential.

The expansion and contraction of a gel by gelation and solation are not the only colloid-chemical concepts having possible applications to mitotic movement. Another is anisotropic hydration. For example, we have mentioned Belar's observation of the elongation of the spindle under conditions of dehydration (p. 279). This might prove to be a successful model of the normal elongation of the spindle at anaphase. As for the movements of the chromosomes, we may recall that many if not most of the available models of contractile systems—actomyosin threads, cell models, etc. (Szent-Györgyi, 1951; Hoffmann-Berling, 1959)—involve changes in hydration as an important aspect of contractility. Thus, the approach to chromosome movement through colloid chemistry may converge with the approach through the concept of contractility, and a modern treatment of the colloid-chemical aspects of mitosis, such as has been outlined by Anderson (1956a, b), is very much in order.

g. Oscillating bodies (Lamb, 1907; Pfeiffer, 1956). A physical principle attributed to Bjerknes, to the effect that two oscillating bodies in a fluid medium may attract or repel each other, depending on whether they oscillate in or out of phase, has fascinated students of mitosis for many years; for here we might find a mechanism to account for the interactions of centers and kinetochores. This mechanism, unlike many others, does at least pose an experimental question: Do the bodies with which we are concerned oscillate? Recently, Pfeiffer has reported observations on the centers in dividing leucocytes, where he finds oscillations of 2–5 μ with a frequency of 0.7–1.4 per minute. This is, of course, interesting in itself. We would like to know whether it is general, whether kinetochores oscillate, and whether the postulated attractions would be adequate to the long distances involved. The simplified theory itself implies that the chromosomes lie free in the mitotic apparatus, whereas we have so much evidence (e.g., from centrifugation studies) that they are restrained.

h. Contractile mechanisms. Under this heading we include the hypotheses that the chromosomes are pushed or pulled toward the poles. They are discussed in some detail in the following section.

2. Criteria for a Theory of Chromosome Movement

Even though we do not yet know the mechanism of chromosome movement, we need not assign an equal value to all the speculations. On the contrary, whole classes of theories may be rejected as inadequate even as working hypotheses. The basis for rejection is the observed facts of chromosome movement, of which the following are relevant here.

1. The chromosomes move *individually* to the poles. Although movement in a group is normal, each chromosome *may* move at a different time and at a different speed.

2. If sister chromosomes separate, they move to different poles.

3. The kinetochore seems to be the only significant part of the chromosome in movement.

4. There must be at least two poles. There can be more, but if there is only one, the chromosomes generally do not move at all.

These few facts, which are discussed at greater length in other sections, insist on specific and individual chromosome-to-pole connections or interactions. Theories involving currents, waves of gelation, repulsions of chromosomes, the expansion of an interzonal mass, etc., do not fare well.

3. Anaphase Movement and Contractile Mechanisms

a. Analogies to other contractile mechanisms. Chromosomal fibers do exist, do connect the kinetochores to their destination, and do shorten as the chromosomes move to the poles. To this extent, the statement that chromosomes are "pulled" poleward is an adequate description of the facts. Similarly, the spindle does elongate in many cases and the separation of the chromosomes may, to that extent at least, be attributed to a "pushing" action. To state that chromosome movement is a matter of pushing or pulling does not explain anaphase movement; it only defines the class of mechanisms among which we must look for an explanation. We are directed to the mechanisms of contractility.

A most attractive unifying hypothesis is that the various types of biological movement, including mitotic movement, have a common molecular basis (e.g., Weber, 1958). That the mitotic apparatus and muscle might be analogous has been recognized for many years (e.g., by Heidenhain, 1895). It has seemed to find dramatic support in the experiments of Hoffmann-Berling (1954a, 1959), who has compared "anaphase models" (fibroblasts in anaphase, killed and extracted with cold glycerol) with the well-known muscle fiber "models" prepared in the same way. Under conditions of ATP concentration, ionic strength, etc., in which the muscle models relax (or are "plasticized"), the "anaphase models" elongate (Fig. 66), and as they do so the chromosome groups move apart. This would seem to show an analogy between the spindle elongation in anaphase and the relaxation phase of muscle contraction. The other anaphase movement—chromosomes to poles—was concealed by the over-all shrinkage of the "models" when these were exposed to conditions under which the chromosomal fibers might be expected to shorten.

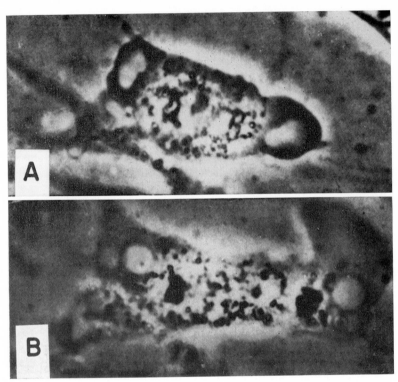

FIG. 66. Chromosome movement in glycerol-extracted fibroblasts ("anaphase models"). Separation of chromosomes as glycerol-extracted cell elongates under action of ATP. A. Without ATP. B. Twelve minutes after addition of ATP. Photographs by courtesy of Dr. H. Hoffmann-Berling (cf. Hoffmann-Berling, 1954a, 1959).

If we carry the unifying hypothesis a bold step beyond analogy, we may ask: Does the supposed contractile system in the mitotic apparatus use the same kinds of molecules as do the muscle cells of the same organism? Is the difference only one of organization? Here recent work gives us an unencouraging answer. If proteins of the mitotic apparatus were genetically similar to those of muscle, they should combine with antibodies to muscle proteins of the same species. Holtzer et al. (1959) have prepared antibodies to muscle proteins of chick embryos, labeled them with fluorescent groups, and studied their reaction with dividing chick fibroblasts. Fluorescence microscopy gave no evidence of binding of the antibodies by the mitotic spindles. Conversely, Went (1959b; Went and Mazia, 1959) has tested the lantern muscles of sea urchins, extracted in various ways, against the antiserum to the mitotic apparatus. There was no reaction. These findings do not exclude *analogies* between muscle proteins and those of the mitotic apparatus. In any case, the concept of a generalized contractile system may have been stretched too far. More recently, Hoffmann-Berling (1959) has described important differences between muscle "models" and other contractile "models." It might be expected that the alleged contractile elements of the mitotic apparatus might be more similar genetically to those of flagella and cilia of the same organism, and this expectation has been sustained in part by immunological tests. In a comparison involving proteins of the isolated mitotic apparatus of sea urchin eggs, isolated flagellar proteins from sea urchin sperm, and antisera to the two, Ruby (1961) has been able to obtain a cross reaction between the two groups of antigens.

Chemically, the proteins of the isolated mitotic apparatus show few similarities to actomyosin. The amino acid composition of the major proteins of the mitotic apparatus does bear some resemblance to that of actin (Roslansky, 1957), and the apparatus does carry ATP-splitting activity. The proteins of the mitotic apparatus also have some points of similarity to those obtained from isolated cilia of *Tetrahymena* (Child, 1959), but these resemblances are not yet interpretable in a functional way and may only suggest certain common features in the design of fibrous protein structures.

The analogies between mitotic movement and other forms of biological motility fare best in molecular terms; something can be said in favor of an hypothesis that mitotic movement involves the interaction of an actin-like molecule with ATP and the splitting of ATP (p. 249). Further analogies are difficult to develop because the mitotic apparatus, unlike a muscle fibril or a cilium, is an unstable structure whose activity is associated with the assembly and disassembly of the structure. A chromosomal fiber may contract, but there is no evidence that it becomes thicker as it does so; rather, it gives the appearance of melting in one dimension. The contraction of the chromosomal fiber may take place before, after, or simultaneously with the elongation of the pole-to-pole connections, and our mitotic apparatus must include and actively expand units in close proximity.

  b. Traction, pulsion, and the activity of the kinetochores. The hypotheses attributing the anaphase movement to traction or pulsion by fibers operating on kinetochores are based on visual evidence, much of which has already been mentioned.

The general situation is summarized by the statement that the chromosomes move toward the poles, and not merely away from each other, by the translation of individual kinetochores along paths defined by visible chromosome-to-pole fibers. Nowhere are these relationships more vivid than in multipolar mitotic figures (Figs. 30, 31). It is against this background that we may speculate on the question, are they pushed or are they pulled by fibers? If they are pulled, the chromosome-to-pole fibers could account for both the motive force and the path of movement. If they are pushed by fibers expanding between sister kinetochores, their paths would seem still to be determined by the lines of the chromosome-to-pole fibers, and the latter would have to be regarded as a guiding element in the over-all propulsion system. This follows from the observed paths in divergent mitotic figures, multipolar figures, etc.

The difference between a traction model and a pulsion model would then lie at the level of the application of the force itself, and it is extremely difficult to distinguish between the two on the basis of visual data. The one point that must be stressed is that if the chromosomes are pushed to the poles, they are pushed individually, and not in groups. It is true that the normal picture may be one of remarkable uniformity of movement of the chromosomes of a set. But this uniformity is not necessary. Sometimes, indeed, after failure to form an accurate metaphase plate, individual chromosomes may move past in each other in opposite directions (e.g., Oestergren and Bajer, 1960).

For the sake of clarity, we must recall that the over-all movement of the chromosomes does involve the elongation of the spindle, and to this extent a "pushing" movement is involved. In some cases, it is the major factor in the separation of the chromosomes, in others a minor one (Fig. 63). When the chromosomes separate by virtue of this increase in pole-to-pole distance without moving closer to the poles, we may ask whether they are moved by the elongation of an "interzonal" region itself or by the action extending from one pole to the other, an elongation of the central spindle. If the latter is the case, we can imagine that the chromosomes are being dragged by fibers anchored at the poles, which are not themselves shortening. If the spindle elongates by the growth of an equatorial "pushing body," we must imagine that the so-called half-spindles carrying the chromosomes are rigid.

A good many of the phenomena of anaphase movement could be explained equally well by a traction mechanism or by a pulsion mechanism, provided that the latter provided for the guidance of the kineto-chores by the chromosomal fibers. The case for the pushing of the chro-mosomes was well summarized by Carlson (1952, 1956), who also pointed out some difficulties. Cornman (1944) has assembled the cytological evi-dence for a traction mechanism. The shapes of the chromosomes, the behavior of chromosomes in which two kinetochores are linked by a bridge, and other visual evidence is equally compatible with both views. In favor of a traction mechanism is the fact that we do see the chromo-some-to-pole fibers by all methods, but we have no good cytological evi-dence for bodies pushing individual kinetochores apart. Perhaps the only physical evidence for a traction mechanism is the birefringence of the chromosomal fibers, which is compatible with their being under stress, and the fact that these fibers *do* shorten as the chromosomes advance. In fact all we really mean by traction is that the advance of the chro-mosomes to the poles is the result of events observed as the shortening of the chromosomal fibers. The rest may merely be misleading analogies with the crude devices of classic mechanics, ropes, hooks, elastic bands, etc.

Most of the criticisms of the traction principle express dissatisfaction with some inference made from it, rather than with the principle itself. For example, it has been stated that the theory fails because it is doubtful if the spindle has enough rigidity to pull the chromosome without de-formation of the poles, and that the speed of anaphase movement does not seem to be in good agreement with what would be expected if it were the result of the shortening of an elastic fiber. Since we do not know what degree of rigidity is required, nor whether a simple elastic fiber is the correct model, we cannot discard the principle that the chromosomes are pulled to the poles on such grounds. There are in fact phenomena which suggest a considerable longitudinal rigidity in the mitotic ap-paratus at metaphase. For example, when a "bridge" is produced by a dicentric chromosome in a newt fibroblast (Zirkle and Bloom, 1953), the elongation of the spindle or the resistance of the bridge to the pull of the centers (or both) causes the anaphase chromosome groups to bend toward the centers in a "hinge" configuration. Attempts have been made to calculate whether a system of contractile fibers could mechanically ac-count for the observed velocity of the chromosomes. The most detailed analysis we have, that of Jacquez and Biesele (1954), gives a positive answer, but a good many assumptions are involved.

As an example of situations in which a traction mechanism seems impossible if we regard the chromosomal fibers as stable ropes, we may cite the case of chromosomes with diffuse kinetochores in which chro-

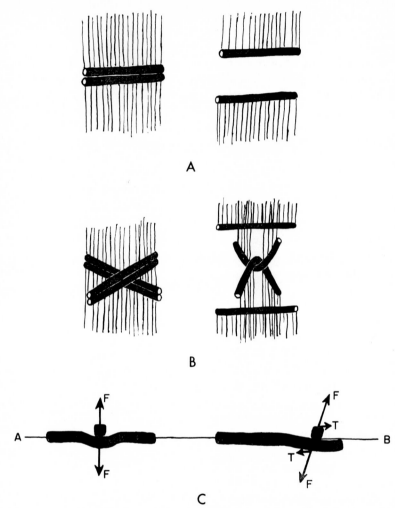

Fig. 67. The problem of separating chromosome with diffuse kinetochores by a traction mechanism, as formulated by Oestergren (1949). A. Chromosomes lie parallel at metaphase. There is no difficulty in separating them. B. Chromosomes crossed at metaphase. They might be expected to interlock as they are pulled apart. The crossed configuration is observed, but locking as diagrammed does not occur. Either the traction model is incorrect or else the chromosomes do separate without permanent rupture of the connections to the poles. C. A suggested means of separation. If the chromosomes are not crossed *exactly* at their midpoints, the forces separating them will have a transverse component and the chromosomes will tend to slide one over the other. The diagram shows this situation, the chromosomes being seen in side view. To retain the traction hypothesis, it is necessary to assume that the broken "connections" to the poles will re-form.

mosomes sometimes lie across each other at metaphase (Fig. 67). The difficulty is self-evident from the figure and was used as a basis for an interesting article on "The Uselessness of the Spindle Fibers for Moving the Attached Chromosomes" (Piza, 1943). In analyzing this case, Oestergren (1949) points out that unless the chromosomes were crossed exactly at their midpoints, they would tend to slide transversely across each other. Really stable fibers would, of course, tend to prevent such a movement, but if the fibers could break and be re-established the chromosomes would ultimately separate without losing their attachments to the poles. There is no great difficulty in imagining how this could happen. Oestergren formulates it in terms of the molecular interactions in tactoid bodies. We may describe it also in terms of the continued action of the "exclusion principle" described earlier; if a chromosome at the end of metaphase is still capable of making connections to a pole, it will tend to join only the pole to which it is already connected by some fibers. Other ways of picturing the situation are possible. This way is introduced here only to illustrate for the noncytologist the traditional "difficulties" and "exceptions" in the formulation of mitotic mechanisms. The cytologist will think of other examples.

In the most naive version of a traction mechanism, a stable fiber would shorten at constant mass, growing thicker, and the tension on the fiber would be uniform along its length. None of these expectations is realized by a real chromosomal fiber. It grows shorter without growing thicker, so far as has been judged by any method of observation from classic fixation and staining, through observation of isolated mitotic figures, to polarization microscopy and electron microscopy. The tension along the length can best be judged by birefringence measurements. In the work of Swann (1951b) the birefringence of the whole spindle (individual fibers not being observed) decreased in the region of the kinetochore, and the decrease proceeded poleward in a wave ahead of the moving kinetochore (Fig. 70). Inoué (1953), finds that the region of the kinetochore in *Lilium* endosperm tends to be more highly birefringent than the rest of the chromosomal fiber and that the specific birefringence of the fiber itself does not decrease as it shortens (Fig. 69).

The idea that the kinetochore is an active participant, and not merely an anchorage for a chromosomal fiber, is not a novel one. One version of it, as developed by Belar (1929a) (and summarized succinctly by Schrader, 1953, p. 76), involves a gliding movement of the kinetochore along the spindle fibers (Fig. 68). In contemporary terms, such a gliding movement could be assimilated with the "sliding" models of muscle contraction (Huxley, 1960). It may be frivolous, but it is not uninteresting, to imagine that the spindle fibers are analogous to I bands of striated muscles and the kinetochores analogous to A bands which crawl along the fibers by breaking bridges and re-forming them at adjacent poleward sites. Another, and recent, hypothesis, developed by Mota (1957), envisages a jet propulsion of the kinetochore poleward by modification of material of the chromosomal fiber ahead of it and the retrojection of the modified material into the interzonal region. It is difficult to judge whether any appreciable force can be developed in this way, but we

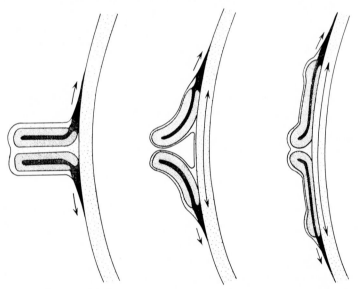

Fig. 68.   Belar's speculation on chromosome movement. The lightly stippled fibers are spindle fibers, viewed as guiding the chromosomes. Black regions represent the traction fibers. This model does not provide for metakinesis. From Belar (1929a).

shall see that the interzonal region does change in anaphase (Section X, E, 4).

Still another view (Mazia, 1956b, p. 109) imagines that the kinetochore brings about a local contraction of the adjacent region of the chromosomal fiber. The contraction, it is supposed, involves the loss of some molecules from the contracted region to the background and consolidation of the rest to maintain continuity. The apparent result is that the fiber is largely "consumed" as the wave of local contraction proceeds

A mechanism of this general type has been presented by Inoué (1959). His analysis of the problem is based on the observed relationship be- toward the pole.

tween the birefringence of the spindle and the temperature (Fig. 52), from which he concludes that its oriented structure represents a temperature-sensitive equilibrium. Further thermodynamic treatment of the data suggests that the ability of the orientation in the spindle reflects its dependence on bonds whose energies are comparable to those of hydrogen bonds. On the basis of the consideration that the chromosomal fibers represent oriented regions, the orientation being imposed by kinetochore and centers, Inoué concludes that "anaphase movement of chromosomes may be explained by local reduction in the quantity of oriented material and the consequent shortening of the chromosomal fibers." The chemical problem in such a mechanism, as was mentioned by Mazia (1956b), is to account for the maintenance of continuity of the chromosomal fiber as a portion of its molecules pass from the oriented region to the unoriented background. It is not difficult to imagine "a statistical disaggregation in which some of the molecules are lost and those that remain are consolidated in a new and smaller association" (Mazia, 1956b), but this does not necessarily move a bulky chromosome through a resistant medium or tear a chromosome bridge.

The plausibility of any hypothesis involving the activity of the kinetochore in mitotic movement would depend on evidence that it *is* active, and is not merely the attachment-point for a chromosomal fiber. Direct evidence is not available, but ingenious deductions from genetic evidence in *Drosophila* lead to the conclusion that the aptitude of a kinetochore to reach a pole does depend on properties of the kinetochore itself (Novitski, 1955). The experiments themselves deal with the genetic consequences of the presence of two kinetochores on certain chromosomes as a result of rearrangements. Such dicentric chromosomes tend to form a bridge at anaphase (Fig. 46) and there is a tug-of-war between the two kinetochores as they tend to move to the opposite poles. It was observed in some cases that the consequences of the division were lethal, and this was interpreted as a result of the breaking of the bridge. In other cases, however, it was found that half the products of the division were lethal and half were not. The latter result is completely interpretable in terms of the hypothesis that the dicentric chromosome contains a "weak" kinetochore and a "strong" kinetochore, and that the "strong" kinetochore wins the tug-of-war and carries the entire chromosome into one daughter cell, which is then viable while its sister is not. Further, it has been shown by Lindsley and Novitski (1958) that the strength of a kinetochore in this situation may depend on the adjacent chromatin.

In a speculation proposed by Oestergren and Bajer (1960), the traction of chromosomes is associated with the shortening of chromosomal fibers; this shortening involves a loss of material, but the driving mechanism is an imaginary molecular pump operating along the sides of the fibers. In a figure of speech, the pump is compared with a wind and the chromosomal fibers are compared with sails. While no specific physical model is proposed, this speculation does draw attention to the variable meaning of "contraction" when viewed in molecular dimensions and does account for a number of puzzling observations, especially observations on the transport of acentric fragments and other particles by the spindle during anaphase.

These formulations have no substantial basis and are mentioned only to illustrate categories of hypotheses.

4. Conclusions

The ingenious speculations on the mechanism of chromosome movement appeal to principles ranging from electric attraction to jet propulsion. In general, we may imagine that the chromosome-to-pole movement (which is not always the predominant movement in the separation of the sister chromosomes) is a consequence of the shortening of chromosomal fibers. Difficulties arise when we try to interpret this grossly as a contractile mechanism. It is obvious that the problems lie in the molecular realm, where we are doubly handicapped by inadequate knowledge of the molecular relations in the mitotic apparatus and of the molecular basis for *any* form of biological movement, even in the popular muscle fiber.

E. The Mitotic Apparatus in Anaphase

1. Birefringence of the Spindle

At present, the most powerful tool we have for following the molecular physics of mitosis is the polarization microscope. As we have seen, the mitotic apparatus is birefringent, the largest component being a positive form birefringence relative to the fiber axes. The most general change observed in anaphase is an over-all *decrease* in birefringence. This has been found in eggs (Schmidt, 1939; Swann, 1951b; Inoué and Dan, 1951) and in chick cells in culture (Hughes and Swann, 1948). In addition to this loss of anisotropy in the "half-spindles," the several authors note that the *interzonal region* between the separating chromosomes is isotropic (Fig. 69). In addition, Swann (1951b) finds that the decline of birefringence in the chromosome-to-pole region is not uniform, but passes toward the poles as a wave moving ahead of the moving chromosomes (Fig. 70). On this basis he attributes the changes in bire-

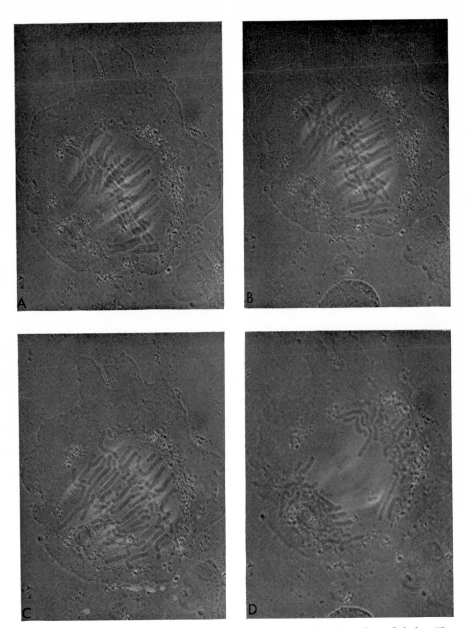

Fig. 69. Anaphase in *Haemanthus* endosperm, observed with polarized light. The cell is somewhat flattened, but the chromosome movement still tends to be convergent. Birefringence is strongest in the chromosomal fibers but is also seen in the interchromosomal regions. Photographs by courtesy of Drs. S. Inoué and A. Bajer.

fringence to the effects of a "structure agent" originating in the chromosomes which may, as we have seen, be a part of the mechanism of chromosome movement.

With a polarization-optical system of higher sensitivity and resolution, it has been possible to observe the spindle fibers as such during anaphase in *Chaetopterus* eggs and in plant cells (Inoué, 1953; Inoué and Bajer, 1961). It is seen that the chromosomal fibers, which are the regions

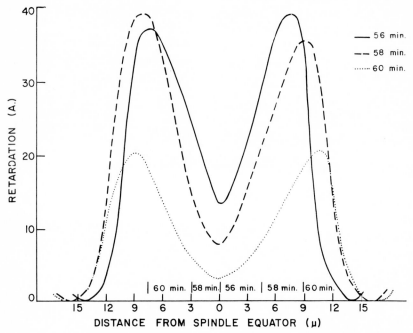

FIG. 70.   Birefringence changes along the spindle at successive stages of anaphase in sea urchin eggs. Marks along base line show the position of the chromosomes. The net impression is that a wave of disorientation passes from equator to poles in advance of the chromosomes. From Swann (1951b).

of higher birefringence, retain most of their birefringence as they shorten, and the portion adjacent to the kinetochore remains highly anisotropic. Although the interzonal region as a whole is isotropic, birefringent fibers are definitely seen to run through it from pole to pole, and other fibers, not connected with chromosomes, tend to fade in the equatorial region (Fig. 69).

As we acquire more data by the polarization-optical methods, they are bound to influence the theory of mitotic movement greatly. But the limitation is not only in the amount and precision of optical data, but also in the lack of auxiliary information without which they remain merely descriptive. For example, a decrease in birefringence may indicate causal events in a "contraction" process (shortening of molecules by contraction of chains of molecules) or may passively reflect mechanical stresses that are closer to the primary events. As an example of the latter, we may cite the observation of Inoué and Dan (1951) that the birefringence of astray rays, in medusan and sea urchin eggs, may actually be *reversed in sign* as a result of pressure from the cell surface. This decrease and reversal of birefringence does not reflect a tendency of the fibers to shorten, but rather it measures a resistance to their lengthening.

2. Volume and Mass

The mitotic spindle at anaphase appears to be a growing body. This is evident from simple observation, from cytochemical observation and from measurements showing that elongation of the spindle may take place without decrease in diameter (Fig. 63). The growth of the asters in cells where they occur is even more striking (Swann, 1951b).

An attractive explanation for the change in size would be that it reflects a change in hydration. It does not seem likely that this is the whole story; the data at this time are not as complete as they might be, considering the methods available. For example, we may make inferences about the mass of the spindle and asters of the sea urchin egg in anaphase from polarization-microscopic data and by calculations involving mass and retardation (Swann, 1951a, b). These tell us that there is an increase in mass along with the growth in volume. The mass of the mitotic apparatus can be measured by interference microscopy (e.g., Ross, 1954, Barer and Joseph, 1957) and by X-ray absorption methods (e.g., Stich and McIntyre, 1958); detailed studies on changes associated with anaphase will be welcome.

There is no reason to suppose that the growth involves active synthesis, although nothing excludes this possibility. If the mitotic apparatus is assembled in the first place from a reserve of preformed molecular constituents its growth at anaphase need only involve the drawing of available substance from the background into the ordered region whose growth is being measured.

3. Asters

In all our discussion thus far, little attention has been paid to the asters, which are a conspicuous part of the mitotic apparatus in many animal cells and perhaps may have a counterpart in plant cells.

No differences between spindle and aster material have been observed in studies on isolated material. Both dissolve under the same conditions and both share common antigens. However, the astral region of the cell may differ from the spindle. The latter is a unified gel that excludes large particles. The astral rays seem to run into the cytoplasm individually, with cytoplasmic particles observable between them in the living cell (Fig. 50). It is not surprising, therefore, that the astral region may have cyto-chemical properties different from those of the spindle. Immers (1957), for instance, finds that the astral regions of the sea urchin egg contain more material that stains with the periodic acid-Schiff reaction than the spindle region.

The astral regions of eggs have been found to stain *in vivo* with a number of dyes: neutral red, toluidine blue, methylene blue (Iida, 1942; Pasteels, 1955; Dalcq, 1957; Mulnard, 1958; reviewed by Rebhun, 1959). This staining is attributed to an interesting class of particles that seem to follow the centriole and to concentrate in the vicinity of the astral rays.

In the course of anaphase the asters grow to a remarkable extent (Swann, 1951a), and the rays reach the cell surface (K. Dan, 1943; Inoué and Dan, 1951). Swann (1951b) describes how the wave of decreasing birefringence originating near the chromosomes at anaphase sweeps to the centers and then out along the astral radii to the surface. Thus far, we have no good basis for assigning to the asters a role in mitosis itself, but, as we shall see, they play a prominent part in speculations about cytokinesis.

4. The Interzonal Region and Spindle Elongation

It is a remarkable fact that the region between the separating chromosomes at anaphase has very different properties from the polar regions. This "interzonal" region obviously does increase in length as the chromosomes move apart, and the idea that it acts as a "pushing body" has been attractive to many cytologists. At first sight, its physical properties would not favor such a view. Micromanipulation studies suggest that it is a region of low rigidity, easily deformed by a needle, compared to the rest of the spindle. As anaphase proceeds, cytoplasmic particles may intrude into it (Carlson, 1952; Ris, 1949). All observers describe it as a region of low birefringence, although this is an ambiguous datum, reflecting either lack of organization or the counterstress to a pushing action. In studies on the isolated mitotic apparatus it appears to be a region of weak bonding. All too often, isolated anaphase spindles break in the interzonal region to yield half-spindles. The electron microscopic studies (Fig. 61, D) show that the chromosomes at anaphase leave in their wake an interzonal region whose structure is indeed entirely different from the structure of the spindle between chromosomes and poles. Aside from the continuous filaments, one sees an amorphous mass of material lacking all resemblance to the gel at the poles. All told, it would appear that the interzonal region is a different kind of gel, neither strong nor stable, from the rest of the mitotic apparatus.

Continuous pole-to-pole fibers do run through it. These, rather than the interzonal region as a whole, may be the important agents in spindle elongation. This is obviously the case in *Barbulanympha* (Fig. 31), in which the chromosomes lie entirely outside the central spindle. The conjecture that a small number of submicroscopic fibers is responsible for what seems like the violent pushing action of the spindle is disconcerting at first, but we should view these visible fibers not as floating in space, but as associated with a mass of less well oriented substance that may be participating in the work of elongation.

At some time in anaphase, some remarkable chemical changes appear in the interzonal region. These will be discussed in Section XI, A.

5. Temperature and Pressure Effects; Blockage at Anaphase

The rates of both the elongation of the spindle and the chromosome-to-pole movement are temperature sensitive; this is illustrated by the data of Ris (1949) reproduced in Fig. 64, B.

We would, of course, expect that anaphase movement could be stopped by agents that would affect the structural organization of the mitotic apparatus. The results of Pease (1941, 1946), who studied the effects of high hydrostatic pressure on *Urechis* eggs and *Tradescantia* pollen mother cells in anaphase, suggest that the fibrous associations of the mitotic apparatus are first loosened and then disrupted, and the chromosomes stop moving and behave as though they are no longer under control of the poles. These results are in accord with experiences with other "gel" systems involved in cellular movements (Marsland, 1956). When the pressure is released, the chromosomes reestablish connections with the poles. In the case of *Urechis*, these connections may be complex as a consequence of the appearance of supernumerary poles (cytasters), but it is clear that the *chromosomes and centers have not lost their capacity to establish fiber connections by the time of anaphase.* In *Tradescantia* Pease observes the re-establishment of the connections to the original poles to be the typical case, along with some provocative exceptions such as the connection of sister kinetochores to one pole only and occasional kinetochore-to-kinetochore connections.

On any grounds, we would anticipate that anaphase movement would be slowed down at lower temperatures, but if the mitotic apparatus had the properties of an "endothermic gel" (Marsland, 1951) and if its oriented structure depended on a temperature-sensitive equilibrium such as is illustrated in Fig. 52, we could predict that lowering the temperature would affect its structure, and not merely the rate of movement. Such an effect has been demonstrated by Rustad (1956) in a study on the sea urchin egg; he finds that a brief exposure to a low temperature (e.g., 5°C.) during the period of chromosome movement causes a considerable delay in the completion of division when the cells are returned to a standard temperature.

We have as yet no generally applicable chemical agent for blocking anaphase movement, comparable to colchicine as a tool for blocking the completion of the mitotic apparatus. On the whole, we may view the anaphase proceedings as events that are extraordinarily difficult to stop once they have started. There are many descriptions in the voluminous literature on antimitotic agents (summarized by Biesele, 1958) on blockage at anaphase ("stathmoanaphase"), but the effective agents generally are active also at other mitotic stages. Such observations are extremely important in linking anaphase to the physiology of the cell as a whole and in disabusing us of the impression that we are dealing with the snapping of prestretched rubber bands, but it would be extremely useful to have at our disposal an experimental agent that did specifically arrest cells in anaphase.

XI. Telophase Problems

If we view the mitotic cycle as a whole, the dismantling of the mitotic apparatus is quite as striking a feature as its construction, and the reestablishment of the interphase structure of the nucleus is almost certainly a prerequisite to further growth. The available information calls our attention to a few specific problems, but it does not go much further.

A. The Mitotic Apparatus at the End of Anaphase: Completion of "RNA Cycle"

The completion of the movements of the chromosomes is accompanied by some very striking changes in the interzonal region. One is an apparent accumulation of RNA, which has been related to the chromosomal RNA cycle. Jacobson and Webb (1952) and Boss (1955) have described what appears to be a streaming of RNA (or at least of material staining as RNA) from the polar regions toward the equator, concomitant with a loss of RNA staining by the chromosomes.

Ideally, it should be possible to follow these changes in living dividing cells by ultraviolet microscopy. In fact, an apparent accumulation of ultraviolet-absorbing material in the interzonal region was observed by Davies (1952), working with chick fibroblasts. The technique used involved fairly heavy irradiation, so that continuous ultraviolet observation through mitosis was not possible. The technical problem has been solved by Montgomery and Bonner (1959), by the conjunction of the flying-spot principle with television viewing, but their photographs show no conspicuous accumulation of material absorbing at 2600 A. in the interzonal region at anaphase or telophase in newt endothelial cells in culture. They state that: "the centrioles and the spindles have not been observed by us to be ultraviolet absorbing structures at any time during mitosis." We are left to wonder whether the observations of RNA in the interzonal region at late anaphase or telophase represent artifacts of injury or fixation, or whether the RNA of the mitotic apparatus in some cells may be overshadowed by other absorbing substances when they are observed by UV in the living condition. The body of evidence we are discussing is not easy to dismiss on grounds of artifact.

In plant material, the basophilic interzonal region may appear to be concentrated in the phragmoplast (Shimamura and Ôta, 1956). Ris and Kleinfeld (1952) have analyzed by cytochemical methods the so-called "chromatin elimination" that is a feature of mitosis in certain insects. At anaphase basophilic bodies corresponding in number to the chromosomes are shed by the chromosomes and move toward the equator, where they form an "elimination plate." In *Solenobia*, a lepidopteran, they find that the bodies eliminated by the chromosomes give positive tests for RNA and protein but react negatively in tests for DNA and polysaccharides.

Little can be said about the character of the protein of the interzonal region. Sandritter and Krygier (1959) find that its concentration of protein-bound SH, as measured by cytophotometry, is about 40% higher than that of the cytoplasm of the HeLa cell. On the other hand, it would not appear from the photographs of Fig. 57 that the concentration of protein SH in this region is higher than that of the rest of the mitotic apparatus in sea urchin eggs.

Thus, although the morphological expression varies from one kind of cell to the other, there is evidence that the terminal phases of mitosis do involve a movement of material toward the equator, that the material is ribonucleoprotein in character, and that it may derive at least partially from the chromosomes.

Apparently the material moving toward the equator can remain firmly associated with the mitotic apparatus, for it has now been detected in late anaphase figures isolated from the sea urchin egg by the alcohol-digitonin method. Rustad (1959) has studied isolated figures with the

interference microscope and observed an increase in the mass of the
interzonal region just at the end of anaphase (Fig. 71). This is accompanied by an increase in basophilia in the same region. A similar increase
in mass in the interzonal region during anaphase of meiotic divisions in

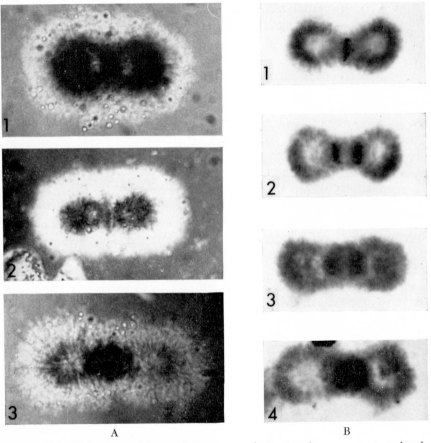

A   B

FIG. 71. Shift of material toward the equator during anaphase, as seen in isolated
mitotic apparatus of a sea urchin egg (*Strongylocentrotus purpuratus*). From Rustad
(1959).

A. Observations with the interference microscope. *Relative* darkness of a region
indicates a higher density of material. Regions of each photograph may be compared
with each other, but the several photographs are not comparable. 1. Early anaphase.
2. Mid-anaphase. 3. End of anaphase. It is seen that the density of the interzonal
region increases at the end of anaphase.

B. Mitotic apparatus stained for RNA. 1. Metaphase. 2. Mid anaphase. 3. Later
anaphase. 4. End of anaphase. There is a concentration of RNA-containing material,
which takes place at the end of anaphase.

wheat has been observed by interference microscopy of fixed preparations (Longwell and Mota, 1960). Before these apparent changes in mass can be interpreted, we shall have to have observations and quantitative data on living material, as well as information about chemical changes which might influence the refractive increments in various regions of the division apparatus.

In discussing the RNA of the mitotic system at anaphase, we are confronted with two problems. One is the apparent loss of RNA (or decrease in its stainability) of the chromosomes, which reverses the changes seen in prophase (Section VI, B, 2) and completes a cycle. The second is the increase of RNA (or ribonucleoprotein) in the interzonal region at about the same time. It has seemed logical to relate the two and to postulate a chromosomal origin of the interzonal RNA. The simplest picture of the "RNA cycle" is that chromosomes pick up ribonucleoprotein at prophase and discard it in an equatorial direction at anaphase. A rather provocative interpretation is that spindle material is modified by the kinetochores and retrojected toward the equator, providing a jet mechanism for propelling the chromosomes (Mota, 1957). Against this is the observation (e.g., Rustad, 1959) that the interzonal accumulation of ribonucleoprotein may not begin until the chromosomes have completed their anaphase movements.

Finally, it is possible that the RNA collecting in the interzonal region does not derive principally from the chromosomes. In the case of the sea urchin material (Fig. 71) one receives the impression that the amount of RNA (and other contributions to the mass) is very large compared to what could have come from the tiny chromosomes of these cells. This would be open to quantitative study. More significant is the electron microscopic description by Porter and Machado (1960) of the behavior of the endoplasmic reticulum during mitosis in *Allium* root tips. They describe a striking accumulation of elements of the endoplasmic reticulum (including fragments of the nuclear membrane) at the poles during the period between the end of prophase and the beginning of anaphase; the spindle contains very little of this material at this time. During anaphase the spindle is progressively invaded by double-membranous material of the reticulum, apparently coming in from the poles (Fig. 72). This behavior obviously could account for the cytochemical observations of the accumulation of RNA in the interzonal region. The increase in density as well as RNA concentration in the interzonal region suggests still another interpretation: that some of the substance of the spindle itself dissociates from the poles and contracts toward the equator. None of these proposals excludes the others.

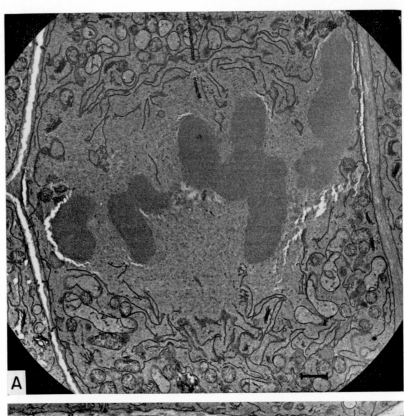

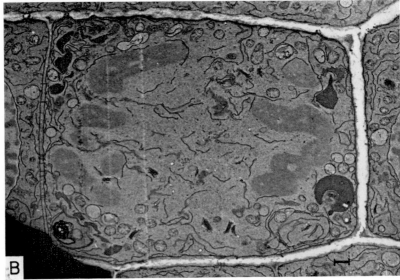

B. The Reconstitution of the Interphase Nucleus

1. Chromosomes

The restoration of the interphase nucleus calls for the reversion of the chromosomes to the interphase condition and the inclusion of non-chromosomal constituents. The latter has been studied by interference microscopy (cf. Fig. 29). According to Richards (1960), the non-chromosomal protein added to mouse nuclei late telophase is equal to the amount in a pre-prophase nucleus, while in a plant endosperm (*Leucojum*) it is considerably less. It would please our sense of symmetry if the telophase events could be viewed as a film of prophase that was run backward, but this is not always the case. Very often, the chromosomes do not elongate but rather "swell" and form what is termed "chromosomal vesicles" (Fig. 73). These vesicles then seem to coalesce. It has been argued (e.g., by Lewis, 1947) that the interphase nucleus consists of such vesicles, adhering to each other but with each chromosome retaining its membrane or boundary.

Where chromosome vesicles are not formed, the telophase changes do have the aspect of a breakdown of the coiling of the chromosomes. The transformation from a compactly coiled thread to a randomly extended one is attributed by Cleveland (1949) to the collapse of the matrix. He describes this in detail for the flagellate *Holomastigotoides*, in which the resultant uncoiled chromosomes can be seen clearly.

In living newt fibroblasts (Boss, 1959), the early telophase changes are described as a clumping of the chromosome group followed by an elongation of the chromosomes (Fig. 74). As they elongate, their doubleness can be discerned and it can be seen that the chromonemata of a chromosome are wound around each other.

The most remarkable fact about the telophase behavior of the chromosomes is that it depends on some reaction of the individual chromosome to a condition prevailing in the cell as a whole. The kineto-

---

FIG. 72. The movements of the endoplasmic reticulum during anaphase in the onion root tip. This material was prepared for electron microscopic observation with $KMnO_4$, which brings out the membranous elements but does not show details of the spindle structure. A. Metaphase, longitudinal section. The membranes of the endoplasmic reticulum are concentrated near the pole and are scarce inside the spindle. B. Anaphase, longitudinal section. Chromosomes near the poles. Membranes have penetrated into the spindle. Photographs by courtesy of Dr. Keith Porter (Porter and Machado, 1960).

chores, centers, or the rest of the mitotic apparatus do not seem to be involved directly. This is proved by the fact that a piece of a chromosome, broken off by irradiation, lacking a kinetochore and lying outside the mitotic apparatus will swell and form a "nuclear membrane" around itself. This "micronucleus" forms at exactly the same time when the or-

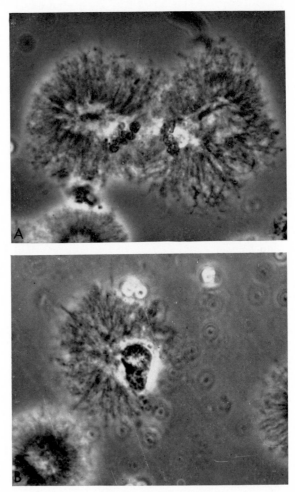

Fig. 73. One type of telophase behavior: the apparent swelling of the chromosomes to form "chromosomal vesicles," followed by the fusion of the vesicles into a compact nucleus. Isolated mitotic apparatus of sea urchin egg. A. Earlier telophase; spindle remains, though in a disoriented condition. Asters have grown very large. Chromosomal vesicles. B. End of telophase. Chromosomes have merged into a nucleus. Spindle has broken down, but aster persists. Compare Fig. 75.

dinary nucleus is being formed by the chromosomes that have completed anaphase movement. The formation of such "micronuclei" or "karyomeres" has been recognized for a long time, and examples are cited by Tischler (1922, p. 232) and by Wilson (1925, p. 133). It can be the normal state of affairs in cells in which the chromosomes diverge at anaphase (e.g., K. W. Cooper's, 1939) observations on *Pediculopsis;* divergent mitosis in maize: Clark, 1940 [Fig. 8, B3]; Crosby, 1957). It can be induced experimentally by chemical means, e.g., action of ether (Wilson, 1901) and of podophyllin (Cornman and Cornman, 1951) on sea urchin eggs, and

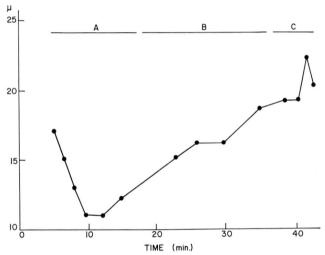

FIG. 74.   Telophase behavior of chromosomes in newt fibroblasts (Boss, 1959). Measurements on the length of one chromosome in the living cell in early telophase. In region *C,* the chromosome was seen as a pair of relationally coiled chromonemata.

is one of the results of the interruption of mitosis by high hydrostatic pressure (Pease, 1946).

The production of karyomeres offers a powerful tool for the study of the activity of individual chromosomes. The subdivision of the nucleus into "micronuclei" is not immediately fatal to the cell itself, although it may lead to abnormalities in subsequent divisions. It should be possible, for instance, to relate the times of DNA synthesis in the several chromosomes of a cell once they are segregated into separate nuclei. As an example of the interesting possibilities, we may cite the finding by Crosby (1957) that only those "micronuclei" that carry the normal nucleolus-organizing regions can form visible nucleoli. This observation suggests that direct contributions of other chromosomes are not necessary. What is more important, the survival of such cells tells us that some of the functions of chromosomes are independent of compact nucleoli. At least the nucleoli and the chromosomes do not have to be within the same nucleus.

2. The Nucleolus at Telophase

The nucleolar cycle in mitosis is a reproductive event of an odd kind. We begin with nucleoli in definite numbers, located at definite "nucleolar organizer" sites [or "nucleolar zones" in less committal terminology (Rattenbury and Serra, 1952)]. Most, if not all, of the substance disappears by metaphase. By telophase each daughter nucleus has the same complement of nucleoli, and at the same sites, as did the parent cell. We shall have occasion later (Section XIV, A) to consider the significance of this strange reproductive process; the present problem is to account for the reappearance of nucleoli.

The simplest conception of the organizers (perhaps implied by the name itself) is that they are the sites of syntheses of the nucleolar substances, but this does not seem to be so.

A good many cytological observations (reviewed by Geitler, 1938; Gates, 1942; Rattenbury and Serra, 1952; and others) suggest that the nucleolar material appears in irregular and dispersed forms in the course of anaphase or telophase and is gathered together into compact nucleoli. More recent work utilizing specific staining for RNA (e.g., the work of Kleinfeld and van Hamm, 1959, on rat liver) and the silver-staining method for an unknown nucleolar substance (Das and Alfert, 1959; cf. Fig. 33) confirms the impression that the nucleolar materials gather among and along the chromosomes at anaphase and are assembled into the definitive nucleoli as telophase proceeds. Still further confirmation comes from electron microscopic studies by Lafontaine (1958) on *Vicia* and onion root tips. In these studies the "prenucleolar" substance is first identified as small dense bodies containing a class of particles, 140 A. in diameter, which are characteristic of nucleoli.

It is not known to what extent the new nucleoli are formed from material lost to the cytoplasm at prophase and to what extent it is newly synthesized. Figure 33 is compatible with the idea that the silver-staining component was recovered from the cytoplasm by the nuclei, but hardly proves it. Evidence that at least some of the nucleolar RNA is newly synthesized at telophase is given by Woods and Taylor (1959), who fixed root tips of *Vicia faba* after 1 hour of exposure to tritiated cytidine and observed that the nucleolar material of cells in telophase was radioactive.

It will now be necessary to distinguish between nucleolar material and the compact and morphologically consistent nucleoli in dealing with functional problems. We have seen that the concentration of the material in the nucleolar region is a terminal step following its formation and assembly, and we are not encouraged to think of the organizer region as the site of its formation. Das and Alfert (1959) have now shown that micronuclei (karyomeres) produced after chromosomes breakage by X-rays contain the characteristic silver-staining nucleolar substance. Therefore, a chromosome or nucleus lacking a compact nucleolus is not necessarily deprived of the functions associated with nucleolar substance. Further investigation of such functions as the synthesis of DNA, RNA, and proteins by such karyomeres without compact nucleoli will be of the greatest interest.

3. Restitution of the Nuclear Membrane

In the present state of knowledge, an understanding of the morphological events in the reconstruction of the nuclear membrane at telophase will go a long way toward defining the process. Such descriptions are now available (Porter, 1961). For example, Barer et al. (1959) have presented electron microscopic data that formulate the genesis of the nuclear membrane as an interaction between the chromosomes and elements of the endoplasmic reticulum. This seems entirely reasonable in view of wealth of information on relationships between the nuclear membrane and the reticulum during interphase (e.g., Bernhard, 1959). In the grasshopper spermatocytes studied by Barer et al. (1959) vesicles about 0.5 μ in length, "indistinguishable from endoplasmic reticulum," collect around the chromosomes at a stage when they are swelling, orient along the surface of the chromosomes, and fuse to form membranes. In the authors' words: "Each chromosome is at least partially surrounded by the vesicular elements at first but the latter seem to be squeezed out at places where the expanding membranes come into contact. The result is that a continuous membrane is formed around the whole group of chromosomes, following which it seems to be elevated from the chromosomal surfaces, possibly by the accumulation of 'nuclear sap.'" On the basis of this picture, it is easy to understand how chromosomes separated from the main group can form micronuclei with membranes apparently just like those of a normal nucleus. A rather similar picture of the relationship between the endoplasmic reticulum and the chromosomes in the formation of the nuclear membrane is seen in onion root tip cells by Porter and Machado (1960) and by Ito (1960) in spermatocytes of Drosophila virilis. In sea urchin eggs, the assembly of the material of the future nuclear membrane around the chromosomes has already begun during anaphase, and the

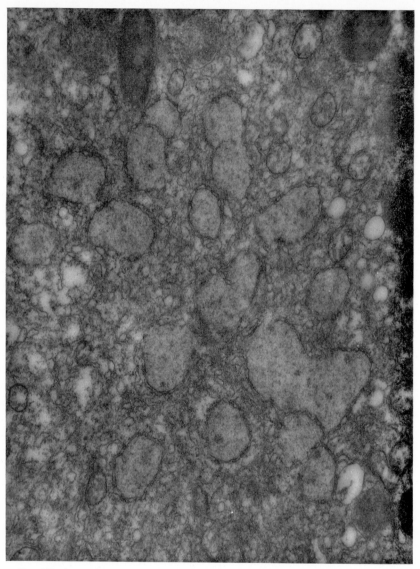

Fɪɢ. 75. An early stage in the formation of the nuclear membrane. Early telophase in a cell of a sea urchin embryo *Strongylocentrotus purpuratus*. In this material, the chromosomes begin to be surrounded by a double membrane during anaphase. This membrane is similar in structure to the normal nuclear membrane as seen in interphase. In the photograph, some chromosomal vesicles have merged, others are merging. When they have coalesced, they are surrounded by a common membrane. Note the structure of the aster in which the chromosomal vesicles lie: the gel appears to be a mass of tubules, membranes, and vesicles, from the center of which large particles such as mitochondria, fat droplets, and yolk granules are excluded. Magnification: × 16,000. Photograph by Patricia Harris.

membranes around the chromosomal vesicles show the typical "pore" structure of nuclear membranes even before the chromosomes have merged into a single interphase nucleus (Fig. 75).

It now seems certain that the nuclear membrane as such does not persist through mitosis in cells of plants and higher animals and that it is formed from material already present in the cytoplasm during telophase.

It should also be mentioned that the reconstruction of the nuclear membrane is sensitive to inhibitors such as iodoacetamide, and there is some reason to think that sulfhydryl reagents would be a good tool for experimental analysis of the process (Hughes, 1949, 1950). Obviously, it is normally well correlated in time with other aspects of the mitotic cycle, but it is not absolutely dependent either on the completion of ana-phase or on the expansion of the chromosomes. In experiments with colchicine and other mitotic inhibitors the chromosomes may go through a complete cycle except for anaphase separation, and a membrane forms at the end around the now tetraploid chromosome complement.

C. Summary

The conspicuous events of telophase are: (1) reversion of the chromosomes to their interphase condition by a process that often resembles a swelling rather than a despiralization; (2) re-formation of nucleoli; (3) re-establishment of the nuclear membrane, and (4) the dismantling of the mitotic apparatus. The formation of nucleoli is described by the appearance of small masses of nuclear substance in the vicinity of the chromosomes and their assembly at the "organizer" regions. Some of the substance is newly synthesized. The formation of the nuclear membrane is the result of the assembly of material of the endoplasmic reticulum around the chromosomes.

Little can be said about the dispersal of the mitotic apparatus because the problem has not received attention.

XII. CYTOKINESIS

A. General Plan

In this discussion we shall use the term cytokinesis to cover all schemes of cytoplasmic division.

If we contemplate the diverse mechanisms by which the cell body may divide, we are hardly encouraged to generalize. Nuclear divisions may not be followed by cytokinesis at all: such is the case in plasmodial growth. Then there are multinucleated cells which divide regularly by binary fission and in which there seems to be no relation between the divisions of the nuclei and the cleavage of the cell body. Examples are the protozoans *Actinosphaerium eichhornii* (a heliozoan) and the opalinid *Opalina ranarum* (Grell, 1956; p. 86). In the giant amoeba *Pelomyxa*, a synchronized mitosis of the nuclei precedes the division of the cell body into two multinucleated masses, but there is no apparent spatial relation between mitotic apparatus and fission. The production of many nuclei by mitosis may be followed much later by a phase in which the cytoplasm around each nucleus is partitioned off to form an independent cell, as though the new cells were carved out of a cytoplasmic mass. There seems to be no common term for such partitioning; it is designated as "Zerkluftung" in the German literature and as "cloisonnement" in the French. There are many examples of this in the plant world; one of the most studied is found in endosperm. Among the protozoa, as in the gamogony, sporogony, and schizogony of some rhizopods and flagellates and especially Sporozoa, large numbers of cells having very characteristic forms may be carved out in this way. Perhaps the most familiar examples are seen in the life cycles of the malarial parasites. The forms of such partitioning may be quite elaborate; for example, the daughter cells, each receiving one nucleus, may be formed at the surface and separated off. When all the nuclei are used up in this way, a mass of cytoplasm may be left behind.

In the "typical" association of nuclear and cytoplasmic division there seem to be two fundamental plans of cytokinesis, which accord roughly with the design of plant and animal cells, respectively. Animal cells are not encased in a rigid wall, and they generally divide by furrowing. In typical plant cytokinesis, the proplast is encased in a rigid wall and the essential feature of cytokinesis is the formation of a *cell plate,* a membrane crossing the equator which develops into the definitive wall between the daughter cells. In the formation of the cell plate (Fig. 76) we note that the interzonal region of the spindle differentiates as a *phragmoplast,* and the thin plate forms across its equator. The phragmoplast contracts toward the equator and broadens toward the equatorial surface, with a parellel broadening of the plate, and finally the plate meets the surface and the phragmoplast disappears. The cell plate becomes the middle lamella in the further differentiation of the new wall, but we shall not discuss the interesting further events which must take place before the complex wall is completed. In comparing this form of division with the animal type, the cell biologist is bound to ask: At what stage and how are the daughter cells separated by true plasma membranes, functional permeability barriers? This question had not been answerable by microscopic observation, but an answer can be expected from electron microscopy, as we shall see.

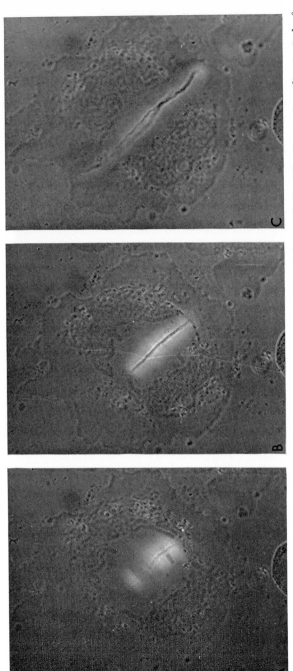

FIG. 76. Telophase and cytokinesis in *Haemanthus* endosperm, observed in polarized light. The picture is rather typical of plant cytokinesis. Material of the interzonal region collects toward the equator as a phragmoplast. A cell plate is formed, the cell plate and the phragmoplast grow toward the surface, and birefringent material of the new cell wall appears. Photographs by courtesy of Drs. S. Inoué and A. Bajer.

The reasons for the occurrence of the two types of cytokinesis are not so obvious as they may seem. Although furrowing seems to be a logical enough device for a cell with a flexible surface, it is not observed in some plant cells which lack a rigid membrane. For example, endosperm cells, whose surface is as active and flexible as that of any animal cell, do not form furrows but divide by means of cell plates (Fig. 76). In some plant cell divisions, such as the division of microsporocytes into four spores, cytokinesis may take place by furrowing alone or may involve both furrowing and the deposition of a new wall internally. Among the algae, cleavage by inpushing of the cell wall has been described in some detail (e.g., Conard, 1939; survey in Sharp, 1934, pp. 165-169). Although we do not observe full-fledged cell-plate formation in animal cells, we shall consider evidence of analogous telophase events.

Cytokinesis in bacteria and yeasts is not discussed here only because of the relative paucity of information about the mitotic mechanisms. Actually, the literature is a fascinating one, and some remarkable cytokinetic devices have been discovered. For example, the division of yeasts by budding has been analyzed in considerable detail and seems to involve the action of an enzyme, a disulfide reductase, upon the proteins of the cell wall at the point where the bud will appear (Nickerson and Falcone, 1959). The bud is initiated as a "ballooning" of the cytoplasm at this weakened point. In bacteria, cytokinesis seems to involve the inward growth of the cytoplasmic membrane (Chapman, 1959).

B. Determination of Cytokinesis; Relation to the Mitotic Apparatus

1. The Normal Picture

If we observed only normal cell division, we could not escape the conclusion that cytokinesis was governed by the mitotic apparatus, both in time and in place. In each kind of cell the beginning of cytokinesis is nicely adjusted to the period of telophase. Division may fail to take place at all, but it does not begin prematurely. The plane of division normally is exactly related to the position of the mitotic apparatus; in fact, it corresponds to the equatorial plane. A generalization to the effect that a successful cleavage must cut through a spindle was made by Boveri in 1896. If the mitotic apparatus is not centrally located, it still appears to govern division, and unequal daughter cells are produced. This applies both to plant and animal cells. A classic example from the plant world is to be found in van Wisselingh's (1909) study of *Spirogyra*, where the nucleus is ordinarily suspended in the middle of the cell but is sometimes found in a displaced position. When it is naturally displaced the division is correspondingly unequal.

Some recent experiments by K. Kawamura (1960b) illustrate a quite rigorous relationship between the mitotic apparatus and the plane of cytokinesis. The mitotic apparatus of the grasshopper neuroblast was displaced in various ways by means of a microneedle. This cell normally divides unequally, the larger daughter cell having 6.5 times the volume of the smaller. It can be seen in Fig. 77 that the plane of division could be shifted at will by moving the mitotic apparatus, and even in the ex-

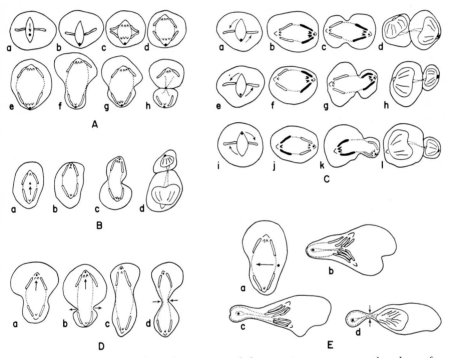

FIG. 77. Effect of shifting the position of the mitotic apparatus on the plane of cytokinesis in grasshopper neuroblasts. Black circles show position of the micro-needle holding the spindle (K. Kawamura, 1960b).

A. Spindle is moved toward ganglion cell side. It is normally shifted to this side by unequal growth of asters. Division into large neuroblast and smaller ganglion cell is normal.

B. Spindle shifted to neuroblast side. Larger cell is formed at pole where smaller cell would normally form.

C. Spindle rotated 90°. Cleavage furrow at right angles to new spindle axis.

D. Spindle shifted just as furrowing begins. Furrow regresses and reforms at new equatorial plane.

E. Needle applied to interzonal region, bending spindle back on itself. Cleavage into nucleated and anucleate daughters.

treme case when the spindle was bent back on itself the furrow still appeared over the spindle "equator." The determination of the division plane by the spindle may not be quite so rigid in all cases, and we shall cite instances where the correlation is violated experimentally, but our basic generalization is that *the plane of cytokinesis is normally perpendicular to the midpoint of the spindle.*

2. Unequal Division

Unequal cell division occurs normally in very many situations, and it may be regarded as one of the mechanisms operative in tissue differentiation. For example, the small daughter produced by the division of a neuroblast (Fig. 77) goes on to form a ganglion cell, whereas the larger daughter remains a neuroblast and continues to produce more ganglion cells. In the development of annelids and mollusks unequal cleavages are the basis of the cell lineages by which differentiation is traced back to the egg. If the plane of division is related to the mitotic apparatus, unequal division must involve some asymmetry in its relation to the cell as a whole. One such device, applicable to animal cells, has been proposed by K. Dan (1943). He suggested that the spindle might be displaced mechanically from the center of the cell if the asters are of unequal size. In invertebrate egg cells, at least, the asters are very large at anaphase, the rays extending to the cell surface. The predicted inequality of the asters was confirmed by K. Dan et al. (1952) for cleaving eggs of the clam *Spisula* and by K. Dan and Nakajima (1956) for the unequal divisions leading to micromere formation in the embryo of a sea urchin *Hemicentrotus pulcherrimus*. In these studies the mitotic apparatus was isolated from unequally dividing cells, and it was noted that the pole at which the larger aster formed was the one at which the larger daughter cell was produced, the plane of division corresponding to the midpoint between the centers (Fig. 78). Dan and Nakajima noted that the asters were of equal size until early metaphase; after this time one grew larger than the other. The actual situation may not be described simply in terms of the unequal growth of astral rays, for it was noted (Fig. 78; and Fig. 20 of the paper by K. Dan and Nakajima) that the aster which defined the smaller daughter cell was flattened at its polar end, as though it were being pushed or pulled toward the cell surface. The important point, however, is that inequality of the asters is closely correlated with unequal division, and the rule of correspondence between the division plane and the equator of the spindle is preserved.

A further illustration of the validity of this rule in cases of unequal division is given by certain invertebrate eggs that lose their spherical shape and bulge out a "polar lobe" at one end during cleavage. In this way, the cytoplasm is disposed asymmetrically around a mitotic apparatus, and the cleavage through the equator of the spindle yields unequal cells.

To describe mechanisms of unequal division in animal cells in terms of the positions of the centers and the growth of the asters is not to explain how the polarity is determined in the first place. In plants, where we cannot rely with conviction upon centers and asters to account for the mechanisms, the processes of tissue differentiation proceed with incredible precision and do depend to a large extent on the positions of

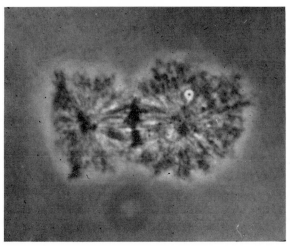

FIG. 78. Mitotic apparatus isolated from the dividing egg of the clam *Spisula solidissima*. The inequality of the asters corresponds to the inequality of the daughter cells (cf. Dan and Nakajima, 1956).

the mitotic apparatus in the cells. An example is given in Fig. 79. The literature on polarity and unequal division in plant tissues has been reviewed by Bünning (1957).

3. Delayed Cytokinesis

Cases where cytokinesis not only comes much later than nuclear division but takes place after the nuclei have divided numerous times have already been mentioned. The cells seem to be carved out of the common cytoplasm shared by the nuclei. The nuclei are said to be in an interphase condition at the time when the partitioning takes place. At first glance, it would seem unlikely that this form of cell division would be correlated with the mitotic apparatus. But some examples from the literature of plant cytology suggest an analogy between the exception

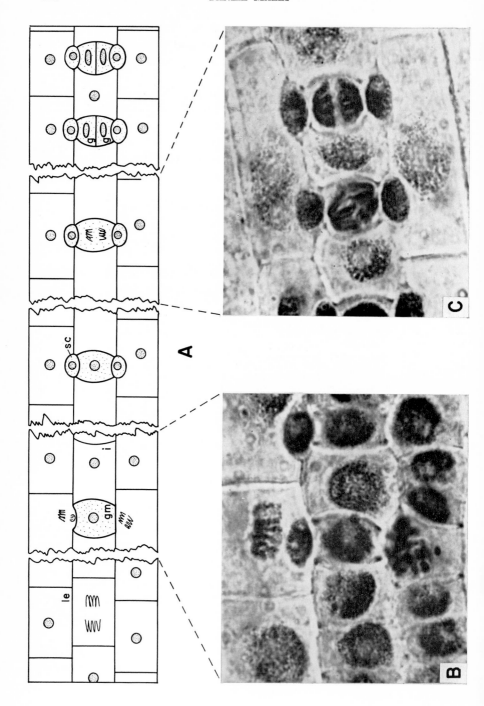

and the normal. In accounts of the partitioning of multinucleated plant tissues the appearance of a fibrillar system between adjacent nuclei is often described. Tischler (1922), in a review of the voluminous older literature, traces the observation back to Strasburger (1880), whose description is confirmed by later work (e.g., Jungers, 1931; Buchholz, 1939). In Jungers' detailed study of division in *Iris* endosperm the fibrous connections between the nuclei are interpreted as being equivalent to those seen at telophase in the normal type of division (Fig. 80). We could easily invent an explanation if we were permitted to assume that centrioles or their functional equivalents were associated with the nuclei. The picture is just what would be expected from our experience with multipolar mitosis, where spindles form between centers regardless of whether they engage chromosomes or not. If the formation of new cell walls does in fact require that the cell retrace its steps and form something like a spindle, it would be a remarkable demonstration of a fundamental association between the mitotic apparatus and cytokinesis.

The partitioning of plant syncytia into cells is described as proceeding quite rapidly and, in a given region, synchronously. The earlier workers suggested that it might be triggered by an agent that was specific for cytokinesis (a "Teilungswecker," as Tischler designates it). This proposal is quite in line with the recent demonstrations (Das *et al.*, 1956) that the presence or absence of auxin determines cytokinesis when the kinins are available to promote nuclear preparations.

4. Relation of Cytokinesis to the Mitotic Apparatus

a. Relation to the poles. Some idea of the relation between the mitotic apparatus and cytokinesis in animal cells can be gained from the

---

FIG. 79. Asymmetry and polarization of mitosis in differentiation. This example, the formation of the stomatal complex in seedling leaves of barley, illustrates two points: (1) Differentiation may take place at a single division; that is, the daughter cells may be different and have different fates, and (2) the organization of a tissue may depend on the orientation of the mitotic apparatus in a decisive division. In drawing A, the stages of the formation of the stomatal complex, beginning with three rows of cells, are shown in sequence from left to right. An asymmetric division in the middle row produces two kinds of cells, one of which is the guard mother cells (*gm*). A very asymmetric division of nuclei in the epidermal cells on either side of the guard mother cell produces two subsidiary cells (*sc*). Note, in photograph B, upper middle, that the differences between the two daughter nuclei are evident even before the division is completed; the chromosomes of the subsidiary cell nucleus uncoil before those of the epidermal cell nucleus. Finally, the guard mother cells complete a mitosis at right angles to the leaf axis, producing guard cells (*g*). The stomatal complex then completes its differentiation (not shown) without further division. Photographs by courtesy of Dr. C. L. Stebbins (Stebbins and Shah, 1960).

study of multipolar mitosis. Ordinarily, the rule is that each center is
connected with every other (Fig. 30) and a furrow bisects each spindle.
In certain situations all the poles may not be connected to each other by
spindles, for a variety of reasons, and such cases let us decide if fur-

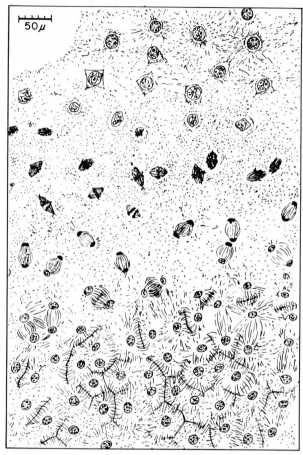

FIG. 80.   Gradient of mitotic stages in endosperm of *Iris pseudoacoris*, persistence
of "spindles" after telophase, and partitioning into cells by formation of phragmoplasts
and cell plates at equators of "spindles." From Jungers (1931).

rowing is necessarily determined by a spindle. Favorable material was
found by Roberts and Johnson (1956) in the spermatocyte divisions of
a beetle *Popilius disjunctus*. In these divisions, mitochondrial filaments
collect along the spindles, outlining them vividly in the living cell. Multipolar figures of various types are observed. Figure 81 tells the story:

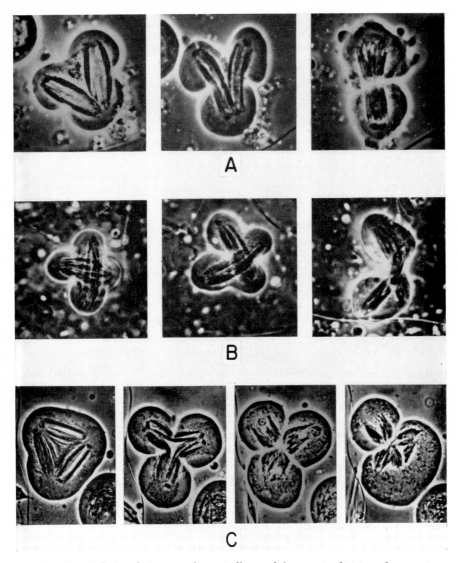

Fig. 81. Relations between poles, spindles, and furrows in division of spermatocytes of the beetle *Popilius disjunctus*. The spindles are not actually seen, but are marked by the sheaves of mitochondria aligned along their surfaces. A. Three poles, two divergent spindles. Furrows form between each pair of poles, but are completed only where the poles are connected by spindles. B. Four poles, two spindles. Four furrows begin, but the cell cleaves at midpoint of the two spindles. C. Three poles, three spindles. Three furrows form and are almost completed. One regresses. Photographs by courtesy of Dr. Henry S. Roberts (Roberts and Johnson, 1956).

the planes of furrowing do not seem to be governed by the equators of the spindles, but by their poles. The furrows appear midway between the poles whether or not a spindle connects them, and the cell attempts to make as many daughters as there are poles. Obviously this conclusion relates only to the role of the spindle as geometry master and says nothing about its part in the mechanism of cytokinesis in animal cells.

   b. Experimental dissociation of division plane and mitotic apparatus. Having stated some of the normal associations between the mitotic apparatus, it must be admitted that the correlation of the mitotic apparatus and the plane of cytokinesis can be perturbed experimentally. The extreme case is that in which mitosis runs its course, but the division plane is so displaced that one daughter cell receives two nuclei, the other none. A few illustrative cases out of many may be cited. In grasshopper spermatocytes normal mitosis may be accompanied by an unequal cytokinesis, producing an "anuclear bud" (Makino and Nakahara, 1955). In cultures of chick fibroblasts, division to produce one anucleate and one binucleate daughter cell has been induced by exposing the cell to a double gradient of diethylstilbesterol and testosterone (H. Lettré and Siebs, 1956). This was done by placing a crystal of one compound on one side of the cell, and a crystal of the other on the opposite side. Other examples could be cited. Carlson (1952) described an experiment in which the whole mitotic apparatus was pressed into one end of a grasshopper neuroblast by means of a microneedle, and he observed that the cleavage furrow formed "in the usual position," leaving all the chromosomes in one daughter cell. But a smaller displacement, such as was later investigated by K. Kawamura (1960b) (Fig. 77) was followed by a corresponding shift of the division plane with the equator of the spindle. In the sea urchin egg movement of the spindle by centrifugal force applied before some time around metaphase was followed by a corresponding shift of the division plane (E. B. Harvey, 1934). Centrifugation at a later time had no such effect; the furrow "came often in the exact position that it would have come had not the mitotic figure been moved." These are only a few examples from work on animal cells.

   It is interesting to consult some remarkable older literature for comparable cases among algal cells, in particular the work of Gerassimov (1905) and van Wisselingh (1909) on *Spirogyra*. The former found that the chilling of the cells or exposure to anesthetics was often followed by a division in which one cell received both nuclei, the other none. Van Wisselingh (1909) observed that when the spindle was displaced to one end of the dividing cell by strong centrifugation, mitosis took place at that end, but the new and normal cell wall appeared at the normal position midway between the ends of the cell. The spindle completed its division, producing a binucleate cell beside its anucleate sister. (This experimental result contrasts with his observation that when the nucleus is normally displaced from the center of the cell, the division is correspondingly unequal.) In later experiments he observed the production of binucleate and anucleate sister cells from parent cells in which division had not begun at the time of centrifugation, and he was one of the first to propose that the plane of cytokinesis is determined at an early stage. (The writer has often wondered why later students of nuclear function and cell division have not exploited this beautiful experimental system.)

We would not expect to be able to dissociate cytokinesis in cells of higher plants from the mitotic apparatus, since the cell plate seems to originate in the apparatus. There is, however, an interesting experimental system for testing the autonomy of the phragmoplast. If plant cells are centrifuged at telophase, the heavier nuclei move toward the centrifugal pole while the phragmoplast is displaced peripherally. According to Beams and King (1938) the cell wall is not completed after this disruption of the telophase organization of the mitotic apparatus.

c. *Cytokinesis after damage to the mitotic apparatus: the "point of no return."* To account for the deviations from the rule of the normal coordination of the geometry of nuclear and cytoplasmic division, we may imagine that any plane of division is possible and that the actual plane is determined by a signal of some sort from the mitotic apparatus. This general formulation, which we shall deal with later in terms of real structures, implies that we can find a "point of no return," before which cytokinesis does depend on the mitotic apparatus and after which it is no longer dependent. Let us consider some examples.

We have already mentioned evidence on the centrifuged sea urchin egg which suggests that the furrow is determined around metaphase. In similar material it was observed (Cornman and Cornman, 1951) that damaging the spindle by the antimitotic agent podophyllin would prevent cytokinesis if the drug were introduced before mid-anaphase, but the agent could no longer stop it if it were applied after that stage, even though mitosis was seriously disturbed. Quite similar results were obtained on sea urchin eggs with colchicine (Swann and Mitchison, 1953) in experiments in which the disorganization of the mitotic apparatus, especially the asters, was evaluated by means of polarization microscopy. These authors cite earlier and similar results of Beams and Evans (1940).

The irradiation of the cytoplasm or the spindle of newt fibroblasts with ultraviolet microbeams (reviewed by Zirkle, 1957) results in a characteristic and drastic disturbance of mitosis. The spindle can no longer be detected as such by phase contrast or polarization microscopy, and the sister chromosomes do not split apart. Unsplit chromosomes do move toward the centrioles and gather around them with their kineto-chores pointing toward the center in what has been called a "quasi-rosette" configuration (Fig. 82). Yet the cells do undergo cytokinesis.

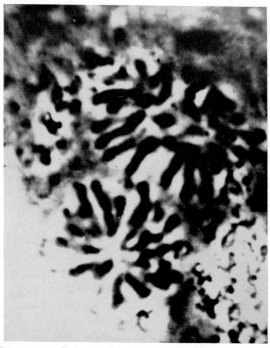

Fig. 82. "Quasirosette" form of separation of chromosomes after damage to the mitotic apparatus resulting from ultraviolet irradiation. The sister chromosomes have not split, but unsplit chromosomes are carried to the poles in approximately equal numbers. Cytokinesis follows. Photograph by courtesy of Dr. R. E. Zirkle.

This type of "false anaphase" is not restricted to animal cells. It is de-scribed, for instance, in onion root tips after treatment with colchicine and γ-cyclochlorohexane (Hyppio *et al.*, 1955). A similar story is told in a more extreme form by observations of the effect of a microbeam of alpha particles on animal cells in culture (Davis and Smith, 1957). The beam was aimed at the metaphase spindle, avoiding the chromosomes. As a result, no chromosome movement was seen, but the cells did divide to produce one anucleate daughter and one containing all the chromo-somes.

A common feature of all the experiments, which differ otherwise in so many ways, is that the poles were established, even though the mitotic apparatus suffered damage. We may therefore ask, without being able to give the answer, whether it is the polar determiners, represented by centrioles in animal cells, which also determine irrevocably the plane of division at a critical time. From our earlier discussion of the time of separation of the centers (Section IV, B, 3) we could well imagine that this critical point would vary considerably among different kinds of cells.

d. *Cytokinesis without chromosomes and after removal of the mitotic apparatus.* The chromosomes do not seem to be essential for cytokinesis. Observations of division without chromatin have been presented by Dalcq and Simon (1932) and others for amphibian eggs; by Harvey (1936, 1951) and Lorch *et al.* (1953) for sea urchin eggs; and by Cleveland (1956) for flagellates of the genera *Trichonympha* and *Barbulanympha*. No attempt has been made to collect all the published evidence. The methods used to perform these experiments have been of various kinds. For example, Harvey studied the division of parthenogenetically activated egg fragments, Lorch *et al.* removed nuclei by micrurgical means, and Cleveland discovered that exposure of the flagellates to high oxygen concentrations (70–80%) during gametogenesis caused the disintegration of chromosomes. Although these results may be surprising in themselves, they are rather damaging to the interesting hypothesis that the movement of RNA from chromosomes to the equator at anaphase (p. 329) is related to cytokinesis (e.g., Boss, 1955). In all the cases mentioned a mitotic apparatus of some kind was present, although it did not contain chromosomes. In the experiments on sea urchin eggs, "cytasters" were present, and they could have taken over normal polar functions. In Cleveland's experiments the mitotic apparatus was complete except for chromosomes.

Having seen that a cell may suffer severe damage to the spindle and complete loss of chromosomes without necessarily losing its ability to divide, we are bound to ask whether any element of the mitotic apparatus is essential for determining cytokinesis. Only a few pieces of evidence, limited to sea urchin eggs, are available. Lorch (1952) removed the entire "astrophere" (centers and associated asters) from sea urchin blastomeres, along with the nucleus, at a stage when the nucleus was still whole. She found that the cells did not divide for 8 hours and that then they fragmented into many pieces in a manner described as "pathological." The effect of removing the whole mitotic apparatus of the sea urchin egg at various stages has been observed in a skillful micrurgical study by Hiramoto (1956). Up to a point of no return in

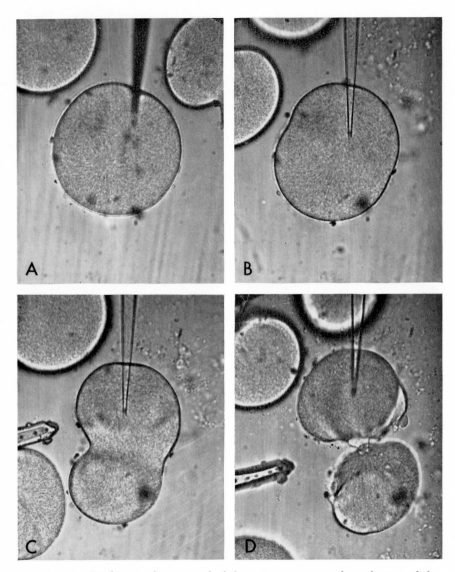

FIG. 83.   Cytokinesis after removal of the mitotic apparatus from the egg of the heart urchin *Clypeaster japonicus*.   A. Micropipette inserted.   B. Spindle being sucked out of cell, just as it begins to elongate before furrowing.   C. Furrowing begins 2.5 minutes later.   D. Division complete. Photographs by courtesy of Dr. Y. Hiramoto (cf. Hiramoto, 1956).

mid-anaphase, the eggs failed to divide without a mitotic apparatus. After this point cytokinesis proceeded without a mitotic apparatus, with the cleavage plane in its normal place with respect to the sites of the poles before the operation (Fig. 83). Moreover, if some cytoplasm were sucked out of the cell after mid-anaphase, the cleavage plane was normal with respect to the mitotic apparatus and unequal daughter cells were produced. Clearly, then, the mitotic apparatus does determine the oc-

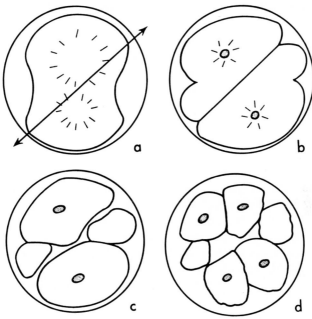

Fig. 84.   Effect of transecting the dividing cell and the mitotic apparatus after the furrow has begun to form. Experiments on sea urchin eggs. The original furrow is completed, and the fragments receiving nuclei divide again. After Chambers (1951).

currence and location of cytokinesis but does not seem to be necessary for its completion.

The independence of cytokinesis from the mitotic apparatus at the later stages is demonstrated in still another way by an experiment of Chambers (1951) illustrated in Fig. 84, where it is seen that furrowing, once begun, continues even after the cell and the mitotic apparatus have been transected.

e. Time relations of mitosis and cytokinesis. In normal cell reproduction mitosis and cytokinesis are closely coordinated in time. If cytoplasmic division is blocked, mitosis may proceed normally, producing a binucleate cell. There are few means of imposing a controllable delay of cytokinesis, the most elegant being the application of hydrostatic pressure, as described by Marsland (1956, 1958). One of his most interesting findings (1958) is that the furrowing of a sea urchin egg can be delayed for only a limited time, after which the cell loses its ability to cleave and omits that division. At the following division the binucleate egg divides directly into four cells. Thus, cytokinesis is not governed by an independent rhythm, but is linked to mitosis, with some leeway.

We need not be surprised at the rarity of premature cytokinesis if we imagine that this process is set into motion on signal from some elements of the mitotic apparatus. There are, however, some recent experiments by Marsland et al. (1960) in which furrowing could be induced in sea urchin eggs even before prophase by exposing them to high centrifugal forces (40,000–50,000 g) under high hydrostatic pressures (in the neighborhood of 800 atmospheres). The cells divided completely in a plane at right angles to the centrifugal axis. In experiments described by E. B. Harvey (1960), unfertilized eggs of a number of species of sea urchins were stratified by centrifugation, then activated parthenogenetically by exposure to a hypertonic medium. Such eggs might form a distinct cleavage furrow in a plane at right angles to the direction of the centrifugal field, even though their nuclei seemed to have made no progress toward mitosis. These observations hardly imply a capricious stimulation of the ability of the cells to make a furrow. The plane of the induced furrow is well defined with respect to the centrifugal axis, just as the plane of the normal furrow is well defined by the mitotic apparatus. It is suggested that the stratification of the cytoplasmic fractions concentrates material of which the furrow will be made in a definite and compact layer and that in the normal case the mitotic apparatus may be performing a comparable function. This line of reasoning will be pursued below.

f. Conclusions. A strong case can be made for the determination of the time and site of cytoplasmic division by the mitotic apparatus, but it is difficult to defend the idea that the mitotic apparatus is immediately essential for the performance of the cytokinetic acts themselves. Rather, *the determination seems to take place previous to the visible beginnings of the division of the cell, and after the "signal" has been given cytokinesis may proceed with some degree of autonomy.* The geometric requirements would be satisfied by the hypothesis that the centers (or euphemisms applicable to the poles of plant cells) determine the plane of division. This might seem to be a somewhat ambiguous proposition since the poles in turn define the spindle and the paths of the chromosomes, either of which could be involved. But we can exclude the chromosomes, as unessential for cytokinesis, they are, and can recognize that the spindles can be abused in many ways without influencing cytokinesis. Of experimental evidence on the indispensability of the centers, perhaps the most interesting examples are the cases where only one pole is present Here we observe a complete mitotic cycle with the exception of anaphase movement of the chromosomes, but we never observe cytokinesis until a second pole is formed.

5. Interaction of the Mitotic Apparatus and the Cell Surface; Speculations

It would appear that there must be some *communication* between the spindle and the cell surface, fixing the site where the surface will form a wall or furrow. What form might this communication take? In vacuolated plant cells (Sinnott and Bloch, 1941; Esau, 1953) some of the strands of cytoplasm passing across the vacuole from the nuclear area to the periphery of the protoplasm may take up a position at right angles to the spindle. It has been proposed that this plate of cytoplasm, called the *phragmosome*, provides the foundation of the new cell wall. If this is so, could such a simple and direct channel of communication between the mitotic apparatus and the cell surface exist in other cells in the form of strands obscured by the cytoplasmic background?

What geometrically defined form of communication other than a direct physical connection between the spindle equator and the site of division can we imagine? It has been proposed (Cornman and Cornman, 1951) that an "organizer" substance is released at some point in mitosis and finds its way to the surface. Cornman and Cornman give reasons for considering the nucleus to be the source of the substance. Boss (1954) considers the possibility that the link between the mitotic apparatus and the surface involves the ribonucleoproteins, the behavior of which in anaphase and telophase we have discussed earlier (Section XI, A). It will be recalled that these seem to collect toward the equator as anaphase proceeds. In newt fibroblasts Boss describes a further apparent streaming of the staining material from the interzonal region toward the surface, just about the time that the "bubbling" of the surface in such cells marks the beginning of cytokinesis. While the general hypothesis attributing the action of the mitotic apparatus on the cytokinetic mechanism to diffusing substances is one of the few possibilities, a nuclear origin of such substances does not seem plausible, since the nucleus need not be essential for cytokinesis.

It is an obvious possibility that some activity at the poles and not at the equator determines the division plane; after all, it is the poles that specify both the equator of the spindle and the site of the division. Moreover, we have seen that a pair of poles may determine a cleavage plane even when no spindle connects them. The hypothesis of Dan (K. Dan, 1943; summarized by J. C. Dan, 1948) accounts in a beautifully logical way for the localization of the furrow when asters are present. In the course of their normal growth the astral rays from the two poles do cross at the equator and reach the surface on either side of the equator. Dan had proposed that the crossed astral rays defined the site of the furrow by mechanical means; as the spindle elongated, the points of attachment of these rays to the surface came closer, relaxing the surface in the equatorial region (Fig. 91). Objections have been raised to the mechanical aspects of this hypothesis, but it could have a deeper meaning. The visible astral rays may be merely a gross manifestation of an orienting mechanism that issues forth from the centers, and their form may be a superficial expression of a diffusion front of an agent responsible for the orientation. Such a view is developed as an "Astral Relaxation Theory" by Wolpert (1960). Even if microscopic asters were not present for one reason or another, the diffusion fronts could still be imagined, and they could bring about structural changes such as a "peripolar gelation," to quote Dalcq and Simon (1930), which need not involve orientation so strong as to be expressed as astral rays. Viewed only geometrically, these fronts would meet halfway between the poles if the latter act symmetrically, and their meeting point at the surface would be midway between the poles. Or, if we consider possible internal changes, the structural effect emanating from the poles might encompass expanding "spheres of influence" that would meet at the equator and thus define a plane of division. Such a picture was developed by J. Gray (1924, 1931), who, however, identified the polar spheres as the asters themselves. Dalcq and Simon advocated such a view in accounting for observations on the frog egg, and they state the opinion, "le point de départ de la cytodiérèse est profond et non pas cortical." A more complete hypothesis, stated by Swann (1952), is based on a correlation of birefringence changes in the mitotic apparatus and optical changes in the cell surface. Swann pictures a wave of a "structural agent" passing from the chromosomes at anaphase, conducted to the poles along the spindle, and then moving out along the asters to the surface. Its effect on the surface first appears at the polar ends as a decrease in cortical birefringence and spreads toward the equator, where the waves from the two ends meet and presumably initiate the furrowing of the surface.

This line of speculation does not demand the involvement of actual asters in division. On the contrary, it views the asters seen in some kinds of cells as a "visual aid" giving a clue to an activity of the poles. Where there are asters, their visible expansion to the surface must follow and not precede the action of the centers on the surface, for we have seen that the mitotic apparatus is no longer needed for cytokinesis by mid-anaphase and sometimes earlier. The experimental challenge is to discover an activity that radiates from the poles to the surface at a sufficiently early stage, else all this remains an idle speculation.

It is interesting to note that we may find a coordination between the nuclear events and surface changes, even when division does not occur. In sea urchin eggs whose mitotic apparatus has been disorganized by colchicine, the chromosomal cycles continue, without cleavage (Zeuthen, 1951; Holter and Zeuthen, 1957). In such eggs the changes in surface birefringence associated with normal division take place at the normal times (Monroy and Montalenti, 1947) and the cycle of surface rigidity changes also occurs normally (Mitchison and Swann, 1954; Swann and Mitchison, 1958). It is as though the surface were receiving its "signal" at the proper time, coordinated with the chromosomal changes, but these changes in themselves are not sufficient to determine and to drive a furrow without the cooperation of a reasonably normal mitotic apparatus. As to the source of the "signal," if the chromosomes are not necessary, we can ask whether the reproductive cycle of the centers as well as that of the chromosomes is proceeding in the presence of colchicine.

C. Mechanisms of Cytokinesis

Superficially, the act of cytokinesis appears to involve one of three procedures: wall-building around or between the nuclei, constriction of the cell surface between the nuclei, or the extrusion of part of the cell along with one nucleus, followed by a pinching off of the extruded part.

The cleavage of animal cells has been studied by a greater variety of approaches than other types of cytokinesis and will serve as an example. It has been reviewed in some detail by Swann and Mitchison (1958) and by Wolpert (1960).

1. Cleavage and Locomotion

Two general forms of cleavage are most familiar. The first, observed in ameboid cells, including tissue cells, involves a period of striking activity at the cell surface around anaphase and telophase, following the typical rounding-up and quiescence of such cells during the earlier phases of mitosis. This has become very familiar through the many excellent films of dividing cells. It has been suggested that the active ameboid crawling of the sister cells in opposite directions is a major factor in their separation. This approach has been discussed by Lewis (1942) and by Chalkley (1951), who find close parallels between factors that inhibit

the normal locomotion of *Amoeba proteus* and those that inhibit cytokinesis without influencing caryokinesis. Chalkley could produce binu-
cleated cells at will by exposing the dividing amebae to a variety of
agents known to interfere with locomotion.

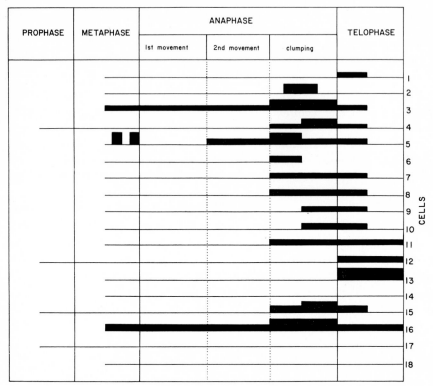

FIG. 85. Time of occurrence of "bubbling" in individual newt fibroblasts. Each
bar refers to bubbling of a single cell, and the line under bar represents time during
which it was observed. "First movement" refers to initial poleward movement of
chromosomes, "second movement" refers to spindle elongation (Fig. 63, D). "Clumping" refers to aggregation of chromosomes after they have completed their movement.
The bubbling is consistently associated with telophase, but may occur earlier. From
Boss (1955).

In cells of higher animals, generally but not always observed in culture, the period of cytokinesis is commonly marked by active "bubbling"
of the surface. Hughes (1952b, p. 145) describes and illustrates the details of the "bubbling" process. The time at which it appears may vary,
but it is generally concentrated in late anaphase and telophase (Fig. 85)
or about the time of cytokinesis. The existence of a link between the

"bubbling" and the behavior of the mitotic apparatus was inferred by Boss (1955), who observed that the most active "bubbling" in newt fibroblasts appeared in the areas of the surface nearest to the chromosomes. This was especially evident on occasions when the bubbling began prematurely, at metaphase. The "bubbling" so typical of dividing cells may be induced in nondividing cells, as shown by Dornfeld and Owczarzak (1958). Chick fibroblasts treated with EDTA (ethylenediaminetetraacetic acid) in interphase "bubble" actively, and similar treatment of dividing cells enhances the normal bubbling at anaphase but does not elicit it at metaphase. Earlier (H. Lettré, 1952b, H. Lettré and Schleich, 1955), similar effects were observed with the dye Victoria Blue. Dornfeld and Owczarzak speculate that the spindle binds divalent cations during mitosis and releases them to the surface as it breaks down after anaphase, setting off the "bubbling" and permitting continued "bubbling" in the presence of EDTA.

We have no complete hypothesis directly linking the "bubbling" observed in so many cells to the actual fission process. We might extend Chalkley's view relating fission to the deeper mechanism of ameboid movement; localized expansions of the surface near the poles would be a reflection of contractile activity near the equator. Swann and Mitchison (1958) suggest that the "bubbling" may reflect the activity of an actively expanding membrane, of which more will be said below.

2. Constriction and Contraction

In the cleavage of eggs—the archetype of the cleavage process— changes in surface contour are not conspicuous and play no part in current theorizing. All the mystery can be buried in the bland assertion that the cell "pinches in two." This also applies to many other animal cells: many protozoa, spermatocytes, etc. The idea that the process actually is the result of an active contraction around the equator has been developed ably by a number of workers (e.g., Lewis, 1942), but most thoroughly by Marsland (summaries, 1951, 1956, 1957) and associates. Their major assumption is that the property of contractility may be assimilated into the concept of the gel state, thus permitting inferences about contraction (which is difficult to study directly) from measurements of "gel strength," for which they have developed elegant methods. "Gel strength" is an operational concept that is related to, but not necessarily identical with, viscosity. By centrifugation of eggs under high hydrostatic pressures at controlled temperatures and by observation of the displacement of cortical granules, it has been concluded that the cortex belongs to that class of gels which tend to lose rigidity at high pressures and increase in rigidity as the temperature is increased (the so-called "endothermic" gels). In studies on cleaving eggs the effects of temperature and pressure conform to theory: high pressure lowers cortical gel strength and blocks cytokinesis, but temperature works in the opposite sense. The observations themselves are very striking. If pressure is applied to a cleaving egg, the furrow will recede, even though it may have advanced almost to completion. As the temperature is elevated, the pressure required to

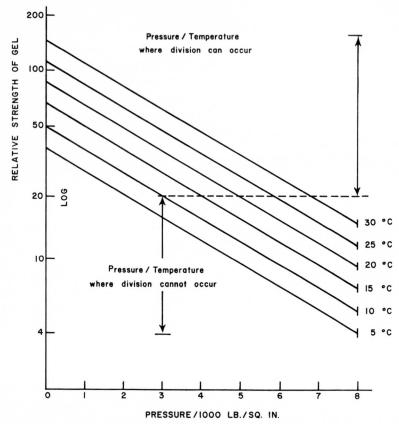

Fig. 86.   Relation between the "gel strength" of the cortical layer of sea urchin eggs (*Arbacia*) and their ability to furrow. This graph also relates the "gel strength" to hydrostatic pressure and temperature. The ordinate expresses "gel strength" in terms of the experimental criterion used to measure it; the time of centrifuging, at constant force, which is required to displace certain granules from the surface layer of the egg. Above a certain value of the ordinate, the cells divide; below it they do not, and existing furrows recede. As the temperature is raised, a higher pressure is required to reduce the "gel strength" below the critical value that permits the completion of the furrow. From Marsland (1957).

reverse the furrow increases (Fig. 86). The large body of evidence assembled by Marsland and his associates leaves little doubt that the gel state of the "cortex" is essential to the cleavage process in eggs, and relates the cleavage to ameboid movement and cytoplasmic streaming in a convincing and quantitative way (Marsland, 1951).

The hypothesis involves three levels of inference: that furrowing involves a gel, that the sol-gel transformation is an indicator of a contractile mechanism, and that the contractile mechanism is expressed in a constricting "ring" around the equatorial periphery. The first is based on experiment, the second can be assimilated into other theories if we assume that contraction and elongation are related processes, and the third is subject to direct test. One such test is morphological: can we observe such a ring with optical or electron microscopic methods? Mercer and Wolpert (1958) have described the appearance of a dense layer in the furrow of cleaving sea urchin eggs—a layer thicker than the plasma membrane but still of submicroscopic dimensions—which seems to be formed by the aggregation of tubular elements. They suggest that it may correspond to the hypothetical contractile ring. If it does, it shifts attention from a cortical gel of microscopic thickness, in which particles are embedded, to a much thinner layer. Clear evidence for a surface differentiation in the furrow would be important for any of the theories of cleavage.

Evidence for a contractile ring appears in Mota's (1959) study of individual grasshopper spermatocytes which undergo mitosis without cytokinesis. Phase contrast observation showed the presence of a distinct, thick refractile ring, constricting the mitotic apparatus and the mitochondrial layer which surrounds it in these cells. One reasonable interpretation is that in the abnormal cells a contractile ring was detached from the cell surface and thus became visible. Only if it were attached to the surface would a furrow be formed. Mota proposes that the formation of the ring would be determined by the release of material from the chromosomes into the interzonal region. This attractive hypothesis would not explain the formation of furrows between centers in multipolar figures which are not joined by spindles (Fig. 81).

The analogy between animal cytokinesis and muscle contraction inevitably makes a strong appeal to our sense of biological unity. One link has been sought experimentally through possible effects of ATP on cleavage. Nothing so obvious as the induction or acceleration of normal cytokinesis has been observed. Perhaps it is not to be expected, even if furrowing is analogous to contraction. The furrowing might well involve a local effect of ATP associated with a relaxation of other regions of the cell surface, as Lettré and Schleich (1955) have pointed out, and this localized condition could not be reproduced merely by bathing cells in ATP. Fibroblasts immersed in a high concentration of ATP (1 mg./ml.) tend to retain their normal extended form during division, rather than rounding up and bubbling, and this has been taken as evidence that ATP does affect the surface rigidity or "tonus" (Lettré, 1952b).

A more successful experimental design has involved the demonstration that ATP could help a cell to overcome a block to division. For ex-

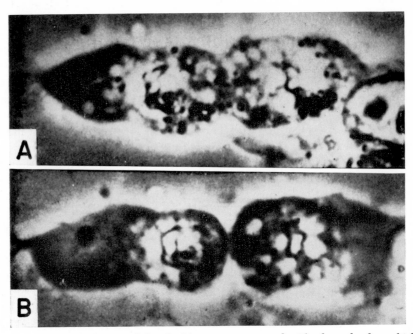

Fig. 87.   Telophase model. Fibroblasts were extracted with glycerol, after which a cell in early telophase appeared as in photograph A. Upon the addition of ATP, the furrow advanced, as seen in photograph B. The cells did not separate. Photograph by courtesy of Dr. H. Hoffmann-Berling (Hoffmann-Berling, 1954b).

ample, Landau et al. (1955) have found that eggs of Arbacia and Chaetopterus did cleave in the presence of ATP under pressures and temperatures at which they would ordinarily be blocked and that the cleavage was paralleled by an increased cortical "gel strength" in the presence of ATP. In none of this work was the penetration of the ATP, its hydrolysis, or its possible role as a chelating agent rather than as source of "high-energy phosphate" fully excluded. The one experiment that does relate cytokinesis directly to the contractile mechanisms of muscle was done by Hoffmann-Berling (1954b, 1959), who observed that "telophase models"—glycerol-extracted fibroblasts in which cytokinesis had begun—completed their furrowing when ATP was added under conditions identical with those that elicited contraction from corresponding "muscle models" (Fig. 87).

The case against the theory that cleavage is primarily an equatorial contractile process has been presented most fully by Mitchison (1953; summary in Swann and Mitchison, 1958). Some micrurgical experiments by Mitchison (1953) are impressive. For example, he has impaled cleaving eggs on microneedles which pass through the path of a furrow. A perforation in a contracting ring might be expected to expand into a "gaping wound" as constriction proceeded. In fact, the furrow simply passed through the needle (Fig. 88). This objection, however, depends on the assumption of one of a number of images of what contraction actually is, and again we are faced with the looseness of the conception of contraction when we essay a molecule's-eye-view.

Abstractly, "contraction" of the equator can be converted to an inward growth or expansion of the surface merely be reversing our symbolic arrows. Both expansion (in the sense of an unfolding of the existing cell surface) and growth (in the sense of formation or new cell surface as the furrow advances) have been proposed. The "growth" theory has been developed mainly by observers of cleavage of amphibian eggs, which are very large and whose furrows must travel very long distances. Direct observation and manipulation, for which these large cells are favorable, seem to argue against a stretching of cell surface in the furrow (Selman and Waddington, 1955). Surface pigment does not seem to be diluted, and the mechanical properties of the surface in the furrow region (resistance to mechanical deformation) are no different from those of the rest of the surface, as would be expected if this region were being stretched.

3. The Expanding Membrane

The "expanding membrane" theory, elaborated by Mitchison (1952; review Swann and Mitchison, 1958), is based on optical and mechanical studies of the surface of the dividing sea urchin egg and on a novel interpretation of the structure of the cell surface. The cell surface is viewed as being rather thick, of micron dimensions, by virtue of the intimate association of the paucimolecular permeability barrier with an underlying "structural layer," the latter being composed of highly folded molecules. The mechanical properties associated with cleavage are those of this thick membrane as a whole. The elastic modulus of the sea urchin egg

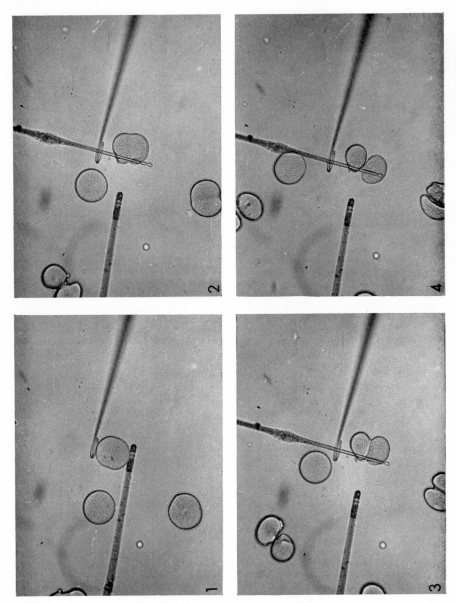

FIG. 88. Impalement of a dividing sea urchin egg on a microneedle passing through the furrow. Cleavage proceeds normally. Photographs by courtesy of Dr. J. M. Mitchison (Mitchison, 1953).

surface was measured by means of an ingenious micro-"elastimeter," a precisely regulated micro suction cup by which the degree of deformation of a point on the surface could be related quantitatively to the applied suction. The relationship found was not that expected of a thin elastic membrane having a "surface tension," but rather that of a thick elastic membrane; as Swann and Mitchison put it, a tennis ball is a better

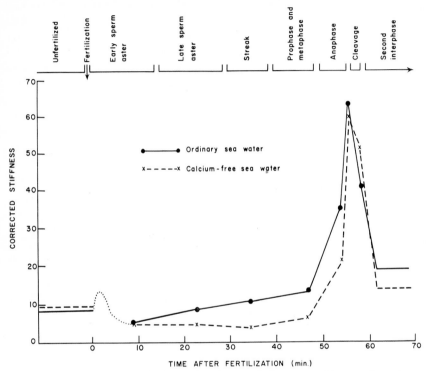

FIG. 89. The stiffness of the surface layers of the sea urchin egg (membrane plus cortex) from fertilization through cleavage. Ordinates represent the relation between negative pressure applied at the surface and the deformation of the surface, calculated as Young's modulus (elastimeter method of Mitchison and Swann, 1954). After Mitchison and Swann (1955).

model than a rubber balloon. At cleavage there appears a dramatic rise in the rigidity of the surface, measured in this way (Fig. 89), and this is most important as one of the precious few data we have on the physics of the surface of the dividing cell, regardless of theory.

Optical changes at the surface at the time of cleavage, notably a decline in birefringence, have been observed by a number of workers (Monroy and Montalenti, 1947; Mitchison and Swann, 1952). In the "expanding membrane" theory these changes are regarded as evidence of disorientation accompanying the expansion of a thick layer of protein molecules folded in a regular array. The changes seem to begin at the poles and to spread toward the equator.

The general picture of the "expanding membrane" mechanism begins with the initiation of the surface changes by a signal received from the centers (possibly in the form of a "structure agent" originating in the chromosomes). The expansion begins at the poles, develops toward the equator, and pushes the equatorial surface progressively into the furrow. In the latest version the surface of the furrow itself is not stretched.

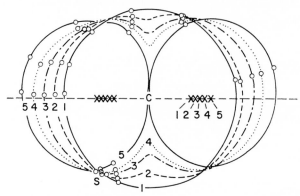

Fig. 90. Movements of the cell surface during cleavage in a sea urchin egg (*Mespilia globulus*). Successive stages of furrowing are superimposed. The small circles mark the successive positions of carbon particles that adhere to the surface. The polar surface stretches, particles moving outward. Particles at the edge of the furrow are carried downward into the furrow. There are four points, one of which is marked S in the diagram, at which the surface is stationary. In three dimensions, these would be represented as stationary rings on either side of the furrow. After Ishizaka (1958).

The topographic details of the behavior of the cell surface are now very well known for the case of the sea urchin egg, thanks to ingenious studies initiated by Dan *et al.* (1937), which have been summarized most recently by Hiramoto (1958). The simple and elegant technique of the Japanese workers consists of mapping the relative movements of kaolin or carbon particles adhering to the surface. Those who wish to do theoretical work on this problem will find an abundance of data in these papers. The essential facts (Fig. 90) are: (1) the cell volume remains constant during cleavage (Hiramoto, 1958); (2) the surface expands at the poles; (3) particles attached to the equatorial surface are pushed or pulled into the furrow; and (4) there are circumferential rings at latitudes just above and below the equator which are stationary (Ishizaka, 1958). The existence of the stationary rings raises interesting problems for any of the theories of cleavage.

Apart from the question whether the driving force in cleavage is best described as a contraction, expansion, or growth, the idea that an *activity* of the surface is involved has considerable appeal to the experienced observer of cell division. Furrow formation often is *localized* to a portion of the cell surface. There are remarkable experiments by Chambers (1951) in which a dividing egg was cut in two along a plane oblique to the equator. The normal furrow continued in its path, dividing each cell fragment into a nucleated portion (at the original poles) and an anucleate fragment (Fig. 84).

4. Reversibility of Furrows

One of the fundamental properties of the cleavage mechanism is that it is reversible up to a "point of no return"; only at this point can we say that the cell actually has divided. Reversal of division furrows is a commonplace event in experimental work. To cite studies that have already been mentioned: Marsland (1951) finds that application of high pressure reverses furrows that seem to the eye to be completed; Roberts and Johnson (1956) state that the furrows in the multipolar *Popilius* spermatocytes often regress so that only two cells actually are produced; and Hiramoto (1956) observes that removal of the mitotic apparatus from sea urchin eggs causes the furrows to regress if the cells are in a calcium-free medium. Many more cases could be marshalled.

5. Internal Events

Hypotheses emphasizing the active role of the cell surface in cleavage have held the center of the stage recently and for very good reasons. But this need not be the whole story and may be only the more conspicuous part of the story. In the early history of the question, a good deal of attention was devoted to the internal events and especially to the asters. The view that the progressive organization of material round the poles was important to the cleavage process played a central part in concepts of cleavage developed by Dalcq and Simon (1932) and J. Gray (1931). The ingenious theory of K. Dan (1943; summary by J. C. Dan, 1948) stimulated a body of experimental work which has lent strong support to the hypothesis that the attachment of astral rays to the cell surface (demonstrated to be a fact under normal conditions in a variety of cleaving eggs) and the elongation of the spindle (which we have seen to be a widespread concomitant of anaphase) might determine the initial stages of furrow formation. This would, of course, apply only to cases where asters were present. In this ingenious model (Fig. 91) the essential points are that the astral rays will cross at the equator and that the elongation of the spindle will bring the tips of the crossed rays (and the points at the surface to which they attach) closer together, "relaxing" the surface in an equatorial band. A number of lines of experimental evidence support particular points in this theory (cf. Ishizaka, 1958), but the natural evidence comes from the correlations between the growth and positions of the asters and the sites where furrowing begins; correla-

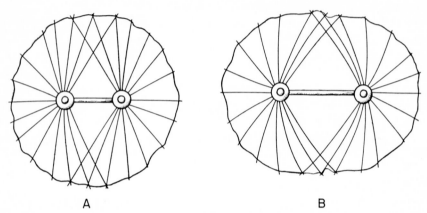

A   B

Fɪɢ. 91. A mechanical model showing the possible relations between spindle elongation, the astral rays, and the determination of the furrow. A. Initial condition. Cell is spherical, astral rays extend to surface. B. Spindle (rigid bar) elongates. The displacement of the astral rays crossed at the center lowers the tension at the equator. The elongation of the spindle, the elongation of the cell as a whole, the expansion of the polar surface, and the initial contraction of the equatorial surface are confirmed by observation. From Dan and Dan (1947).

tions are best seen in cases where the asters are located eccentrically, where the mitotic apparatus is curved, etc. Apart from any specific physical model, the evidence assembled by Dan and his collaborators reopened the question: What is the significance of the asters, which occur so commonly in animal cells and cells of lower plant groups?

There have been a few speculations on the manner in which the mitotic apparatus might influence the furrowing process itself. For example, J. Gray, and later K. Dan, proposed that the growth of the asters might draw cytoplasmic material into the polar spheres, thus developing a "suction" at the equator.

In the above discussion, we have considered only the relations between the mitotic apparatus as a fibrous structure and the formation of the furrow. But there is an interesting body of evidence for the participation of certain substances and particles. Some years ago, Moore (1938) performed a remarkable experiment in which sand dollar (*Dendraster excentricus*) eggs were centrifuged strongly, forming the well-known "dumbbells" in which the centripetal end contained the nucleus, and then were activated chemically. Divisions occurred regularly at the centrifugal end to which the heavier particles were thrown. Although there was no nucleus, the cytasters produced by activation presumably supplied the essentials of a mitotic apparatus. At the nucleated centripetal end of the dumbbell the nucleus sometimes went through division, but the cytoplasm either did not divide at all or division was retarded. Moore concluded that a "cleavage substance," essential for cytokinesis, was associated with the heavy-particle fraction. This observation has been given new meaning by recent work. We have already noted that furrowing of sea urchin eggs, according to Marsland *et al.* (1960), may be induced prematurely by pressure centrifugation. They state that this furrowing seems to depend on the breakdown of certain cytoplasmic particles characterized by vital-staining properties. We have also seen that such particles normally behave in a polarized way during division and concentrate at the asters (p. 298). Kojima (1959b) has shown that if the particles staining with neutral red and other vital dyes are concentrated by centrifugation in eggs of a number of sea urchins and of the echiuroid *Urechis unicinctus* and are unequally distributed between the daughter cells, then only those cells receiving the granules will divide again.

Altogether, it seems likely that cytokinesis may indeed depend on substances present and active in the cell interior. Attempting an interpretation of what they may be contributing, we may take the plant cell as a limiting case. Here it seems that the cell surface that separates daughter cells is formed from within, since there is no sign of furrowing. In Section XII, C, 7 the details of its formation will be considered in terms of the movement of membranous material of the endoplasmic reticulum from poles to equator. At the microscopic level the characteristic features of equatorial partitioning in plants are associated with phragmoplast. Comparable differentiations have been described for animal cells. For example, Selman and Waddington (1955) describe equatorial differentiation in dividing amphibian eggs which includes a group of fibers running perpendicular to the cleavage plane. It is a speculation, but not an absurd one, that even in animal cell division there is a contribution of new membrane from inside the cell, that furrowing is not entirely a matter of stretching or of expanding the original membrane. If so, we might make the following comparison between plant and animal cytokinesis: In plant cytokinesis, to be discussed below, vesicles of the endoplasmic reticulum collect at the poles, move toward the equator, and organize new surface. In large animal cells, such as sea urchin eggs, we may imagine that the vital-staining particles which collect in the astral regions are a similar source of new surface. We need not specify whether this material moves into the equator, expands the surface at the poles, or contributes in both ways. If the plantlike behavior is involved, we can understand why one finds phragmoplastlike structures in some animal cells. If this speculation is not nonsense, one would imagine that the vital-staining granules would be comparable in structure to the material of the endoplasmic reticulum, and this seems likely in view of Rebhun's (1959, 1960) description of their vesicular structure.

There have been a number of attempts to answer the question of the formation of "new" surface in the furrow, and it must be admitted that the answer is sometimes negative (K. Dan, 1954). But the experiments do not exclude at all the idea that the polar regions are expanded by the inclusion of new material.

The total surface area increases at each division, and over a series of divisions the increase obviously exceeds any imaginable "stretching." The question is only whether the cell adds new surface material *during* cytokinesis. Considering the paucimolecular thinness of the plasma membrane, it might not be possible for it to stretch as much as is required at division (28% to 50% according to Wolpert, 1960); the addition of new material from the interior might be necessary. We are now beginning to appreciate the dynamic character of the cell surface, its "turnover" in pinocytosis, the apparent interconvertibility of internal membranes and the plasma membrane. We can imagine that the addition of membrane material at the surface may increase the area in various ways; for example it might bring about the evaginations seen as "bubbling" in dividing mammalian cells or the polar expansion at the surface in eggs (Fig. 90). In short, the surface changes invoked by several theories of furrowing might reflect transactions between the surface and the interior, governed by the poles of the mitotic apparatus.

6. Other Problems

One aspect of cleavage that we do not understand at all is the final process whereby the ingrowing surfaces meet and seal off the daughter cells from each other. All we can say is that this may involve mechanisms of its own, judging from the number of cases where cleavage seems to the eye to be completed but can still be reversed by a variety of means, as by high pressure (Marsland, 1951). Conversely, when a "spindle remnant" persists the furrow may be stabilized at a point where a cytoplasmic bridge is left between the sister cells. The details of such bridge formation in animal cells are given in an electron microscopic study by Fawcett *et al.* (1959).

Another problem—and it is an important field of research in itself—is the association between the formation of the cleavage furrow and the laying down of intercellular "cements" that hold the daughter cells together. This is crucial in all multicellular organisms where embryonic development, and metazoan existence itself, depends on the effectiveness of the binding together of daughter cells.

7. Cytokinesis in Plant Cells

One striking difference between cytokinesis in plant and in animal cells is the early formation of the phragmoplast in the former. It can be clearly seen (Fig. 76), especially in time-lapse films, that the phragmoplast appears in the equator of the mitotic apparatus at late anaphase or telophase, as though it were a product and a part of the mitotic apparatus. We do find counterparts of the phragmoplast in the mitotic apparatus of favorable animal cells. For example, there is the classic "midbody" which appears on the equator of the spindle at telophase (Wilson, 1925). Using isolation procedures, it has been possible to show that the nuclei of sea urchin eggs at the end of telophase are still connected by a bar, the remnant of the spindle, and that this bar is crossed at the equator by a row of granules, very reminiscent of the phragmoplast (K. Dan and Nakajima, 1956). As we have mentioned (Section XI, A), the collection of basophilic material toward the equator is a common feature of the late stages of mitosis in both plant and animal cells. In plant cells, according to Shimamura and Ôta (1956), "a plentiful accumulation of pentosenucleic acid is seen for the first time in the phragmoplast, which is a characteristic mitotic organelle of plant cells, and the phragmoplast begins to develop after the daughter chromosomes contract at the poles."

Electron microscopic evidence now takes us a long way toward a unified picture accommodating many of these facts. In the work of Porter and Machado (1960), it is seen that elements of the endoplasmic reticulum, tubules and lamellar bodies, move from the poles toward the equator during anaphase, passing between the chromosomes in a way that suggests to the authors that they move through channels of least resistance between the fibrous elements of the spindle itself. This movement, as we have remarked, may account for the interzonal RNA described by light microscopy. As the fronts meet at the equator, they form a rather tight latticework that extends laterally toward the surface and

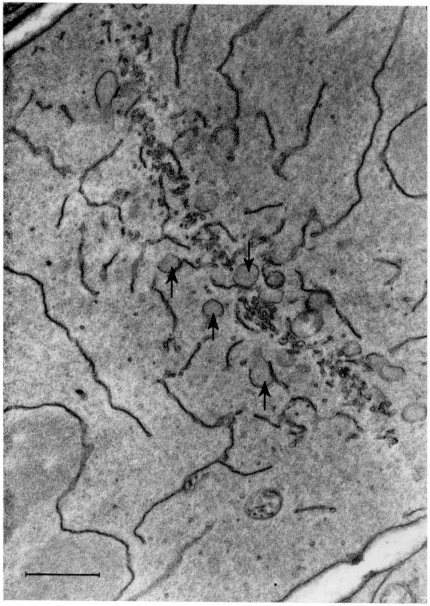

FIG. 92. An early stage in cell-plate formation in onion root tip. Telophase nuclei are seen. Endoplasmic reticulum is concentrating at the equator as a cell plate, whose edges have not reached the surface. Particles marked with arrows are phragmosomes, which are thought to contribute to the formation of the new cell wall. Photograph by courtesy of Dr. K. Porter (Porter and Machado, 1960).

marks the beginnings of the partition between the sister cells (Fig. 92). A membrane-limited class of particles called the "phragmosomes" also collects at the equator. If such a development of the endoplasmic reticulum takes place in the animal cell, corresponding to the movements of RNA, it would account for the equatorial granules observed by Dan and Nakajima (1956) and for the apparent lateral "flow" of basophilic material from equator to surface in the newt fibroblast (Boss, 1955). What is more appealing for speculative purposes is that the collection and fusion of the membranous components of the endoplasmic reticulum presents an ideal solution to the problem of formation of new plasma membrane between the daughter cells. This is a problem in animal cells, for even there cytokinesis may involve the organization of some area of new membrane. In plant cells it is critical, since we cannot, on the basis of present knowledge, invoke the stretching of the parent cell membrane to account for the partitioning of the cells.

The subsequent events of cytokinesis in plant cells involve the completion of a cell wall in all its complexity.

8. Conclusions

There is substantial experimental support for a number of hypothetical mechanisms of cytokinesis in animal cells, stressing (1) mechanisms analogous to those used in ameboid movement, (2) a contractile equatorial ring, (3) expansion of the membrane, and (4) the interaction of the spindle and asters with the cell surface. No one of these has been accepted as the definitive solution of the problem, and it may turn out that all are involved in one way or another. (5) In plant cells the movement of elements of the endoplasmic reticulum from the poles, through the spindle, and the fusion and later spreading of this material at the equator, may be the essential event of normal cytokinesis.

XIII. PHYSIOLOGY OF THE DIVIDING CELL

In the preceding sections, we have attempted to dissect the mitotic mechanisms as such from the operations of the cell as a whole. It goes without saying that the mitotic equipment does not function autonomously, and we now will consider the status of the entire cell in division.

A. The Synchrony of Mitotic Events

The most vivid demonstration of the influence of the "internal environment" of the cell on mitotic processes is given by the synchronous performance of so many of these processes. Let us review some examples: (1) The whole mitotic cycle proceeds synchronously in many, although not all, multinucleated cells. (2) Even more remarkable is the observation that a mitotic cycle and endomitotic cycle will proceed synchronously when only one of two nuclei in a cell is provided with mitotic centers. (3) Cleveland's (1949) observations on *Holomastig-otoides*, where the chromosomes can be observed through their whole life cycle, indicate that both chromosomes of this organism remain perfectly in step throughout the cycle. (4) It has been noted that even in an unusual case where two nuclei in a cell do not go through mitosis at the same rate, they may enter prophase at the same time (Holden and Mota, 1956). (5) During division itself, the initial separation of the sister chromosomes at the beginning of anaphase happens at the same time in chromosomes that are engaged by the mitotic apparatus and in akinetic chromosome fragments that are not (Carlson, 1956; Zirkle, 1956). (6) At the end of mitosis, the chromosomes appear to surround themselves with nuclear membranes and to enter the interphase condition even when they fail to fuse, and instead form karyomeres or micronuclei. (7) Individual chromosome movements in metakinesis and in anaphase normally are well coordinated. Descriptions of lagging and precocious chromosomes are very common in the cytological literature, but even here, we can contemplate the controls imposed by the cell as a whole. For example, if a chromosome is delayed in reaching the metaphase plate, as in the case of the "centrophilic" chromosomes in newt cells, the others will "wait" for it to arrive before they enter anaphase.

From the synchrony of so many processes we infer that rate-determining events may be governed by underlying changes in the intracellular environment that can be shared. We shall hardly understand how the mitotic cycle is driven if we look only to the internal economy of the mitotic equipment.

B. *Energetics of the Mitotic Cycle*

The act of mitosis obviously involves the performance of work. Possibly because lazy humans tend to associate "real" work with active movement, in contrast with the kinds of work that we know only through thermodynamic symbols, we might intuitively expect to find mitosis to be associated with high levels of the metabolic processes associated with energy mobilization. We shall see that this is not so. Either the energy requirements of division are not as great as we imagine, or else they are met by a pre-established hoard, the "energy reservoir" discussed earlier (Section III, D, 4).

1. Respiration and Glycolysis

A linkage of mitotic cell division to aerobic processes obviously cannot be obligatory, for the cells of anaerobic organisms reproduce by mitosis. Aerobic sources can be obligatory for the division of certain cells, for example, the sea urchin egg (Krahl, 1950) and mouse ear epidermis (Bullough, 1952): cells that are preparing to divide fail to do so if the oxygen supply is curtailed. Even in these cases, the oxygen requirement is associated only with the predivision events or possibly with prophase. In one case where mitosis has been stopped at all stages by removal of oxygen, it was necessary to lower the oxygen tension of the cells—pea root tips—far below the level at which respiration became negligible (Amoore 1961a, b). Thus the arrest of mitosis was not attributable to energy requirements, but to some other oxygen requirement. In this connection, it is interesting that oxygen at high pressures will arrest division in sand-dollar eggs (Rosenbaum and Wittner, 1960). Prolonged exposure to anoxic conditions may lead to mitotic abnormalities. For example, Marty (1954) and Gavaudan (1956) describe disturbances of spindle formation in wheat seedlings after a period of growth under lowered oxygen tension. Cells other than those adapted to anaerobic existence can divide in the absence of oxygen. Examples are frog eggs (Barth and Barth, 1954), fish eggs (Devillers and Rosenberg, 1953), a number of vertebrate cells in culture (Laser, 1933; Harris, 1956), and grasshopper neuroblasts (Gaulden et al., 1949).

The attempt to correlate the work of cell division with respiratory changes has a long history, well summarized by Brachet (1947).

Several detailed studies using methods of high sensitivity are now available. Erickson (1947) and H. Stern and Kirk (1948) have exploited the synchrony of microspore divisions in *Lilium* and *Trillium,* respectively, using sensitive capillary respirometers. Both studies show a striking *decrease* in the oxygen consumption of the cells *during* mitosis and a rather definite increase in the period just preceding mitosis (Fig. 93). Zeuthen (1946, 1949, 1953a, 1955) has followed the respiration of eggs of amphibians, sea urchins, sand dollars, ascidians, and of the gephyrean worm *Urechis* by means of his ingenious series of Cartesian diver respirometers, and he finds in each case that the oxygen consumption fluctuates rhythmically during a series of divisions (Fig. 94) though the fluctuations are not large. These cells are all of the type in which there is no growth between divisions and no prolonged interphase, and it can be assumed that the respiratory rhythms are associated with the mitotic cycle itself. Correlating the rhythms with the state of the nuclei, he comes to the conclusion that the rising phase is associated with the period when the nuclei are "closed" (the chromosome material being

contained within a nuclear membrane) and the falling phase with the
period when the nuclei are "open" (the period of chromosome movement). In colchicine-treated eggs, where the chromosome cycles persist
even though there are no divisions, the respiratory rhythms are preserved. Therefore, both the studies on microspore divisions and on the
cleavage of eggs seem to be telling us that the visibly active part of the
mitotic cycle is associated with a lowered respiration, while immediate
preparations for division may involve increased oxidative activity.

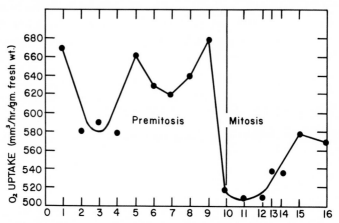

Fig. 93. Respiration of *Trillium* anthers during preparation for microspore divisions and during division. During the period of preparation, the microspores are
growing. The respiration drops before the beginning of the period of active division
and is low during that period. Stage 10 marks the appearance of mitosis. By stage
15, most of the nuclei have divided. After Stern and Kirk (1948).

Scholander *et al.* (1952; 1958) have examined the respiration of a
number of echinoderm eggs during division, employing a new "reference
diver" respirometer capable of measuring the oxygen consumption of a
single egg. They did not consistently observe the waves of respiration
found by Zeuthen, though these appeared in some individual cells. Possible reasons for the discrepancies are discussed by Zeuthen (1953a,
1960).

There is a substantial body of literature on the effects of respiratory
inhibitors on cell division, which has been summarized most recently
by Biesele (1958, pp. 15-28). Krahl (1950) tabulated the effects of a
large number of inhibitors on a single cell type, the sea urchin egg. A
generalized conclusion is possible, and it is unnecessary here to review
the details as they apply to particular cell types: cells can be prevented
from entering division by blocking oxidative phosphorylations. The block

may be imposed upon terminal steps (as in the cases of inhibition by anoxia or by CO) or more immediately, as in the effects of substituted phenols (Clowes, 1951). The inhibition must be imposed before the cell has advanced into prophase; it clearly has to do with preparations or trigger events that are not completed until just before the chromosomes visibly go into action. Once the cell has passed the critical point, it cannot

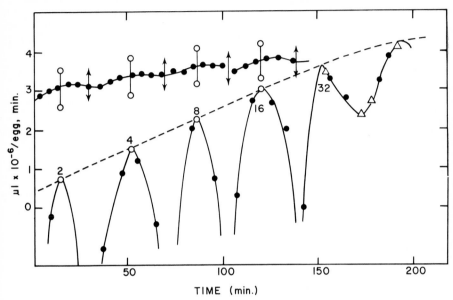

FIG. 94. Respiration of sea urchin eggs (*Psammechinus microtuberculatus*) during the first four divisions following fertilization. The upper curve represents oxygen consumption, measured by a sensitive Cartesian diver respirometer. A sample of 413 eggs was measured. The lower curves show the numbers of interphase nuclei, as determined by direct observation on a control sample. These curves drop to low levels each time the population enters synchronous division. It is evident that the period of actual mitosis (⟷ on the respiration curve) is the time of minimum respiratory activity, whereas the interphase period (o—o) is the time of highest respiratory activity. After Holter and Zeuthen (1957).

be stopped by metabolic inhibitors unless these also have some direct action on the structure of the mitotic apparatus. Some substances, urethane for example (I. Cornman, 1954), may be expected to act both as metabolic inhibitors and as inhibitors of spindle formation, leading to somewhat more complex results.

In cases where the effect of metabolic inhibitors on both respiration and mitosis can be measured, mitosis does not always seem to be very sensitive to the curtailment of respiration. For example, in the best-studied case of the sea urchin egg, the cyanide concentration must be sufficient to suppress respiration to about 35% of its control value before division is fully blocked, and a comparable figure is given for the effects of carbon monoxide (Krahl, 1950).

We can conclude, with Swann (1957), that the work of mitosis does not on the whole make very great demands on the cell's capabilities for providing energy. If there is a period when demands of mitosis call forth increased metabolic efforts, it is at the time of transition from interphase to prophase, as one can see in the curves of Stern and Kirk (1948) and Zeuthen (1953a).

The idea that the energy requirements for mitosis might be met by glycolysis has a long history, as Stern (1959a) pointed out in an important review of the metabolic problems of mitosis. It has roots in Warburg's ideas about the relations between glycolysis and cell multiplication and in some of Rapkine's (1931) work on the significance of SH in mitosis. Yet there has been little in the way of direct investigation based on the study of cells in division rather than mere correlations between population growth and glycolysis. Recently, Nasatir and Stern (1959) have investigated the levels of several enzymes of the glycolytic pathway, aldolase and d-glyceraldehyde-3-phosphate dehydrogenase, in microspores of *Lilium*. They find that the activities of these enzymes, measured *in vitro*, were low during the period of mitosis, compared to activities during other periods in the development of the microspores. This parallels the decline in respiration of the same cells during division.

2. Energy Sources for Mitosis

The straightforward study of metabolism during the kinetic phases of mitosis has given us no evidence that the operations of the mitotic apparatus depend on oxidations that take place during this period. The evidence is not sufficiently detailed to exclude a glycolytic channel, but the hypothesis that mitosis proceeds at the expense of *stored energy* has excited the greatest interest.

The simplest possibility—to the biologist of this generation, if not to the cell—would be that ATP was stored in preparation for division and that the operation of the mitotic apparatus was a case of mechanochemical coupling not unlike that observed in muscle models (Weber, 1955, 1958). Some evidence in favor of this view can be cited. The work of Hoffmann-Berling (1954a), demonstrating changes in the spindle when "anaphase models" (cells in anaphase killed and extracted with cold glycerol) are supplied with ATP has already been mentioned. Barnett (1953) reported that the inhibition of mitosis in *Arbacia* and *Chaetop-*

terus eggs by a number of means, including cyanide and anoxia, was reversed upon addition of ATP. Butros (1956) could obtain no such reversal in eggs of *Ilyanassa*. H. Lettré (1952b, 1954) correlates chromosome movement with ATP on the basis of experiments in which ATP appears to overcome the blocking effects of colchicine in tissue cultures. Benitez *et al.* (1954) describe similar experiments but interpret them in terms of effects of ATP and colchicine on the length of interphase.

Kriszat and Runnström (1951) observed that the inhibitory effects of dinitrophenol, colchicine, and hypertonic conditions on the division of sea urchin eggs were somewhat relieved by ATP, but adenylic acid and pyrophosphate were also effective (Kriszat, 1954), and the authors refrain from interpreting the results in terms of an energetic role of ATP. These few fragments of evidence do not make the strongest case for the driving of mitosis through stored ATP. Perhaps we cannot expect too much from experiments in which ATP is supplied to the living cell. It would have to be established that it penetrates cells without being dephosphorylated and that its action is not attributable to its properties as a chelating agent. In the case of the living yeast cell there is evidence that it is dephosphorylated at the surface (Rothstein, 1954), and in the case of living muscle its activity has been attributed to its chelating power (Falk, 1956).

It is necessary to distinguish clearly the possible role of ATP as the immediate agent of energy transfer to the mitotic apparatus and as the site of the "energy store." The former hypothesis implies that ATP combines specifically with the mitotic apparatus, and it is a testable possibility. But there are many cases where the "bulk storage" of "energy" (to compound an atrocity) must be located in a compound other than ATP, to be transferred to a working mechanism via a low concentration of ATP which is functioning essentially catalytically. An example of such an ATP-regenerating system is that driving the incorporation of amino acids into liver microsomes (Zamecnik and Keller, 1954). Thus, ATP might well be the immediate energy source for mitosis, and quite another substance could serve as the "reservoir."

Information on the actual levels of ATP and related compounds during the mitotic cycle is sparse. Swann (1953, 1954b) states that the ATP level in the sea urchin egg does not appear to fluctuate during division. However, Barnett and Downey (1955) do describe a cyclical change in "high-energy phosphate" (defined by hydrolysis properties) during the division cycle in the sea urchin *Lytechinus* and the polychete *Chaetopterus*, the values rising between divisions and falling at the end of each division. We have already considered the data on the rise and fall of nucleoside triphosphates before division in *Tetrahymena* (Fig. 20). The time course is not exactly that to be expected if these triphosphates were being stored for division and expended during the visibly active part of the division process, but the fluctuations could be part of a somewhat more complex energy storage and transfer system. A rather similar, but not identical, fluctuation of soluble phosphate in *Tetrahymena* has been described by Scherbaum *et al.* (1959).

The hypothesis that the energy for cell division is drawn from a prefilled "reservoir" is one of the most stimulating guides to the physiology of cell division. It does account for the indifference of the dividing cell to metabolic inhibition, but it is not a simple hypothesis once the specifications of the reservoir have been drawn up precisely, as has been done by Swann (1953). A puddle of ATP will not do, for we would expect it to be drained during the inhibition of division of CO and similar agents. The putative reservoir is not so drained in the sea urchin egg at least, though it may be in *Tetrahymena* (Section III, D, 4). Since the hypothetical reservoir for the next division can be filling while that for the current division is being drained (Fig. 18), it is imaginable that the energy supply is actually associated with the mitotic apparatus. Indeed it might be *built into* the MA, which would be looked upon as an activated system whose visible "work" required no further demands on external energy sources. Such a view would be in harmony with our other experiences with the performance of biological work, where activation precedes the purposeful end reaction, and the latter appears to go spontaneously.

An intermediate possibility would be the discovery of a pool of some special high-energy compound which combined only with the mitotic system at the time of division. Such a compound is being sought (Swann, 1957) but has not yet been found. Finally, we must leave open the possibilities that the energy is supplied by metabolic pathways not affected by inhibitors which have been tried, or that the energy requirements are so very low that the residual supply after experimental inhibition is adequate.

C. *Metabolic Status of the Dividing Cell*

Although the main outlines of the energy problems of the dividing cell have been drawn, the study of its metabolism at a level worthy of modern biochemistry has scarcely begun. As we have seen, only fragments of information are available even about so simple a matter as the ATP levels. The patterns of enzymes, of their activators and inhibitors and of their associations with functional particles and other cell structures remain to be studied.

1. Thiols

Much of the work that has been done so far has drawn its inspiration from Rapkine's conception of the regulatory role of SH groups in the mitotic process (reviewed by Brachet, 1947). Some of its possible implications for the mitotic apparatus itself have been discussed (Section IX, B, 2), but, as has been stressed by H. Stern (1956, 1959a, b), changes in the concentration of glutathione and other soluble thiols would certainly have broader meaning for the metabolism of the dividing cells. Working with the synchronized anthers of *Lilium*, H. Stern finds a striking rise in the soluble SH at the onset of nuclear division, or just preceding it. One such rise precedes zygotene of meiosis, the second precedes microsporocyte mitosis. The division period itself seems to be associated with a decline in soluble SH. The details of the picture are somewhat different in *Trillium* (Fig. 60), where the second peak is replaced by a "shoulder" in the decline following the meiotic peak, but again there is a decline of soluble SH during the division periods. Stern's conclusion is that "meiosis and mitosis have comparatively high requirements for soluble sulfhydryl compounds." While the total protein SH of the cells did not simply mirror the soluble SH, a decrease in the former was associated with meiotic diakinesis and with microspore mitosis (Fig. 60). This may be related to the bonding of the mitotic apparatus, but it is bound to have broader import for the activity of the numerous SH enzymes that must be participating in the work of the dividing cell. Stern and Timonen (1954) have also described changes in ascorbic acid levels associated with mitosis in lily anthers.

In the alga *Chlorella*, whose growth-division relations may be controlled by cyclic illumination (Section XV, B), sulfur metabolism can be shown to play a unique part in cell division (Hase *et al.*, 1957, 1958). If the nutritional sulfur supply is limited, a level can be found at which the cells can still grow and synthesize DNA in the light but cannot divide. The cells can complete one nuclear division without cytoplasmic division under these conditions. Division can be restored by supplying sulfate and nitrate. It was shown that a sulfur-containing compound soluble in trichloroacetic acid increased greatly in quantity at the time of division, and this compound was identified as a peptide-nucleotide complex containing cysteine, several other amino acids, adenine and uracil in nucleotide linkages, and some unidentified components (Hase *et al.*, 1959). These observations recall the findings of Sakai and Dan (1959) on sea urchin eggs, in which a "Rapkine cycle" was associated with a TCA-soluble polypeptide other than glutathione (Section IX, B, 2).

A comparable demonstration of a special relation between sulfur metabolism and division in algal cells has been given in studies on temperature-synchronized *Astasia* (Padilla and James, 1960) and light-synchronized *Euglena* (Cook and James, 1960). In both the time of division was very much reduced, relative to the total generation time, by supplementation of the defined nutrient medium with the sulfur-containing amino acids.

2. *Mitochondria*

Long before the emergence of the modern conceptions of the function of mitochondria as centers of enzyme activities associated with oxidative phosphorylations, it was recognized that they comport themselves in a definite way during mitosis. "Chondriokinesis" was described by Wilson (1925, pp. 163-165) as one of the characteristic phenomena of the dividing cell. The mitochondria typically are not contained *within* the mitotic apparatus, as has been shown most clearly in recent electron microscopic studies (e.g., Selby, 1953; K. R. Porter, 1955; Kurosumi, 1958; Gross, 1957), and indeed a satisfactory explanation of the formation of the mitotic apparatus must include an explanation of how mitochondria are evicted from the space that is occupied by the apparatus. In some cases, such as the meiotic divisions of the scorpion *Opisthacanthus*, described by Wilson (1916), the mitochondria seem to aggregate into a definite number of spherical masses, which seem to enter the mitotic apparatus and are distributed equally to the daughter cells with high but not perfect accuracy. In other cases, they may form equal groups at the polar sides of the nucleus, possibly in association with the centers. Wilson cites numerous cases among insects in which the rodlike mitochondria or chains of mitochondria seem to be oriented with respect to the centers. Recent photographic and cinematographic studies on a favorite material, the living grasshopper spermatocyte, have brought to light a number of details of chondriokinesis (Fig. 95). The following description is taken from Nakahara (1952). At metaphase the mitochondria are still in the form of short rods scattered through the cell. At anaphase they assemble in long chains, lying very close to the surface of the spindle. As anaphase proceeds the chains gather into bundles which are quite rigorously parallel to the spindle axis and which seem to elongate as the chromosomes separate. At telophase the bundles stretch between the sister nuclei "like bridges" and are cut into two approximately equal masses by the cleavage furrow. In certain abnormal cells Makino and Nakahara (1955) note that the mitochondrial orientation persists even when the regression of the spindle causes the nuclear material to be restricted to one daughter cell, and division thus produces an "anuclear bud." The plane of cleavage still cuts midway through the mitochondrial bundles, leading the authors to conclude that the mitochondrial bundles play a decisive part in cell elongation and the determination of the division furrow. Additional details of mitochondrial behavior in the division of grasshopper spermatocytes are given by Barer and Joseph (1957), who stress associations between the mitochondria and the nuclear membrane. They make the interesting suggestion that enzyme systems involved in the formation of the nuclear membranes at telophase and their "lysis" at the end of prophase might be associated with the mitochondria.

We might well imagine that daughter cells would fare badly if they began their individual lives with an elaborate cookbook in the form of a

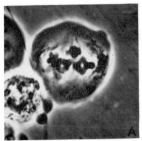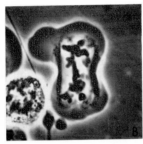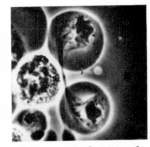

FIG. 95.   The segregation of mitochondria during the first meiotic division of grasshopper spermatocytes. Phase contrast photographs of *Chorthippus*. A. Metaphase. Mitochondria clustering around the equatorial region. Spindle is clear. B. Anaphase. Bundles of elongated mitochondrial masses on either side of spindle.   C. Telophase. Sheaves of mitochondria have been cut in two by division furrow.   Photographs by Drs. R. Barer and E. Joseph (Barer and Joseph, 1957).

set of genes, but no cookstove on which to concoct new substance. We see now that the division mechanisms may include fairly elaborate devices, in the forms of "chondriokinesis," to meet this need. Any understanding of the dividing cell as a whole will have to include an explanation of the behavior of mitochondria, which includes, in some cases, directed movements, aggregation in specific forms, and striking orientations. One older hypothesis relates mitochondrial orientation to streaming movements in the cell (Pollister, 1941), but all too little is known of the behavioral attributes of these organelles, whose structure and biochemistry are beginning to be known so well. Obviously, they may be influenced by the same agencies that guide the mitotic apparatus in time and place.

Some reported changes in the mitochondria of the dividing cell may relate to the metabolic trends that we have been discussing. Chèvremont and Frederic (1952, 1955) and Frederic (1954) describe the attenuation, fragmentation, and even disappearance of mitochondria in cultured chick embryonic cells during mitosis. The "inactivation" of mitochondria during division has also been proposed by H. Lettré and Schleich (1955). Ågrell (1955b) made counts of visible mitochondria in living sea urchin eggs, and recorded a pronounced drop in their numbers, without apparent change in size, at the time of the dissolution of the nuclear membrane, and a rise just before cytokinesis (Fig. 96). These changes are harmonized with Zeuthen's measurements (Fig. 94). Taken together, the two sets of data would be saying that the period when the nuclei are "open" (to use Zeuthen's term) is one of lowered respiration, which in turn is correlated with a lowered number of visible mitochondria.

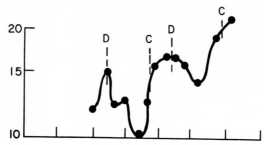

Fɪɢ. 96. Numbers of visible mitochondria in the living sea urchin egg (*Psammechinus miliaris*) during several divisions. Particles stainable with Janus green were counted in slightly flattened living eggs, with the aid of phase contrast microscopy. Ordinates represent the number of mitochondria per 1000 μ^3 of cytoplasmic volume. Abscissa is time. *D* denotes the time of breakdown of the nuclear membrane, *C* denotes the beginning of cleavage. The striking decrease during mitosis may be correlated with the fall in respiration shown in Fig. 94. It is not known whether the mitochondria actually disintegrate or whether they fragment or undergo a change in optical properties which affects their visibility. From Ågrell (1955b).

It is evident that these observations on the breakdown and build-up of mitochondria during division are in accord with the generalization that the period of division is one of depressed metabolic and synthetic functions. But we are hardly in a secure position to assess the metabolic significance of the gross fluctuations that we can see in the living cell.

3. *Endoplasmic Reticulum*

In addition to the mitochondria certain other structures offer clues as to the metabolic status of the dividing cell. For example, the organization of the endoplasmic reticulum is thought to be correlated with synthetic activities. What happens to it during division? K. R. Porter (1955) indicated that the complex endoplasmic reticulum characteristic of interphase in a cultured rat sarcoma loses much of its structure as the cell enters prophase, being "transformed to a discontinuous system of spherical vesicles which are confined to the peripheral regions of the cytoplasm." It is also possible that the system is reduced in volume as well as losing its organization as a "complex of connected canaliculae and vesicles in which the latter elements adopt many bizarre shapes." Early in interphase the reticulum returns to the form just described.

A point of view concerning the endoplasmic reticulum that is particularly revelant to mitosis stresses the opinion (to quote Porter and Machado, 1960) that "the nuclear envelope through its structure and its continuity with the cytoplasmic elements of the endoplasmic reticulum is properly included as part of the system, and since it is present in all forms thus far examined, except bacteria, it may appropriately be regarded as the most universal and constant expression of this membrane-limited system." It this is so, the breakdown or altered structure of the nuclear membrane during mitosis would in itself reflect a close link between the synthetic status of the dividing cell and its structural organization. If the nuclear membrane is a crucial part of the endoplasmic reticulum, viewed as the structural base of protein synthesis, might not the breakdown of the membrane (for which we can find more obvious reasons related to chromosome movements) actually signify a disorganization of synthetic machinery? This question, which we cannot answer, is relevant to the view (Mazia and Prescott, 1954, Stern, 1959a) that entry of the cell into mitosis is in some ways the functional equivalent of enucleation (p. 362).

D. A General View of the Metabolic Status of the Dividing Cell

The entrance of the cell into mitotic division commits it to a complete structural transformation. The chromosomes coil into compact masses, the nucleolus usually breaks down, the nuclear membrane disappears or is changed drastically, nonchromosomal contents of the nucleus are lost to the cytoplasm, the mitochondria undergo a number of changes and some may disappear, and the endoplasmic reticulum may lose its characteristic structure. A mitotic apparatus, sometimes huge, occupies much of the cell interior. Even the surface organization clearly changes in many kinds of cells. Cells which normally are irregular in shape and extend ameboid processes, such as amebae or fibroblasts, become spherical when they enter division. For example, the newt fibroblasts figured by Boss (1954) begin to round up in late prophase and are spherical by the end of metaphase. Dividing amebae lose their ability to adhere to surfaces. In ciliates division is marked by a striking reduction in movement. For example, dividing *Tetrahymena* actually tend to settle to the bottom of a culture, so sluggish they become, and indeed one learns to recognize an individual that is about to divide by its behavior. In plants streaming may stop during mitosis, as in the staminal hairs of *Tradescantia,* but there are plant cells in which streaming continues during division (cases cited by H. Stern, 1956).

Thus, many of the visible activities of cells suggest that the period of division is a sluggish one physiologically, as though the cell concentrates on reproduction to the neglect of its commonplace housekeeping activities. Such a view has been expressed by Lettré (1952b), Agrell (1955b), Mazia (1956b), and others. Nor need this view be restricted to the more obvious physiological activities. C. Stern (1938) has summarized convincing evidence that the genes are operative between divisions, and not during division. When the cell is no longer quite one individual nor yet quite two, it might be confused as well as preoccupied.

What is the physiological status of the dividing cell at a deeper level, and what does it mean? We have seen some evidence that the energy-yielding systems of the cell operate at a lowered rate during division; certainly they do not operate at a higher rate than in the interphase cell. We would like to know whether the biosynthetic activities continue during division. In some cases there is evidence that they do not. For example, Prescott's studies on the life cycle of *Amoeba proteus* (1955) show that the sum of the "reduced weights" of the daughter cells is no greater than that of the parent cell entering division. There is no growth in "dry mass" during division. Similarly, in synchronized populations of *Tetrahymena,* the period of division is one in which growth (measured as increase in cell nitrogen) is arrested (Hamburger and Zeuthen, 1960; Zeuthen, 1958). Mitchison's (1957) measurements with the interference microscope on fission in yeast cells do show a growth in mass during division, but growth in volume is arrested. Much more attention should be given this point. The decision whether simultaneous cell growth and mitotic division is possible or usual, should not rest on a few cases.

A few fragments of evidence suggest that at least certain kinds of biosynthesis come to a halt during division. Perhaps the most elegant study is that of Zeuthen (1953b), who followed the *growth of the respiratory rate,* which is interpretable as a measure of the synthesis of respiratory enzymes and structures, in single *Tetrahymena* growing under optimal conditions. He observed a steady increase between divisions, but a striking leveling at the time of division (Fig. 97). It can easily be concluded that these cells stop making respiratory machinery during the early part of the division period, although other interpretations, such as the intervention of inhibitors, are conceivable. Studies of the uptake and incorporation of isotope-labeled precursors also suggest that biosynthetic activities may decline during division. Taylor and Taylor (1953) found that the incorporation of P^{32} and S^{35} into macromolecules decreased during microspore mitosis. The uptake of $P^{32} O_4$ by sea urchin eggs (Zeuthen, 1951)

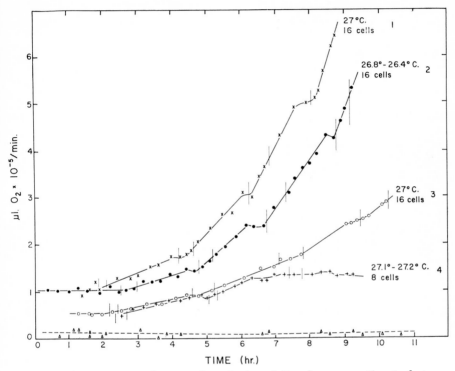

FIG. 97. Increase in the rate of respiration of *Tetrahymena pyriformis* during successive cell cycles, beginning with a single cell. Respiration was measured with a very sensitive Cartesian diver system. At each division, the first vertical mark denotes the onset of division activity, the second the complete separation of the daughter cells. The curves suggest that the growth of respiratory activity, which may speculatively be associated with the synthesis of respiratory enzymes, is arrested before the visible onset of division and is resumed at a *doubled rate* before the completion of fission. These ciliates do not divide by conventional mitosis, and it is not possible to assign the changes to the mitotic phases. After Zeuthen (1953b).

and by synchronized *Tetrahymena* (Zeuthen, 1958; Hamburger and Zeuthen, 1960) declines during division. In *Amoeba proteus* the rate of phosphate uptake during division is less than half that during interphase (Mazia and Prescott, 1954). More recently, de Terra (1960) has measured an extraordinary decline in the uptake and incorporation of radioactive phosphate during division in *Stentor* (Table XII). In all these cases it is conceivable that the transport of the precursor into the cell is the limiting factor, and this would be an interesting finding in itself. So far as the present discussion is concerned, evidence that the levels of biosynthesis change during division is of importance, whichever step in the chain is responsible. Since such evidence is rather fragmentary, a discussion of whether the supplies of precursors or the actual synthetic mechanisms are depressed is premature.

TABLE XII

UPTAKE OF $P^{32}O_4$ BY NORMAL *Stentor* IN INTERPHASE, CONTRASTED WITH DIVIDING CELLS AND CELLS WITHOUT NUCLEI[a]

Experiment no. (duplicate samples in each experiment)	Uptake by 3 cells from medium containing 25 µc./ml. carrier-free $P^{32}O_4$ (counts per minute)			
	Interphase[b] with nucleus	Interphase[b] anucleate	Dividing with nucleus	Dividing anucleate
1	17,108	321	761	535
	16,842	549	288	756
2	9,837	106	214	45
	7,468	32	284	322
3	5,314	327	293	82
	4,294	342	201	25

[a] From de Terra (1960).
[b] Six hours after preceding division.

In an earlier interpretation (Mazia and Prescott, 1954), the physiological depression of the cell in mitosis was correlated with the nuclear cycle. If the interphase structure of the nucleus is thought to be essential to its functions in the growing, synthesizing cell, the prophase transformations might be viewed as a *functional enucleation*. When an *Amoeba* is deprived of its nucleus, there is a sharp and immediate decline in P^{32} incorporation (Mazia and Hirschfield, 1950; Brachet, 1955), and this is one of the most striking stigmata of the anucleate condition. In this respect entrance into division has exactly the same consequences as removal of the nucleus.

Although this view still has a very narrow foundation, it is reasonable enough as a basis for further efforts. The interphase structure of the nucleus *is* characteristic of most growing and synthesizing cells, the nucleus does exert controls over synthetic activities; it is reasonable to imagine that drastic changes in nuclear organization will affect synthetic activities. At the time the hypothesis was stated, the author leaned toward the correlation of these changes with the state of condensation of the chromosome material. More recent work (e.g., Brachet, 1957, pp. 133-135; McMaster-Kaye and Taylor, 1958; Goldstein and Micou, 1959) increasingly draws attention to the nucleolus as the active center of current metabolic transactions involving the nucleus. The prophase changes in this organelle might be the starting point for the physiological depression of the dividing cell.

Conclusions

The questions have been asked: Do important biosynthetic activities of the cell come to a halt during division? Are growth and division activities physiologically incompatible? On the basis of fragmentary evidence, we infer that the period of division is a time of depression for anabolic functions.

E. Some Physical Changes in the Dividing Cell

Mitosis is accompanied by some striking changes in the physical state or texture of the cytoplasm, which have been assessed as viscosity changes. At least one generalization can be drawn from the more complete and more critical studies which we owe to the late L. V. Heilbrunn and his students (Heilbrunn and Wilson, 1948; Heilbrunn, 1956) and to Carlson (1946): *The completion of the mitotic apparatus at metaphase is accompanied by a sharp decrease in the viscosity of the cytoplasm outside the apparatus* (Fig. 98). This viscosity was measured on various marine eggs by the method of centrifugal sedimentation of cytoplasmic particles (Heilbrunn, 1920, 1921; Heilbrunn and Wilson, 1948) and on the grasshopper neuroblast by Carlson (1946) by judgment of the rapidity of Brownian movement. The former method is more quantitative, but the latter is advantageous in dealing with possible local differences. Earlier and somewhat conflicting literature is reviewed by these authors. A high cytoplasmic viscosity is generally thought to be an expression of gelation, the result of linear aggregations of molecules and of the formation of networks of such chains; the clotting of fibrin has been a model (Heilbrunn, 1956). The decrease in cytoplasmic viscosity at the time the spindle is forming could conceivably result from the mere solation of such a gel. But a most reasonable alternative, pointed out by Heilbrunn as long ago as 1920, is that the fibrous material is condensing as a spindle, leaving the peripheral cytoplasm in a more liquid state.

While it seems to be agreed that the cytoplasmic viscosity decreases at the time the mitotic apparatus is assembled, the descriptions of the prior events are in apparent disagreement. In egg cells, which were studied by the Heilbrunn group, mitosis is anticipated by a "mitotic gelation," an increase in cytoplasmic viscosity. In grasshopper neuroblasts, Carlson did not observe such a period of high viscosity. Differences in method could, conceivably, account for the discordant results, but it is more interesting to consider the differences between the types of cells which were studied. In the egg cells, the mitotic apparatus is almost certainly assembled outside the nucleus, and the quantitative contributions from the nucleus could not be large. The first steps in the assembly of the gel, before it concentrates as a mitotic apparatus, could be reflected as an increase in the viscosity of the cytoplasm as a whole, and

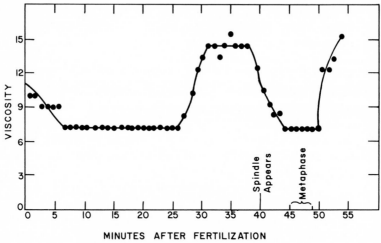

MINUTES AFTER FERTILIZATION

Fig. 98. Changes in relative viscosity of the cytoplasm of *Chaetopterus* eggs in the course of the first division following fertilization. Viscosity was measured in terms of the time of centrifugation required to achieve a certain degree of stratification of cytoplasmic particles at a constant centrifugal force. After Heilbrunn and Wilson (1948).

the mitotic gelation shown in Fig. 98 could be accounted for. In the case of the grasshopper neuroblast, there is reason to believe that a good deal of the material of the mitotic apparatus is assembled in the nucleus, even though a small central spindle is seen in the cytoplasm before the breakdown of the nuclear membrane (K. Kawamura, 1960b). If this is so, we would not expect the assembly to be preceded by a mitotic gelation in the cytoplasm.

It can be seen that a rapid rise in cytoplasmic viscosity follows the decline at metaphase. In both *Chaetopterus* and the neuroblast, this begins at anaphase. The rise can hardly be associated with the dispersal of the mitotic apparatus, which takes place later, but might be correlated with its continued growth between metaphase and telophase. In the egg, at least, the astral system just about fills the cell by telophase (e.g., J. C. Dan, 1948; K. Dan, 1943; Swann, 1951b).

It is sufficiently clear that the events of mitosis are mirrored in changes in the colloidal states of the cytoplasm, and it seems entirely without profit to argue which "explains" which. The next phase of research on these problems should attempt to link the viscosity changes to definite molecules, and the molecular interactions to the mitotic apparatus. Does the mitotic gelation, where it occurs, represent the first stage in the polymerization of the molecules of the mitotic apparatus, and does the subsequent decrease in cytoplasmic viscosity actually reflect the consolidation of the molecular chains into a compact apparatus? What changes in the molecules themselves are involved? For example, can the gelation be correlated with changes in available —SH groups, so strikingly seen in Fig. 57? What changes in the intracellular environment cause or accompany the colloidal changes? Shall we relate the latter to shifts in the concentration of Ca^{+++} (as suggested by Heilbrunn) to the action of organic polycations (as suggested by Anderson, 1956b), to a Rapkine-type cycle of changes in low-molecular weight —SH compounds, to a system analogous to blood-clotting and involving both ionic factors and enzymes (Heilbrunn, 1952)? These are not unanswerable questions.

In dealing with the dividing cell as a colloidal system, molecular hydration is bound to be an interesting variable. It has been mentioned earlier in connection with the problem of spindle elongation. It is technically possible to measure changes in the water content of the cell as a whole by the sensitive Cartesian diver balance, and this has been done on dividing egg cells [sea urchins and *Urechis* by Geilenkirchen and Zeuthen (1958)]. They observe a decrease in the "reduced weight" of the cells, interpreted as an uptake of water, amounting to about 0.15–0.6% per division cycle. The inflow of water seems to be interrupted during anaphase and telophase and to resume at the following interphase. The importance of this rhythm for the mitotic process itself is not understood.

XIV. PHYSIOLOGICAL REPRODUCTION

A. *The Origin of "Twoness"*

The normal reproductive cycle of the cell involves a doubling of all its functional potentialities, which is only to say that each of the two daughter cells at the beginning of its individual career is able to do whatever the parent cell could do. Let us designate this aspect of the cell's life history as *physiological reproduction*, for we shall see that it is distinguishable from genetic reproduction as embodied in the conventional chromosome cycle. We may put it that physiological reproduction involves the doubling of a *growth potential,* which is measured both by the maximum rate at which the cell can increase its working substance and the maximum working mass it can attain without nuclear reproduction. These may be loose terms for the time being, but they express the fact that the maximum size and the maximum growth rate of any kind of cell is, within limits, "inherited." We do not expect a fibroblast to grow to the size of a paramecium without nuclear reproduction, nor do we expect it even under the most perfect conditions to double its mass in 20–30 minutes, as some bacterial cells can do.

We have seen (Section III, B) that the maximum size a cell can attain is roughly related to the nuclear dosage, and that the influence of the nuclear dosage may be conceptualized in terms of the classic concept of the nuclear "sphere of influence." In pursuing this concept, we may imagine that the sites of actual synthesis of proteins are cytoplasmic, for current evidence requires this assumption (e.g., Zalokar, 1960), and we may express the intensity of synthesis in terms of the number of active cytoplasmic sites. The control of the rate of protein synthesis by the nucleus can be described in various ways. Remarkable recent work on microorganisms (Pardee *et al.*, 1959; Jacob *et al.*, 1960) stresses control at the genetic level by an interaction of genes (or their products) determining the specificity of given proteins with other genes (or their products) acting as "repressors." The mechanism of repression at the level of actual synthesis has been visualized as a feedback action of end products on enzyme synthesis (e.g., Vogel, 1957; Maas and Gorini, 1958). Still another way of looking at the problem is in terms of the "replacement hypothesis" of nuclear function. To put it crudely, if the nucleus has a finite capacity for supplying biosynthetic information and if the cytoplasm "consumes" this information, growth can continue only as long as the output exceeds the consumption. The basic assumption is that a continuous output of nuclear products (e.g., an unstable "messenger RNA") is required to maintain the biosynthetic units in the cytoplasm, so that the maximum number of active units is limited by the maximum capacity of a nucleus. The mass level is limited by the number of synthetic units if turnover takes place.

The idea of a nuclear limitation of biosynthesis is stressed because it accounts best for the observed facts of physiological reproduction in a number of cases where it has been found that the growth of an individual cell follows a linear or decelerating course from division to division (e.g., Figs. 3, 99).

In such cells growth seems to be under the control of some factors which do not reproduce functionally between divisions and which are limited genetically. At the time the cell enters division it is usually not capable of further growth. But at some time around the end of division, the ability to grow has been restored and shows itself to have been

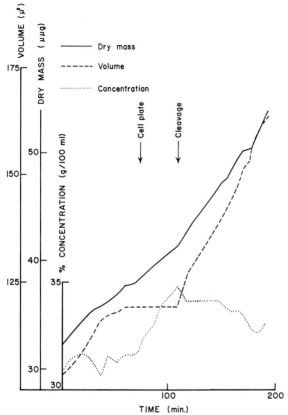

Fig. 99.   Growth curve of a fission yeast, *Schizosaccharomyces pombe*. Mass was measured by an interference-microscopic method. Volume growth levels off during division. Mass growth is linear, continues as the cell enters division, but increases to the rate for the two daughter cells during the division period. Under the experimental conditions, the rate of growth of the two daughter cells was about 1.6 times that of the parent. After Mitchison (1957).

doubled, for the two daughter cells not only grow, but *their combined growth rate is double that of the parent cell at the same stage* (Figs. 3, 99), and they will collectively make twice as much substance before they, in turn, divide. *These cells pass from a state of physiological "oneness" to a state of physiological "twoness" during division.*

An independent demonstration that the doubling of the growth rate may be related to nuclear reproduction is given by Prescott (1956b). Amebae were cut in half, and the regenerative growth of the nucleated halves was compared with the growth rate of daughter cells of a normal division (Fig. 100). Prescott was, so to speak, comparing the effects of an artificial "cytokinesis" on growth with those of a normal cell division.

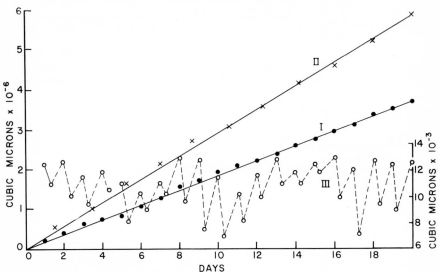

Fig. 100. The growth potential of an ameba (*Amoeba proteus*). Curve *I*. Cytoplasm was amputated periodically, and the size of the anucleate fragment was measured after each amputation. The curve represents the summated volume of the amputated pieces, and therefore the total regenerative growth that had taken place up to a given time. Curve *II*: A single cell was permitted to divide. The volume of one daughter cell was determined, the other was permitted to divide again. The curve represents the summated volume of the daughters produced by that one cell, hence the total normal growth up to a given time. In both cases, the growth potential is seen to be constant over a long period of time. Since the daughter cells produced by normal division would all have had the growth potential shown in curve *II*, it can be considered to be a function of the number of nuclei. Curve *III*. Decrease in nuclear volume each time the cell of curve *I* was cut. After Prescott (1956b).

The *regenerative* growth rate of the nucleated cell halves was almost equal to that of single normal daughter cells. But, since both daughter cells grow at this rate (whereas the enucleated fragments do not grow at all), it is clear that normal division doubles the growth potential. (It is also interesting to note, by the way, that the growth potential of the cell forced to regenerate repeatedly did not diminish. As long as a nucleus is present, the growth potential cannot be "used up.")

When and how does the doubling of the growth potential take place? To determine the time, continuous measurements through the period of division are desirable, and we have these only in a few cases. Zeuthen's (1953b) study on the growth of the respiratory rate in *Tetrahymena* has been cited as a case of arrested synthesis during division. In this same study he observed that the *rate of increase of the respiratory rate* doubled just before the beginning of cytoplasmic fission (Fig. 97). He says: "Although the rate of synthesis appears to be governed by the number of cellular units, the important thing may not be the number of cells *per se*, but the number, in the cells, of undefined centers doubling before each cytoplasmic fission." The time course of increase in respiratory activity in *Tetrahymena* is apparently an accurate reflection of the progress of protein synthesis, for Prescott (1960) observes a constant rate of incorporation of methionine into cell proteins during the interphase of this organism, as measured by an autoradiographic method.

The identical conclusion was drawn from Mitchison's (1957) study of the growth of *Schizosaccharomyces pombe* where the dry mass was measured by means of the interference microscope. Here the rate of increase in dry mass (Fig. 99) appeared double at some point in the division period, between the appearance of the cell plate and the completion of fission.

Unfortunately, neither *Tetrahymena* nor *Schizosaccharomyces* uses a mitotic mechanism that is easily comparable to the "typical" one, and so we cannot refer these findings to standard cytological stages. Undoubtedly, similar data on plant and animal cells will become available before long.

In at least one case, *Paramecium aurelia,* an *exponential* time course of growth between divisions has been reported (Kimball *et al.,* 1959). This study was made by X-ray absorption and interference microscopic methods. As Fig. 101 shows, the cells do double in mass between divisions, in an exponential way. During division, growth ceases, and in fact there is a slight decrease in mass. After division, the instantaneous growth rate is that which existed at the time the cell entered division. We are compelled to say that, in one sense, physiological reproduction in this case has taken place between divisions in a gradual way rather than during division, as in the other kinds of cells that have been considered.

Two approaches to the interpretation of physiological reproduction have been attempted. One of these makes the hypothesis that the cytoplasmic units controlling synthesis may be regarded as self-reproducing. In cases of linear synthesis between divisions and physiological reproduction during division, it is imagined that the synthetic centers all reproduce just once, at the time of division. This hypothesis has been discussed by Mitchison and Walker (1959), who made one test of it by measuring the

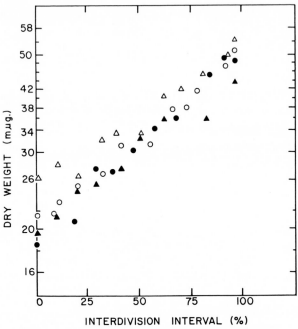

FIG. 101. Growth in mass of individual *Paramecium aurelia*, measured by interference microscopy and X-ray absorption. An exponential increase is seen. After Kimball *et al.* (1959).

RNA content of fission yeast through the cell cycle. They found a steady increase with no evidence of an abrupt change at the time of division. Prescott (1960) measured the RNA synthesis during interphase in *Tetrahymena* and found an increase during the last half of the interphase, during which time protein was increasing at a linear rate. In synchronized cultures of bacteria, the synthesis of RNA, and especially of sedimentable RNA, is discontinuous, but it would appear from present data that it takes place as part of the growth of the cells between divisions, and not as a sudden reproductive event during division (Fig. 102) (Scott and Chu, 1959).

It may well be that RNA is a poor measure of the active centers of synthesis in the cytoplasm, since it is a nuclear product. The history of the "plasmagene" hypothesis cautions us as to the difficulties of demonstrating the existence of such self-reproducing synthetic centers.

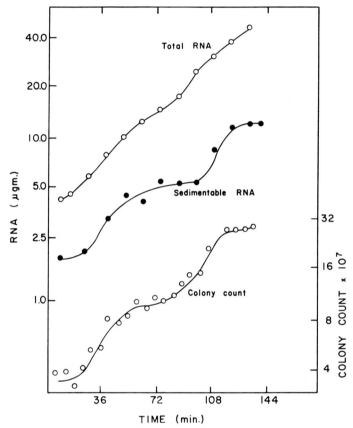

FIG. 102.   RNA synthesis in a synchronized population of the bacterium *Alcaligenes fecalis*. The periods of an abrupt rise of colony count represent the bursts of divisions. After Maruyama and Lark (1959).

The alternative and obvious hypothesis is that physiological reproduction is related to the reproduction of the nucleus. We have already discussed some of the theoretical considerations of the nuclear control of growth and of the nuclear "sphere of influence." This interpretation will appeal most strongly in the cases where growth between divisions is linear, and physiological reproduction takes place during division. This form of physiological reproduction is to be expected if the nucleus is the limiting factor in growth, and if it determines the growth potential. It is not incompatible with the one case of *Paramecium aurelia*—and we may expect others to be discovered—in which growth between divisions is exponential. In such cases we may imagine simply that the nuclear output is not the limiting factor in synthesis. If, for example, a *Paramecium* nucleus had twice the nuclear output, relative to the cytoplasmic "load," as did a *Tetrahymena,* the rate of synthesis would double between divisions, as it does. But it would still require the reproduction of the nucleus to maintain this growth rate from generation to generation.

Pursuing the hypothesis that nuclear reproduction is the basis of physiological reproduction, we note first of all that the *factor "twoness" does not reside in the primary genetic material, if the latter is measured as DNA.* For the DNA (and histone) double during the preparations for division in a way that cannot be related to the growth rate. In forms where the growth rate is the same at the end of interphase as at the beginning, the DNA has doubled by the end of interphase. In the interesting case of *Paramecium* the growth rate is increasing throughout interphase whereas the doubling of DNA is confined to a short interval as the cell is approaching division (Fig. 6).

But we need not limit our search to the chromosomes, whose relation to the synthetic activities of the cell may be largely administrative and correspondingly remote. Other constituents of the nucleus participate in the immediate business of directing the activities of the cell. In recent years the nucleolus had drawn increasing attention as a synthetic control center, beginning with the experiments and theories of T. Caspersson (1950).

We are searching for a controlling system that possesses "oneness" before division and "twoness" after division. If our views concerning the synthetic status of the dividing cell are correct, our controlling system should pass through a phase of "nothingness" in going from "oneness" to "twoness." The *nucleolus (or nucleoli) meet these specifications perfectly.* A given type of cell tends to have a definite number of nucleoli, which are associated with definite chromosomal region—the "nucleolar organizer" regions sometimes associated with "secondary constructions." At prophase these nucleoli normally undergo a "breakdown," at least of the major RNA-containing component, called the *pars amorpha* by Estable and Sotelo (1955). A second filamentous component, a "nucleonema," is claimed to remain associated with the chromosomes and to be carried through mitosis. This component is believed by R. Lettré (1955) to contain DNA and hence to be chromosomal.

The nucleolar bodies which disappear in prophase reappear in telophase, in double the original number. *As a group, they have gone from "oneness" to "nothingness" to "twoness."* The nucleoli may reappear *very early in telophase,* and this is an important point because the data on synthesis, already cited, tell us that synthesis may resume at its doubled rate even before the cell body has divided. Although macronuclear division in a ciliate may differ from typical mitosis in other respects, the nucleolar behavior may conform. V. Schwartz (1956) describes a breakdown of nucleoli in *Paramecium bursaria* early in the division phase and their reappearance at a phase of macronuclear elongation; this timing would correlate very well with the stage at which Zeuthen observed the resumption of the growth of the respiratory activity in *Tetrahymena.*

The suggestion that reproduction of the nucleolus may be the key to physiological reproduction is, then, based on the following hypotheses or parallelisms: (1) the widespread opinion that the nucleolus is an active "middleman" between the genes and their expression in the cytoplasm; (2) the fact that the time of appearance of "daughter" nucleoli corresponds to the time when synthesis resumes at the doubled rate in some dividing cells; (3) the correlation between the disappearance of the conspicuous RNA-containing component and the cessation of growth during division.

Several exotic conditions are relevant to this hypothesis. We have seen, for example, that cells deprived of nucleoli may divide when they do not have to grow between divisions, as in the early development of the *Drosophila* egg (Section VI, B, 4). Indeed, in many cases the dividing nuclei of cleaving eggs produce no perceptible nucleoli, the latter appearing on the scene at developmental stages when active synthesis begins (Brachet, 1947). At the other extreme, we have cells such as animal oöcytes, which grow and synthesize far beyond the usual limits without engaging in genetic reproduction. One of the most striking features of these cells is the presence of either huge nucleoli or great numbers of nucleoli (Vincent, 1955).

An elegant study by Longwell and Svihla (1960) now provides direct evidence of a relationship between nucleolar equipment and the growth potential of a cell. They measured, by interference microscopy, the dry mass of microsporocytes of a series of strains of wheat possessing different numbers of "strong" nucleolar chromosomes. These are chromosomes possessing nucleolus-organizer regions whose ability to generate nucleoli is tested by isolating them in karyomeres, away from the cooperation of other chromosomes (cf. Section IX, B, 2). An increase in the number of strong nucleolar chromosomes from 4 to 6 resulted in a 50% increase in the cytoplasmic dry mass of the microsporocytes, and a corresponding increase in the cytoplasmic RNA content. No such increase was observed as a result of increasing the dosage of non-nucleolar chromosomes. Thus, the growth potential seems to be correlated with nucleolar activity, and nucleolar activity may be the valve which limits the rate and the upper limit of growth by a cell. If this is so, any device which would increase nucleolar activity would increase the growth potential independently from genetic reproduction, but the sequence of events that we actually observe in the mitotic cycle would insure that the genetic doubling before each division was followed by physiological reproduction before each generation began its career.

We can accept physiological reproduction as a fact, and its occurrence *during* the nuclear division (in contrast with genetic reproduction which takes place before division) as a possibility. Its association with the generation of a doubled number of nucleoli is, of course, hypothetical.

B. *Physiological Reproduction and Cell Organization*

There is evidence that constructive activities of the cell are interrupted during division. If the structure of the cytoplasm changes at all during this period, it is in the direction of disorganization. The deplorably fragmentary information about the dividing cell tempts us to make a further hypothesis: that *physiological reproduction implies the erasure of the organization of the parent cell and the fabrication of two brand-new cells, structurally speaking.* It would follow from what has already been said that the organization of the daughter cells would be governed by the nuclei.

If cell organization is in fact wiped out to any degree at each division, and each generation builds anew, this would have rather important implications for the theory of differentiation. So far as the cytoplasm was concerned, each daughter cell would, at the time it was produced, have a clean slate upon which to write its decision as to its future. The decision, as we shall see, is in fact made quite early after division.

C. *Conclusions*

Physiological reproduction, the doubling of the growth potential of the cell, takes place during division and becomes expressed at the end of the division period. Two hypotheses have been presented: (1) that the act of physiological reproduction is observed in the nucleolar cycle, where we go from *one* nucleolus before division to *none* during division to *two* at the end of division; (2) that the cytoplasmic organization is erased at the time of division, and that each daughter cell reorganizes its cytoplasm.

XV. MITOTIC RHYTHMS AND EXPERIMENTAL SYNCHRONIZATION

A. Natural Rhythms

By extrapolating to an absurdity, we might imagine that all cells of a species or an organism would divide at the same time, if their ultimate origin is the division of an ancestral cell. The fact that synchrony is not maintained for very long in a line of cells is, of course, easily explained in terms of the variables that influence the rates of the preparations for division and division itself. Even under what are considered to be very uniform conditions, the progeny of a single cell fall out of phase quite soon. For example, Zeuthen (1953b) finds synchrony in divisions of *Tetrahymena* from one to sixteen cells, and Prescott (1955) was able to maintain *Amoeba proteus* in synchrony for five divisions at best. These are cases in which there is normal growth between divisions, and thus we are dealing with the synchrony of the whole life history of the cells. The reasons why the cells get out of step can be surmised. First, the "microenvironment" of the individuals may not be nearly as uniform as our thermometers, stirrers, etc., lead us to presume. To attack the ultimate basis of so-called biological variability, new standards of experimental control may be necessary (vide F. W. Went, 1957, for an illuminating discussion of biological variability). Second, we may be observing the subtler imperfections of the division mechanism. Sister cells need by no means be perfectly equal with respect to cytoplasmic endowments such as the number of mitochondria. Indeed, we would expect to find such differences unless special devices such as "chrondriokinesis" provided an extremely precise distribution of components which are not normally thought to be part of the mitotic machinery, and these operated very precisely. In yeast, where cytoplasmic inheritance has been studied in such detail (e.g., Ephrussi, 1953), Burns (1956) finds that the mother cell and the daughter cell produced by budding divide in perfect synchrony when growth is at 30°C. or less, but the daughter cell always divides later than the mother at 38°. In *Amoeba* (Prescott, 1956b) the generation times of daughter cells depend entirely on their size, and thus the relatively good synchrony that is sometimes observed is a sign of the high precision of cytoplasmic fission rather than of the existence of special distributive mechanisms.

Relatively synchronized divisions are encountered more frequently in cells that do not grow between divisions, where the preparations for division are not so dependent on external nutrition and massive syntheses. Systems such as animal eggs in early cleavage stages and anthers of some plants in microsporogenesis provide some of the most convenient sources of cell populations dividing in synchrony.

Between the extremes of synchrony and randomness fall the cases where divisions in a population follow anatomical gradients or tend to follow rhythms in time. An example of a mitotic gradient in the plant world is found in the young embryo sacs of certain species (various cases described by Tischler, 1922) at a stage at which the tissue is still a syncytium (Fig. 80).

Periodicity in the occurrence of mitosis in plant and animal tissues is not a rare phenomenon. Tischler in 1922 was able to cite, for plants, a great many descriptions dating back to 1851. The rhythms generally are diurnal and can be influenced by both light and temperature. Among the algae one species may divide by night whereas a closely related one will divide by day. Within a species, the time of the day when the divisions occur may be shifted by means of a period of exposure to low temperature or by artificial reversal of the diurnal cycle of light and darkness. The mitotic rhythms also are observed in higher plants. For example, peaks occur around noon and midnight in onion root tips (Jensen and Kavaljian, 1958). R. Brown (1951) observed a distinct peak around midnight in pea seedling meristems grown in the light from 10 A.M. to 10 P.M. and in the dark for the remainder of the day. But this rhythm was completely absent when the seedlings were grown in continuous darkness.

Most of the available data on mitotic rhythms in animals concern mammalian tissues. Again, the peaks are referred to the time of day, but they vary for different tissues and organisms. Cooper and Franklin (1940) observe a mitotic peak during the night in human epidermis, but a daytime peak (10 A.M.) in mouse epidermis (ear). The occurrence of two mitotic peaks per day has been observed in certain epithelial tissues of the mouse (Bullough, 1948), in some human and rat tumors (Voutilainen, 1953), and in mouse ascites tumors (Ågrell and Welin-Berger, 1957). In regenerating mouse liver there is a maximum mitotic rate at about 2 A.M. which is correlated with a preceding maximum of DNA synthesis (Barnum et al., 1956).

The absolute magnitudes of the mitotic "waves" in normal tissues are not very great. Cooper and Franklin (1940) give a peak value of 0.4% (59 dividing cells per 15,000 counted) for the mouse ear. Such values could easily reflect a triggering of cells which were already prepared for division, as Bullough has suggested. But this would not exclude the possibility that certain preparations for division such as DNA synthesis also tend to proceed rhythmically, as the situation in regenerating liver suggests.

In higher plants and animals we may expect to link the mitotic rhythms to physiological rhythms affecting the cells' environment. In animals, for example, they might be related to diurnal fluctuations in blood sugar (Bullough, 1952). But deeper intracellular "clocks" may make the decisions. For example, Sweeney and Hastings (1958) describe a 24-hour rhythm of cell division in a unicellular organism, the dino-flagellate *Gonyaulax polyedra*. When these cells were grown under a diurnal cycle of light and darkness, cell division in the population occurred in bursts at 24-hour intervals. When transferred to continuous dim light, the 24-hour periodicity of the bursts was preserved. Even if the generation time was much longer than 24 hours, divisions were seen only at the 24-hour intervals. In short it appears that when the appropriate signal is delivered by an endogenous intracellular "clock" those cells which are ready to divide do divide, whereas the rest must wait at least a day before the signal is given again.

B. Experimental Synchronization

The experimental synchronization of cell population has become a necessity of cell biology. It is now apparent that the details of the time travel of cells can be worked out only with the aid of this implement— at least those details which involve biochemistry of any sophistication. The lore of earlier generations of biologists included the germs of synchronization methods, such as the protozoologists' device of chilling cultures in order to collect large numbers of dividing cells shortly after they were rewarmed. But a concentrated attack on the problem has begun only recently (cf. reviews by Campbell, 1957; Zeuthen, 1958; Scherbaum, 1960).

It is necessary to distinguish sharply between the fully synchronous growth of populations through the whole life cycle and the synchronization of division only. So far, the methods of synchronization of division tend to sacrifice normal growth by their very principle; the cells are brought into phase with respect to division either by arresting them at a predivision stage or reverting them to a postdivision stage with respect to one or more preparations for division. No one has succeeded as yet in forcing cells into synchrony with respect to normal growth or in maintaining such synchrony for any length of time. All existing studies on synchronized growth (as of the time of writing) depend on devices for collecting large numbers of "young" cells, which then proceed through one or a few generations in phase.

The pioneer study of the synchronization of division was that of Scherbaum and Zeuthen (1954). Their approach was based on the observation that a temperature shock, in practice an exposure of the cells to a just sublethal temperature of 34°C., not only prevented division, but delayed it for a time longer than the period of exposure to the sublethal temperature. Evidently the cells were *set back in time*. The cells were not equally sensitive to temperature shocks at all "ages" (relative to their last division). Those cells which had passed a certain "point of no return" before division, completed division. The sensitivity of the cells increased with "age" during the latter half of the interdivision period, so that a given temperature shock set the "older" cells back as far as the "younger" ones in terms of the time required before they could divide when returned to a normal temperature (Thomar, 1959). The regime consisted of cycles of 30 minutes' exposure to the sublethal temperature (34°C.) followed by 30 minutes at the optimal temperature of 28°C. Those cells that had been caught in the sensitive part of the interdivision period could not pass the "point of no return" in 30 minutes and were set back again during the next high temperature interval. Those that were not in a sensitive phase during an earlier heat shock advanced to that phase and finally were caught. Six to ten temperature cycles sufficed to entrain the whole population, and to bring it back to the "zero time" status by the end of the last heat shock. After this, the cells were allowed to remain at the optimal temperature of 28°C., at which they divided with remarkable synchrony in about 75 minutes, as contrasted with the normal generation time of 130 minutes. A second and a third wave of divisions followed at about 100-minute intervals, each somewhat less synchronous than the preceding one (Fig. 103).

The details of this remarkable procedure are described by Scherbaum and Zeuthen (1955). It represents the dissociation of cell growth from cell division in almost perfect form. During the period of heat shocks the cells continued to grow and synthesize proteins, DNA, and RNA, although at a somewhat reduced rate. Following the heat shock, the synchronous divisions of the giant cells could take place without growth and indeed without any external organic nutrition at all, the cells returning to normal size. A simple formal interpretation of the sychronization is possible. It is assumed that the preparation for division involves the building up of some system to a critical level and that this system is inactivated or destroyed when the cell is caught by the heat shock during the sensitive part of interphase. In the course of the repeated temperature cycles all the cells will be caught. The time required from the last heat shock to the first wave of divisions, 70 minutes or so at the least, is that required by the cells to complete those preparations for division which had been nullified by the heat shock. Scherbaum (1957a) finds that the results can be treated in terms of the kinetics of the reversible inactivation of a protein.

Of the various general approaches to experimental synchronization, the use of temperature cycles has been pursued most actively so far. Theoretically, the procedure might work in at least two ways. An abnormally low or high temperature might arrest cells in a certain stage while cells at other and less sensitive stages caught up with them. Or, as in the case of *Tetrahymena*, all the cells might be set back to a certain virtual time relative to the next division. A situation that permits the first interpretation is described by Hotchkiss (1954, 1955). A *Pneumococcus* population is grown at 37°C., then held at 25°C. for 10 minutes. Imme-

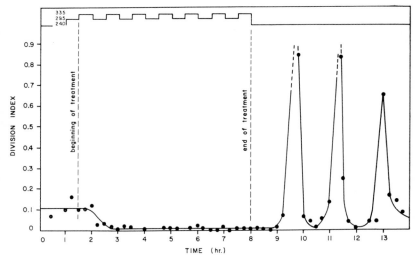

FIG. 103.   Synchronous divisions in *Tetrahymena pyriformis*, induced by a series of temperature shocks. Continuous line at top of figure shows the regime of temperature shifts between 29.5 and 33.5°C. Ordinate shows the fraction of cells observed to be in division. After Scherbaum and Zeuthen (1954).

diately upon return to 37°C., a wave of synchronous divisions is observed, and this is followed by several further waves. Synchronization of division by temperature treatments has been successful with other microorganisms (e.g., *Salmonella*: Maaløe and Lark, 1954; *E. coli*: Scott and Chu, 1958; *Bacillus megatherium*: Hunter-Szybalska *et al.*, 1956).

The problem of the synchronization of animal cells in culture has attracted a great deal of interest, for its solution would lead to some important advances in virus research, chemotherapeutic research, radiobiology, etc., as well as providing needed information about the normal life history of various cell types. Some results of Newton and Wildy (1959) promise the ultimate success of a method based on temperature variations. HeLa cells (a widely used human tumor strain) were grown at 37°C. for 30 hours, then exposed to 4°C. for 1 hour. Upon return to 37°C. there were no divisions for 17–18 hours, then as many as 85% of the cells divided within 1 hour. A second wave of divisions followed within 18 hours. Though this apparent high degree of synchrony in cell division has been achieved, yet the number of cells in mitosis at any time preceding division is rather small; in experiments in which 60–80% of the cells divided within an hour or less, the maximum mitotic index ranged from 3.5 to 8%. Thus the system might be very useful for studying

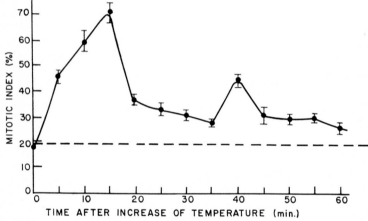

FIG. 104.　Synchronization of mitosis at the blastula stage of a fish (loach: *Misgurnus fossilis*) by cooling to 3°C. for 2 hours, after which the embryos were quickly brought to 18°C. The normal mitotic rate is quite high at this stage of development (lower curve), but the index can be increased to a very high level by the prechilling. The interval between the two division peaks is shorter than the normal period between divisions, suggesting that the preparations for division proceeded beyond the normal predivision level while division was blocked at low temperature. After Neifakh and Rott (1958).

some aspects of the physiology of division, but it would not be very efficient for the isolation of mitotic figures, for instance. A similar partial synchronization of animal cells after cooling has been reported by Chèvremont-Comhaire and Chèvremont (1956) for cultures of various chick embryo tissues, by Emanuelsson (1958) for regions of the intact chick embryo, and by Neifakh and Rott (1958) for a fish embryo at the blastula stage (Fig. 104).

Temperature variations are not the only means to the end of synchronous division. In microorganisms nutritional controls have been very effective. Perhaps the most elegant principle for phasing cells is the limitation of one preparation for division, such as DNA synthesis, while permitting the others to advance normally. This has been applied in *E. coli* by withholding thymine from thymine-requiring mutants (Cohen and Barner, 1954) and in a *Lactobacillus acidophilus* mutant by depriving it of deoxyribosides which it cannot make (Burns, 1959). When the thymine-requiring mutant of *E. coli* is grown without this pyrimidine, all syntheses proceeded except that of DNA. If thymine is added at the appropriate time (after 30 minutes of deprivation) the cells divide very soon and very synchronously, and they remain in step for several generations. Synchronization through nutritional controls has been attempted on other systems, with varying success. Synchronization of division is observed in a number of microorganisms when they are given nutrition after a period of starvation (Campbell, 1957; Scott and Chu, 1958). In the case of photosynthetic organisms variations in the light regime should provide a powerful tool. This has been exploited by Tamiya and collaborators (Tamiya *et al.*, 1953; Iwamura, 1955) in studies on the growth of *Chlorella*. Cells were grown at low light levels, then heavily illuminated. The cells grew in size without dividing, being transformed into the so-called "light cells." At a certain point these "light cells" entered a period of rapid division without further growth, each giving rise to four small cells having the appearance of the original "dark cells." The sharp separation of growth-without-division, which covers some 30–40 hours, and division-without-growth, which is completed in 5–10 hours, makes this an extraordinarily useful system.

Some of the methods of synchronization of division involve a sacrifice of synchrony of growth. There is as yet no system in which sustained synchrony of the complete cycle has been accomplished. However, in a good many of the cases, synchrony is maintained for a generation or two after pretreatments such as temperature shocks, and these later generations may be useful for the study of synchronized growth, or at least of preparations for division. Synchronized growth may be approached by methods that are simple in principle, involving only the initial collection of cells of the same age. For example, Maruyama and Yanagita (1956) have collected the small, early interphase cells of *E. coli* by filtration and by centrifugation, and these cells proceed through at least one generation in good synchrony, as judged by the well-defined phases of synthesis of RNA, protein, DNA, and fission (Maruyama, 1956)—just the type of information on the time course of the cell cycle that is the objective of the synchronization techniques. For other types of cells techniques exploiting the special properties of dividing cells—sluggish movement, loss of adhesiveness, etc.—offer possible alternative means of separating them from a random population.

XVI. Blockage and Stimulation of Division

In this section we shall not attempt to analyze in detail the great literature on inhibition and stimulation of cell division. The known facts concerning antimitotic action are thoroughly summarized in Biesele's valuable book (1958), and Swann (1958) has written a critical and stimulating summary of the problem of mitotic stimulation. Rather, our discussion here seeks only to illustrate how the present image of cell division directs our thinking about how it is controlled.

A. *Suppression of Division; Targets of Antimitotic Action*

Throughout this discussion, our premise will be that *the normal tendency of a cell is to divide, and that a destiny other than division must involve blockage somewhere on the time map of a typical cellular life history* (Fig. 2). The normal suppression of division in multicellular systems is often related to differentiation, but both in turn depend on the environment of the cell (including its neighbors) within the organism. This postulate is demonstrated by the well-known fate of differentiated tissues when explanted into cultures; the cells regain the capacity to divide and lose their differentiated character to a considerable extent, if not entirely. The organismal suppression of division may involve intercellular contact, hormonal or immunological effects, nutritional factors, or anything that may be reckoned as part of a cell's environment. Artificial suppression may be achieved by the greatest variety of physical and chemical means; there is hardly any device for perturbing a cell that has not been described as "antimitotic." But we have no reason to think that the intracellular targets of antimitotic action are as varied as the external weapons. We probably can specify the main points of attack for the suppression of mitosis, without doubting that still others will be discovered.

1. *Blockage at the End of Division or at the Beginning of Interphase*

Here we are dealing with cells that do not seem to enter the pathway to division at all. In the normal differentiation of higher organisms it is probably the most important category of mitotic inhibition, and a true control of mitosis (in contrast with the mere killing off of dividing populations) depends on our understanding what is happening. Such blockage can be detected as a failure of DNA synthesis to begin. As we have seen (Section III, D, 1) differentiated cells generally have the diploid DNA content which they received at the last division.

In a tissue in which differentiation is taking place, a cell must "decide" at some time after the division of its parent, whether it will go on to division or whether it will differentiate and not divide again. This problem has been analyzed by Quastler and Sherman (1959) and Quastler (1960). Their analysis of the kinetics of the cell population in intestinal epithelium involves the following variables: the mitotic rate in crypts (where all new cells are formed), the time course of progress toward division (as measured by autoradiographic study of DNA synthesis), and the history of the differentiating populations (as estimated by the migra-

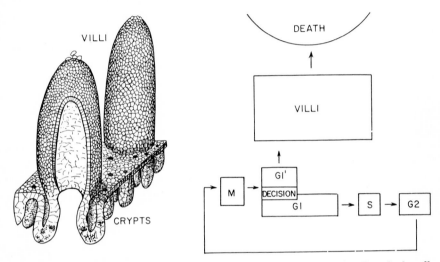

FIG. 105. Population kinetics of a tissue in which differentiated cells, which will not divide again, are replenished by a population of dividing cells. In the system studied, intestinal epithelium, cell divisions take place in the crypts (see diagram on left) and those cells which will differentiate move into the villi. Diagram on right shows the flow of events in terms of the duration of various stages and the fraction of the population in that stage. The symbols are: M = the period of mitosis; G1 = the period between the end of mitosis and the beginning of DNA synthesis; S = the period of DNA synthesis; G2 = the period between the end of DNA synthesis and the beginning of mitosis. The analysis suggested that the "decision" whether to divide or differentiate took place during G1 (or well before the beginning of DNA synthesis). Modified from Quastler and Sherman (1959).

tion of differentiating cells from crypts into villi). The results of this interesting experiment are shown in Fig. 105. The important finding is that the "decision" whether to divide or to differentiate is made shortly after division and certainly within the first 4 hours of a reproductive cycle taking about 19 hours. This is perhaps the most important of all the problems of the regulation of mitosis, for the onset of DNA synthesis does in practice predestine most cells to go through with the division cycle. The problem may exist entirely at the level of the biosynthetic mechanism. For example, one or another aspect of cell metabolism, dictated by the environment in its broadest sense, might determine the suppression or activation of enzymes involved in DNA synthesis or even the formation of such enzymes. Feedback mechanisms for the control of DNA synthesis have been discussed by Potter (1958).

It may also be useful to consider the control of DNA synthesis in terms of the mitotic map itself. We have seen (Section III, D, 2) that duplication of the centers, in animal cells, is the earliest event of a mitotic cycle, the only event we know that takes place before the beginning of DNA synthesis. Could it be a prerequisite of DNA synthesis? If this could be so, we might imagine that an asymmetry of the duplication of the centers at anaphase in a differentiating system might produce one daughter that was ready to make DNA and one that was not. This interesting possibility was put to a test by N. L. R. Bucher and Mazia (1960) with negative results. The experiments took advantage of the finding that mercaptoethanol blocks the duplication of the centers in sea urchin eggs but does not block DNA synthesis if the nuclei are in interphase. The formation of DNA did not seem to depend at all on the antecedent duplication of the centers.

2. Inhibition of Growth

No approach to antimitotic action has been explored more thoroughly than the possibility of preventing division by inhibiting growth, although the rationale has not always been explicit. For example, a large number of studies of the effects of various antimetabolites fall into this category. The investigators are concerned with the effects of agents on the increase in the number of cells in a population, and not with the inhibition of the division process as such. It is helpful to discriminate, within the growing phase of the life history of the cell, between growth as an increase in active mass (typified by an increase in the enzyme content) and the normally concomitant preparations for division. The former, as we have seen (Section III, B), are not essential for the immediately forthcoming divisions, and the inhibition of them would be antimitotic only to the extent that a series of divisions without growth would ultimately diminish the cytoplasmic mass of daughter cells to a point where they could no longer maintain themselves. Such an approach to the killing of dividing cell populations by encouraging division to proceed more rapidly than growth has received some speculative consideration as an attack upon neoplasms (e.g., Berglas, 1957).

3. Preparations for Division

Any of the essential preparations for division may be the target of antimitotic action. Among these the synthesis of DNA has been the most thoroughly studied, especially in connection with the effects of radiations on division. The case for a radiation effect on DNA synthesis has been a strong one. We may mention, for example, the evidence that ultraviolet irradiation inhibits DNA synthesis in microorganisms (reviewed by Brachet, 1957, pp. 251-252; Errera, 1957). A case has been made for direct inhibition of DNA synthesis by ionizing radiation, but this has now been questioned as the basis of radiation effects on cell division. A recent review by Kelly (1957) summarized the argument that ionizing radiations affect primarily some unidentified process essential for cell division. The action is reflected secondarily as an effect of DNA synthesis in long-term experiments on cell populations; in short-term experiments, ionizing radiations do not seem to inhibit DNA synthesis, and may even accelerate it (Das and Alfert, 1961).

The process, or processes, normally dependent on aerobic oxidations, interpreted as the filling of an energy reservoir, have received considerable attention. So far as the evidence goes, the blockage thus imposed is perfectly reversible. Other preparations, such as the separation of the centers and the provision of the substance of the mitotic apparatus have received relatively little attention. The demonstration that inactivation of the nucleolus before division will block division (Section VI, B, 4) provides us with another potential target.

4. Mitotic Blockage and "Triggering"

If "trigger" mechanisms as we defined them earlier—decisive events located in the period of transition into division—exist, we may imagine that cells can be blocked at this point. Several tests would detect this state of affairs: we would expect the chromosome reproduction to have been completed and should find that cells enter division rapidly if the block is removed. Such may be the situation in animal epidermis, judging from studies on wound healing. It has been found, for instance, that cutting of a rabbit's ear sets off a burst of mitoses which appear within 4 hours (Gelfant, 1959, who cites earlier references). The cells which enter division so promptly already have doubled their DNA (Gelfant, 1958). If we were correct earlier in imagining that other preparations for division occupy a considerable proportion of the interphase period, it seems likely that these are at least far advanced in those epidermal cells which divide soonest. In short, it would appear that these cells were blocked at the transition from interphase into the period of division.

This period of "antephase" or "preprophase" may be one of the important targets of antimitotic action. Hughes (1950), in his survey of the chemical inhibition of division of chick cells (bone explants), stated the following criterion of "preprophase" inhibition: cells already in prophase advance through division while no cells enter prophase. Among the "preprophase" inhibitors, he found fluoride, iodoacetate, and chloroacetophenone. A neat demonstration of the sensitivity of the transitional period is given by experiments in which Chèvremont-Comhaire and Chèvremont (1956) exposed muscle and connective tissue cells in culture to the low temperature of 16–20°C. All cells in division completed division; none entered prophase. When the cultures were returned to 37°C., a burst of prophases ensued which indicated that many of the cells in interphase had advanced to a critical stage just before prophase and were blocked at that point.

5. Chromosomal Aberrations

The question of chromosome breakage and chromosome aberrations is a large subject (cf. Symposium, 1952); it is related to our problem only in the sense that the mitotic apparatus "sees" only the kinetochores and distributes them as best it can. Fragments without kinetochores are lost, and chromosomes acquiring two kinetochores by translocation tear themselves when each kinetochore moves to an opposite pole. Here the normal forces of mitosis operate inexorably to establish maldistribution of genetic material, and the end result is often fatal to the progeny.

6. The Mitotic Apparatus as a Target of Antimitotic Action

In almost all cases the blockage of the cell *during* division is associated with structural abnormalities or even the apparent dissolution of the mitotic apparatus. The archetype of an agent producing such blockage is colchicine, whose interesting action has given rise to a huge amount of research, summarized in a volume by Eigsti and Dustin (1955). We have commented on various aspects of blockage of the mitotic apparatus in earlier sections, particularly admonishing against the assumption that the serious disorganization and loss of normal structural stigmata may easily be interpreted as the actual physical dissolution of the mitotic apparatus viewed as a coherent gel. A most significant feature of this type of mitotic blockage—whose visual manifestations often are dreadful—is that it is generally reversible. There are few cases of functional blockage of the mitotic apparatus without visible disordering. One has been described by Mota (1952) in a study of the action of seed extracts on division in plant root tips.

It is remarkable that cells in nature are so seldom blocked in mid-division. One instance is the "dormant" status of unfertilized eggs of certain species. In some cases the egg nucleus is fully mature at the haploid level of both chromosome number and DNA content, but in a great many others it is blocked at some point in meiosis. The cells may be blocked at the first meiotic metaphase (e.g., in some nemerteans, annelids, and mollusks), the first meiotic anaphase (e.g., some annelids), the second meiotic metaphase (e.g., frog, mouse), or the second meiotic anaphase (e.g., bats), according to Wilson (1925; p. 403 ff.). The eggs resume the meiotic divisions when fertilized.

7. Telophase Defects

Blockage of dividing cells at telophase has been described at various times in the literature of mitotic abnormalities, but we have no reason to think of this as a particularly sensitive phase, nor have we character-istic telophase inhibitors of widespread applicability. The aberration of telophase which has been most interesting is the failure of chromosomes to merge: the production of karyomeres. It is, as we have seen, a normal occurrence in some cases and it can be produced by chemical means, as by the action of podophyllin and related compounds (Cornman and Cornman, 1951). Its long-term implications, in terms of mitotic abnor-malities, are related to those of other chromosomal abnormalities. Sub-sequent mitoses may fail to distribute the chromosomes properly, and thus the progeny may die.

8. Conclusions

The blockage of mitosis may be accomplished naturally or artificially (1) by diverting cells from the preparations for division, (2) by inhibiting any one of the preparations for division, (3) by arresting them at the transition stage from interphase into division, and (4) by disabling the mitotic apparatus. These blocks are theoretically reversible and are typi-cally not fatal. Long-term antimitotic action may involve (1) suppression of interphase growth, and (2) production of genetically abnormal prog-eny through chromosome breakage or through telophase abnormalities. Division leading to abnormal progeny is more damaging in the long run than mitotic blockage in the usual sense.

B. Stimulation of Division

1. Stimulation as a Release from Blockage

What do we mean by "stimulation of cell division"? There are two quite different classes of meanings. One is that a normally multiplying cell population multiplies faster. The other is that cell divisions appear in a cell population which normally does not multiply. "Stimuli" of the former class may be considered to be actions that speed up or perhaps bypass one or more of the preparations for division, that overcome any delay at the transitions from interphase into division, or that speed up the division process itself. It may be useful to view the "stimuli" of the second class as actions which remove a block to division. Indeed, it seems constructive to propose that we should look upon *every cell that does not divide as a cell that is blocked at some point on the division pathway.*

The last statement implies that most cells, even highly differentiated ones, are capable of dividing under the right conditions. It is not intended to imply that differentiated cells are to be viewed *merely* as blocked cells. In terms of the views stated earlier about the separable growth and division pathways, we would say that the division pathway was blocked while the growth pathway was given the time and the resources to carry out the additional synthesis and the structure formation that is expressed in cell differentiation. For example, it is possible that the abundant structure proteins of the mitotic apparatus are diverted into structural activity of other kinds (Mazia, 1957; Swann, 1958).

These two classes of actions are commonly confused in discussions of stimulation of cell division and should be distinguished for clarity in experimental design and interpretation. It does not follow necessarily that a given "stimulus" is restricted to the one class or the other. For instance, it has been shown that kinetin (or the kinins), the potent hormone influencing cell division in plant tissues, will throw differentiated cells of tobacco pith into division (Skoog and Miller, 1957) and will also shorten interphase in the dividing meristematic tissue of onion roots (Guttman, 1957).

2. Synchronous Division in Cells with Several Nuclei

Almost any of the processes we have discussed in our description of the division cycle conceivably could be rate-limiting, and therefore an increase in its rate could be seen superficially as a stimulation of division. Intracellular factors influencing division can be approached on a broader front by observations of multinucleate cells and by experiments on the fusion of cells.

If the division cycle is timed by intracellular humoral factors, we would expect that nuclei sharing the same cytoplasm would divide at the same time. This is true in a great many cases; there is no need to list them all. We may quote a statement of Koller (1947) to the effect that synchrony is "the rule in multinucleate tumor cells, in megakaryocytes of human bone, in cells of growing root tips, in spermatocytes of insects and in mammals, etc." The inference of humoral factors is particularly well supported by cases where cytoplasmic continuity is maintained only through tenuous "bridges," and yet the nuclei are synchronized. A number of such cases, in testes of various animals and in certain interstitial cells of *Hydra* are reviewed by Fawcett *et al.* (1959), who describe the fine structure of the bridges. Equally impressive are cases where populations of nuclei which are not separated by walls show a gradient of division stages, as though the mitosis were governed by a corresponding gradient of some exogenous factor. Such a situation occurs in certain plant endosperms (Jungers, 1931). Over-all cytoplasmic control of the division rate is shown also in hybridization experiments, involving division of nuclei of one species within cytoplasm of another. For example, A. R. Moore (1933) removed the nuclei from eggs of the sea urchin *Strongylocentrotus franciscanus* and of the sand dollar *Dendraster excentricus,* and then fertilized each kind of egg with sperm of its own species or of the other species. His results (Table XIII) show complete dominance of the

TABLE XIII

CYTOPLASMIC CONTROL OF TIMING OF DIVISIONS IN ECHINODERM EGGS
[*Strongylocentrotus franciscanus* (S.), A SEA URCHIN AND *Dendraster excentricus* (D.), A SAND DOLLAR][a]

Nucleus-cytoplasm combination at fertilization	Minutes from first to second division
S. egg × S. sperm	47
D. egg × D. sperm	29–30
Enucleated D. egg × D. sperm	29–30
S. egg × D. sperm	46
D. egg × S. sperm	28–30

[a] After Moore (1933).

cytoplasm. [The mitotic apparatus of cells of this type is almost certainly of cytoplasmic origin, apart from the chromosomes (Mazia and Roslansky, 1956). A corresponding experiment involving a mitotic apparatus of nuclear origin would be most interesting.]

An apparent cytoplasmic "control" of the nuclear cycle is seen in experiments on the ciliate *Stentor* by de Terra (1960) in which she grafted nuclei which were in an early division stage into cells which were in interphase. The interphase macronucleus of this organism is a long, beaded body. At the time of division the beads draw together, forming a rounded macronucleus. This then elongates and pinches into two, at which time cytokinesis takes place. When the round, early-division nucleus was grafted into an interphase cell, it did not continue through division. Rather, it "waited" in the rounded form until the host nucleus had reached the same stage, then both nuclei divided synchronously. Clearly, the cytoplasm was calling the turn in this case.

If synchronous divisions of nuclei with a common cytoplasm is the rule, it is by no means an absolute rule (Fig. 106). Among the Protozoa especially we find numerous cases of asynchronous nuclear division in multinucleated cells. The case of certain opalinids (Metcalf, 1923) is

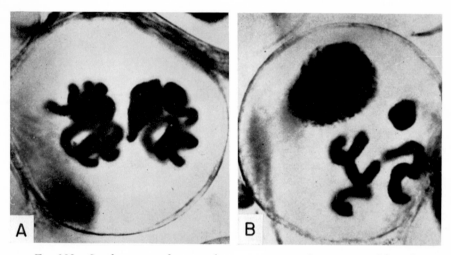

FIG. 106.   Synchronous and nonsynchronous mitosis within a group of binucleate cells. Binucleate pollen grains in *Tradescantia paludosa*, an uncommon condition. Among this group of cells, the two nuclei sharing a common cytoplasm divided synchronously in about 70% of the pollen grains, and nonsynchronously in the rest. Thus synchrony is more probable but is not a mandatory consequence of some cytoplasmic control mechanism.   A. Two chromosome groups perfectly synchronized at late prophase. B. Nonsynchrony, one nucleus in prometaphase, the other in early prophase. Photographs by courtesy of Dr. A. Haque (Haque, 1953).

often cited.   In the heliozoan *Actinosphaerium* (Barrett, 1958) nuclear division is asynchronous. Raikov (1958) describes mitoses in two species of the ciliate genus *Trachelocerca*, which have several micronuclei.   In one synchronous mitosis is the rule; in the other there is asynchrony.

This variability would be most perplexing if we insisted on endowing the idea of "control mechanisms," nuclear or cytoplasmic, with some absolute cybernetic significance. But if we look upon nuclear division as a problem of nucleus-cytoplasm interaction in which either partner may be the limiting one in a given case, the problem is not so serious from a

theoretical standpoint and much more serious—because it calls for work
—from a practical standpoint.

3. Fusion Experiments

Intracellular "stimuli" (if this is not a self-contradictory expression)
of division have been investigated by the fusion of cells of various "age"
with respect to division. An experiment of this form has been carried out
successfully by Weisz (1956) on the ciliate *Stentor*, an organism which
lends itself very well to grafting operations. Weisz made parabiotic grafts
of "prefission" organisms (those within 2–6 hours of division) and "postfission" organisms, which would not be expected to divide before 2 days.
When the "prefission" member of the pair entered division, the much
smaller "postfission" member followed soon after, dividing to produce
abnormally small daughters. Whatever the nature of the activity that
was transmitted from the older to the younger cell, it was found only
during the later stages of preparation for division and disappeared at the
time of division itself. The most obvious interpretation of these interesting
experiments is that a substance appears in the "prefission" cells and diffuses into the younger cells to trigger division. Weisz also presents an
alternative interpretation in terms of a propagated change in cytoplasmic
structure.

The action of an intracellular factor in removing a mitotic block can
also be shown by fusion experiments. For example, Daniels (1959) has
demonstrated that the grafting of unirradiated cytoplasm of the giant
ameba *Pelomyxa carolinensis* to cells in which division has been inhibited
by ultraviolet and Roentgen irradiation will reverse that inhibition.

4. Organismal Factors

The development and the normal operations of multicellular organisms involve the exquisite modulation of cell division. The regulation of
cell division calls into play all the devices we know for coordination of
the parts of the organism. We cannot attempt here to survey the vast
literature that has evolved from studies of nutrition, carcinogenesis, regeneration, wound healing, endocrine action, and experimental embry-
ology, but we may sketch the framework. More complete surveys are
given by Hughes (1952b), Bullough (1955), H. K. Porter (1957), and
Swann (1957, 1958).

A classification of mitosis-stimulating and regulating systems formulated by Abercrombie (1957) for the adult mammal can be applied to
multicellular systems generally. In the *compensatory* type, the mitotic
activity of an organ is regulated to its mature size, and removal of part

of the organ provokes its replacement by new cells. In the *simple target-organ type* growth beyond a certain "resting" size is stimulated by hormones that provoke mitosis in specific target organs. The *reparative* type is, as the term implies, stimulation of mitosis at the immediate site of an injury, mere pressure or distension of the tissue sometimes being adequate.

In all these classes of mitotic stimulation, there is good evidence of the existence of humoral factors. A well-studied example is the regeneration of the liver. If two rats are placed in parabiosis and one is partially hepatectomized, stimulation of mitosis in the livers of both animals is observed (Bucher *et al.*, 1951; Wenneker and Sussman, 1951). Another carefully analyzed case is the initiation of mitosis in wounded rabbit ear epidermis (Gelfant, 1958, 1959). In this material, as we have mentioned, cells whose DNA has already doubled enter mitosis in the wounded region. After other variables, such as increased access to nutrients, are accounted for, it is still clear that the injury to the tissue itself is a factor that elicits the mitosis.

Although we may feel uneasy about the vagueness of relations between "injury" and cell division in higher organisms, it is encouraging to recall that the early hypothesis of "wound hormones" in plants (Haberlandt, 1921) initiated the lines of research that did ultimately lead to the discovery of kinetin and other now-characterized substances that stimulate cell division (e.g., Skoog and Miller, 1957).

The role of the endocrine system in controlling cell division in animals is now coming under direct and detailed study. An interesting finding (Bullough, 1952; Allen, 1956, 1958) has been that hormones which stimulate cell division in specific target organs (e.g., androgens and estrogens) do so also in other tissues, and even in organisms in which these hormones are not presumed to occur normally. Ågrell and Wiman (1957) describe marked stimulation of mitosis in regenerating tissues of planarian worms under the action of estradiol. On the other hand Ågrell (1955a) observed no such stimulation of division by estradiol in sea urchin embryos, but a colchicine-like inhibition. These are far from contradictory results, for the division in sea urchin embryos is not limited by interphase preparations which are probably essential in the planarian cells, and we can conclude that the hormone is unblocking or accelerating these preparations.

The nervous system of animals has also been implicated in the control of mitosis. The work of Singer (1952) and others demonstrates that mitosis in regenerating limbs of urodele amphibians depends on innervation.

The organismal control of cell division may merely be a matter of "on-off" stimulation or inhibition so far as the individual cell is concerned, but for the plant or animal it obviously involves sensitive modulations. The breakdown of even one of these, such as the regulation of the production of leucocytes, may be disastrous. The modulation devices may affect not only the rate of division in a given population, but also its final size, as in the regeneration of a diminished organ to its original size. It involves a high level of specificity, though the specificity may not be perfect; a hormone may increase the mitotic index in many tissues, but it is in its target organs that the greatest increase in cell numbers takes place. Similarly, the action of "hormones" involved in the regeneration of a given organ obviously are focused on that organ. Weiss (1955) has formulated the broad problem of specificity in the regulation of growth in an organism in terms of molecular specificity.

Thus the problem of the modulation of cell division in an organism is summarized by the cliché that it encompasses an interaction between the individual character of the cell and the information-coordinating mechanisms of the organism as a whole. The current literature contains some promising attacks on the interaction, such as studies on tumor transplantation in which the escape of cells from the mitotic discipline of an animal can be followed accurately in terms of cell-host relationships (e.g., Klein and Klein, 1957, 1958).

5. Summary: The Meaning of the "Control" of Mitosis

The control of mitosis may be viewed from the inside, looking out, or from the outside, looking in; the clear questions and answers will be found where these views meet. In the present treatment of the problem mitosis itself is our starting point. The archetypal cell goes through perpetual cycles of growth and division, and the absence of division is regarded as an expression of blockage. From this standpoint the stimulation of division in multicellular systems is the removal of a block; to put it crudely, the stimulus is no more than permission of the cell to do what it would have done had it been left alone in the first place.

Far from being an abstract and idealized way of looking at the situation, this approach asks, in each specific case: Where in the network of the mitotic events are blocks to division imposed in natural situations, and where may they be imposed by artifice? The concept of "control mechanisms" for mitosis thus gains in definiteness what it loses in possible universality. In fact, it is assimilated, by way of a mitotic map of which Fig. 2 is an approximation, into the homely and familiar category of limiting factors in the complex processes. If, as we have observed, nuclei divide synchronously in some multinucleated cells but not in others, this does not challenge some grand concept of a cytoplasmic or nuclear control. It merely means that one or more of the cytoplasmic components of the mitotic cycle is limiting in one case and not in the other, and only a trivial quantitative difference might be involved. If we speak of control mechanisms for definite processes within the mitotic map, that it is another story, and one that is assimilable into our growing knowledge of the regulations of biochemical reactions. At present it is easier to describe the nature of the mitotic inhibition or release than to trace the lines of events connecting inhibition or release to external controlling factors such as hormones, antibodies, cell contacts, etc. Perhaps there is cause for optimism in the fact that it is easier to define a line by two points than by one.

ACKNOWLEDGMENTS

A major part of the preparation of this contribution was done during the tenure of a Research Professorship provided by the Adolph and Mary Sprague Miller Institute for Basic Research in Science, University of California. If it is a thoughtful work, as it is intended to be, the author must thank the Miller Institute for the rare privilege of a period of leisure in which thought was possible. The work of the author's laboratory, which he has presumed to cite extensively on grounds of familiarity if not of importance, has been supported at various times by the American Cancer Society, The Office of Naval Research, The University of California Cancer Research Coordinating Committee, and The National Institutes of Health. The advice of many scientific colleagues is acknowledged in various places in the text, but a complete list of the experts with whom I have taken counsel would be too long to include here. I thank them all. For aid in the preparation of the manuscript and figures, I am indebted to Mrs. Patricia Harris, Mrs. Norma Braver, Miss Frances Kimball, and Miss Alice Krimsky.

Finally, a work as large as this one must, in many ways, reflect the influence of those who were one's teachers, and I am proud to dedicate it to L. V. Heilbrunn and L. J. Stadler, who are no longer with us.

REFERENCES

Abbo, F. E., and Pardee, A. B. (1960). *Biochim. et Biophys. Acta* **39**, 478.
Abercrombie, M. (1957). *Symposia Soc. Exptl. Biol.* **11**, 235.
Adolph, E. F. (1929). *J. Exptl. Zool.* **53**, 269.
Ågrell, I. (1953). *Arkiv. Zool.* **6**, 213.
Ågrell, I. (1955a). *Compt. rend. soc. biol.* **149**, 1322.
Ågrell, I. (1955b). *Exptl. Cell Research* **8**, 232.
Ågrell, I. (1958). *Arkiv. Zool.* **11**, 383.
Ågrell, I., and Welin-Berger, E. (1957). *Nature* **180**, 705.
Ågrell, I., and Wiman, C. (1957). *Arkiv. Zool.* **11**, 37.
Alfert, M. (1954). *Intern. Rev. Cytol.* **3**, 131.
Alfert, M., and Geschwind, I. I. (1958). *Exptl. Cell Research* **15**, 232.
Alfert, M., and Swift, H. (1953). *Exptl. Cell Research* **5**, 455.
Allen, J. M. (1956). *Exptl. Cell Research* **10**, 523.
Allen, J. M. (1958). *Exptl. Cell Research* **14**, 142.
Amano, S. (1954). *Acta Schol. Med. Univ. Kioto* **32**, 5.

Amano, S. (1957). *Cytologia* (*Tokyo*) **22**, 193.

Amano, S., and Tanaka, H. (1957). *Acta Haematol. Japon.* **20**, 319.

Amoore, J. E. (1961a). *Proc. Roy. Soc.* **B154**, 95.

Amoore, J. E. (1961b). *Proc. Roy. Soc.* **B154**, 109.

Anderson, N. G. (1956a). *Quart. Rev. Biol.* **31**, 169.

Anderson, N. G. (1956b). *Quart. Rev. Biol.* **31**, 243.

Bajer, A. (1957). *Exptl. Cell Research* **13**, 493.

Bajer, A. (1958a). *Exptl. Cell Research* **14**, 245.

Bajer, A. (1958b). *Chromosoma* **9**, 319.

Bajer, A. (1959). *Hereditas* **45**, 579.

Bajer, A., and Mole-Bajer, J. (1954a). *Acta Soc. Botan. Polon.* **23**, 69.

Bajer, A., and Mole-Bajer, J. (1954b). *Acta Soc. Botan. Polon.* **23**, 383.

Bajer, A., and Mole-Bajer, J. (1956a). *Chromosoma* **6**, 558.

Bajer, A., and Mole-Bajer, J. (1956b). *Chromosoma* **7**, 558.

Bajer, A., and Mole-Bajer, J. (1960). *In* "Les actions antimitotiques et caryocla-siques des substances chimiques." (J. Turchini and P. Sentein, eds.), pp. 209-214. Colloque No. 88. C.N.R.S., Paris.

Bajer, A., and Mole-Bajer, J. (1961). *Exptl. Cell Research.* In press.

Baker, J. R. (1953). *Quart. J. Microscop. Sci.* **94**, 407.

Baker, J. R. (1955). *Quart. J. Microscop. Sci.* **96**, 449.

Barber, H. N. (1939). *Chromosoma* **1**, 33.

Barber, H. N., and Callan, H. G. (1943). *Proc. Roy. Soc.* **B131**, 258.

Barer, R., and Joseph, S. (1957). *Symposia Soc. Exptl. Biol.* **10**, 160.

Barer, R., Joseph, S., and Meek, G. A. (1959). *Exptl. Cell Research* **18**, 179.

Barnett, R. C. (1953). *Biol. Bull.* **104**, 263.

Barnett, R. C., and Downey, M. (1955). *Federation Proc.* **14**, 9.

Barnum, C. P., Jardetzky, D., and Halberg, F. (1956). *Texas Repts. Biol. and Med.* **15**, 134.

Barrett, J. M. (1958). *J. Protozool.* **5**, 205.

Barth, L. G., and Barth, L. J. (1954). "The Energetics of Development." Columbia Univ. Press, New York.

Barthelmess, A. (1957). *Protoplasma* **48**, 546.

Beams, H. W. (1951). *Ann. N.Y. Acad. Sci.* **51**, 1349.

Beams, H. W., and Evans, T. C. (1940). *Biol. Bull.* **79**, 188.

Beams, H. W., and King, R. L. (1936). *Biol. Bull.* **71**, 188.

Beams, N. W., and King, R. L. (1938). *Biol. Bull.* **75**, 189.

Beams, H. W., Evans, T. C., Baker, W. W., and vanBreemen, V. (1950). *Anat. Record* **107**, 329.

Beatty, R. A. (1954). *Intern. Rev. Cytol.* **3**, 177.

Belar, K. (1921). *Arch. Protistenk.* **43**, 287.

Belar, K. (1926). *Ergeb. Fortschr. Zool.* **6**, 235.

Belar, K. (1929a). *Arch. Entwicklungsmech. Organ.* **118**, 359.

Belar, K. (1929b). *Z. Zellforsch. u. mikroskop. Anat.* **10**, 73.

Belar, K., and Huth, W. (1933). *Z. Zellforsch. u. mikroskop. Anat.* **17**, 51.

Benitez, H. H., Murray, M. R., and Chargaff, E. (1954). *Ann. N.Y. Acad. Sci.* **58**, 1288.

Bennett, H. S. (1951). *Anat. Record* **110**, 231.

Benzer, S. (1957). *In* "The Chemical Basis of Heredity" (W. D. McElroy and B. Glass, eds.), p. 70. Johns Hopkins Press, Baltimore, Maryland.

Berglas, A. (1957). "Cancer: nature, cause, et cure." Inst. Pasteur, Paris.

Berkeley, E. (1948). *Biol. Bull.* **94**, 169.

Bernal, J. D. (1940). *Publ. Am. Assoc. Advance Sci.* **14**, 199.
Bernhard, W. (1959). *Exptl. Cell Research Suppl.* **6**, 17.
Bernhard, W., and de Harven, E. (1960). *Proc. 4th Intern. Conf. Electron Microscopy, 1958* **2**, 217.
Bernstein, J. (1912). "Elektrobiologie." Vieweg, Braunschweig, Germany.
Bessis, M., Breton-Gorius, J., and Thiéry, J. P. (1958). *Rev. hématol.* **13**, 363.
Bibring, T. (1961). Ph.D. Thesis. Univ. of California, Berkeley, California.
Biesele, J. J. (1958). "Mitotic Poisons and the Cancer Problem." Elsevier, New York.
Bloch, D., and Godman, G. C. (1955a). *J. Biophys. Biochem. Cytol.* **1**, 17.
Bloch, D., and Godman, G. C. (1955b). *J. Biophys. Biochem. Cytol.* **1**, 531.
Blum, H. G., and Price, J. P. (1950). *J. Gen. Physiol.* **33**, 285.
Bodenstein, D. (1947). *J. Exptl. Zool.* **104**, 311.
Bodenstein, D., and Kondritzer, A. A. (1948). *J. Exptl. Zool.* **107**, 109.
Boss, J. (1954). *Exptl. Cell Research* **7**, 443.
Boss, J. (1955). *Exptl. Cell Research* **8**, 181.
Boss, J. (1959). *Exptl. Cell Research* **18**, 197.
Boveri, T. (1888). "Zellenstudien," Heft 2. Fischer, Jena.
Boveri, T. (1896). *Sitz. Physiol. Med. Ges. Wurzburg* **9**, 133.
Boveri, T. (1900). "Zellenstudien," Heft 4. Fischer, Jena.
Boveri, T. (1904). "Ergebnisse über die Konstitution der chromatische Substanz des Zellkerns." Fischer, Jena.
Boveri, T. (1907). "Zellenstudien," Heft 6. Fischer, Jena.
Brachet, J. (1947). "Embryologie Chimique." Masson, Paris.
Brachet, J. (1955). *Biochim. et Biophys. Acta* **18**, 247.
Brachet, J. (1957). "Biochemical Cytology." Academic Press, New York.
Bretschneider, L. H. (1950a). *Koninkl. Ned. Akad. Wetenschap., Proc. Ser. A,* **53**, 675.
Bretschneider, L. H. (1950b). *Koninkl. Ned. Akad. Wetenschap., Proc. Ser. B,* **53**, 1476.
Briggs, R., and King, T. J. (1959). In "The Cell" (J. Brachet and A. E. Mirsky, eds.), Vol. 1, p. 537. Academic Press, New York.
Brown, R. (1951). *J. Exptl. Botany* **2**, 96.
Brown, Robert (1833). *Trans. Linnean Soc. London* **16**, 685.
Brown, S. W. (1954). *Univ. Calif. Publs. Botany* **27**, 231.
Brown, V., and Emery, H. P. (1957). *Am. J. Botany* **44**, 585.
Bucciante, L. (1927). *Arch. exptl. Zellforsch. Gewebezücht.* **5**, 1.
Bucher, N. L. R., and Mazia, D. (1960). *J. Biophys. Biochem. Cytol.* **7**, 651.
Bucher, N. L. R., Scott, J. F., and Aub, J. C. (1951). *Cancer Research* **11**, 457.
Bucher, O. (1959). In "Protoplasmatologia" (L. V. Heilbrunn and F. Weber, eds.), Vol. 6/E,1. Springer.
Bucholz, J. T. (1939). *Am. J. Botany* **26**, 93.
Buchsbaum, R., and Williamson, R. (1943). *Physiol. Zoöl.* **16**, 162.
Bullough, W. S. (1948). *Proc. Roy. Soc.* **B132**, 212.
Bullough, W. S. (1952). *Biol. Revs. Cambridge Phil. Soc.* **27**, 133.
Bullough, W. S. (1955). *Vitamins and Hormones* **13**, 261.
Bünning, E. (1957). In "Protoplasmatologia" (L. V. Heilbrunn and F. Weber, eds.), Vol. 8/9/a. Springer, Vienna.
Burns, V. W. (1956). *J. Cellular Comp. Physiol.* **47**, 357.
Burns, V. W. (1959). *Science* **129**, 566.
Burton, A. C., and Haynes, R. H. (1955). *J. Cellular Comp. Physiol.* **46**, 360.
Butros, J. M. (1956). *J. Cellular Comp. Physiol.* **47**, 341.

Campbell, A. (1957). *Bacteriol. Revs.* **21**, 263.

Carlson, J. G. (1938). *Proc. Natl. Acad. Sci. U.S.* **24**, 500.

Carlson, J. G. (1940). *J. Morphol.* **66**, 11.

Carlson, J. G. (1946). *Biol. Bull.* **90**, 109.

Carlson, J. G. (1950). *J. Cellular Comp. Physiol.* **35**, Suppl. 1, 89.

Carlson, J. G. (1952). *Chromosoma* **5**, 199.

Carlson, J. G. (1956). *Science* **124**, 203.

Carlson, J. G., and Hollaender, A. (1948). *J. Cellular Comp. Physiol.* **31**, 149.

Carrière, R., Leblond, C. P., and Messier, B. (1961). *Exptl. Cell Research* **23**, 625.

Caspersson, T. (1936). *Skand. Arch. Physiol.* **73**, Suppl. 8.

Caspersson, T. (1939). *Chromosoma* **1**, 147.

Caspersson, T. (1950). "Cell Growth and Cell Function." Norton, New York.

Caspersson, T., and Schultz, J. (1940). *Proc. Natl. Acad. Sci. U. S.* **26**, 507.

Cavalieri, L., and Rosenberg, B. H. (1961). *Biophysical J.* In press.

Cavalieri, L., and Rosenberg, B. H. (1961). *Biophys. J.* In press.

Cavalieri, L., and Rosenberg, B. H. (1961). *Biophys. J.* **1**, 323.

Chalkley, H. W. (1951). *Ann. N.Y. Acad. Sci.* **51**, 1303.

Chambers, R. (1951). *Ann. N.Y. Acad. Sci.* **51**, 1311.

Chambers, R., and Chambers, E. L. (1961). "Explorations into the Nature of the Living Cell." Harvard Univ. Press, Cambridge, Massachusetts.

Chapman, G. B. (1959). *J. Biophys. Biochem. Cytol.* **6**, 221.

Chapman, G. B., and Hillier, J. (1953). *J. Bacteriol.* **66**, 362.

Chen, T. T. (1948). *J. Morphol.* **83**, 281.

Chèvremont, M., and Frederic, J. (1952). *Arch. biol. (Liége)* **63**, 259.

Chèvremont, M., and Frederic, J. (1955). *In* "Symposium on the Fine Structure of Cells," pp. 33-37. Interscience, New York.

Chèvremont-Comhaire, S., and Chèvremont, M. (1956). *Compt. rend. soc. biol.* **150**, 1046.

Clark, F. J. (1940). *Am. J. Botany* **27**, 547.

Child, F. M. (1959). *Exptl. Cell Research* **18**, 258.

Cleveland, L. R. (1938). *Biol. Bull.* **74**, 51.

Cleveland, L. R. (1949). *Trans. Am. Phil. Soc.* **39**, 1.

Cleveland, L. R. (1953). *Trans. Am. Phil. Soc.* **43**, 809.

Cleveland, L. R. (1954). *J. Morphol.* **95**, 557.

Cleveland, L. R. (1955). *J. Morphol.* **97**, 511.

Cleveland, L. R. (1956). *J. Protozool.* **3**, 78.

Cleveland, L. R. (1957a). *J. Protozool.* **4**, 230.

Cleveland, L. R. (1957b). *J. Protozool.* **4**, 241.

Cleveland, L. R. (1958). *J. Protozool.* **5**, 47.

Cleveland, L. R. (1961). *Arch. Protistenk.* **105**, 163.

Clowes, G. H. A. (1951). *Ann. N.Y. Acad. Sci.* **51**, 1409.

Cohen, A. I. (1957). *J. Biophys. Biochem. Cytol.* **3**, 859.

Cohen, S. S. (1957). *In* "The Chemical Basis of Heredity" (W. D. McElroy and B. Glass, eds.), pp. 651-685. Johns Hopkins Press, Baltimore, Maryland.

Cohen, S. S., and Barner, H. D. (1954). *Proc. Natl. Acad. Sci. U.S.* **40**, 885.

Comandon, J., and deFonbrune, P. (1937). *Compt. rend. soc. biol.* **124**, 1299.

Conard, A. (1939). "Sur le mécanisme de la division cellulaire et sur les bases morphologiques de la Cytologie." Coek, Brussels.

Conklin, E. G. (1912). *J. Exptl. Zool.* **12**, 1.

Conklin, E. G. (1939). *Am. Naturalist* **73**, 538.

Cook, R., and James, T. W. (1960). *Exptl. Cell Research* **21**, 583.

Cooper, K. W. (1939). *Chromosoma* **1**, 151.

Cooper, Z. K., and Franklin, H. C. (1940). *Anat. Record* **78**, 1.

Cornman, I. (1944). *Am. Naturalist* **78**, 410.

Cornman, I. (1954). *Intern. Rev. Cytol.* **3**, 113.

Cornman, I., and Cornman, M. E. (1951). *Ann. N.Y. Acad. Sci.* **51**, 1443.

Corliss, J. O. (1957). *Science* **125**, 988.

Costello, D. P. (1961). *Biol. Bull.* **120**, 285.

Crosby, A. R. (1957). *Am. J. Botany* **44**, 813.

Dalcq, A. (1957). *Bull. soc. zool. France* **82**, 296.

Dalcq, A., and Simon, S. (1930). *Compt. rend. assoc. anat.* **25**, 104.

Dalcq, A., and Simon, S. (1932). *Protoplasma* **14**, 497.

Dan, J. C. (1948). *Physiol. Zoöl.* **21**, 191.

Dan, K. (1943). *J. Fac. Sci. Univ. Tokyo, Sect. IV* **4**, 323.

Dan, K. (1954). *Embryologia* **2**, 99.

Dan, K., and Dan, J. C. (1947). *Biol. Bull.* **93**, 139.

Dan, K., and Nakajima, T. (1956). *Embryologia* **3**, 187.

Dan, K., Ito, S., and Mazia, D. (1952). *Biol. Bull.* **103**, 292.

Dan, K., Yanagita, T., and Sugiyama, M. (1937). *Protoplasma* **28**, 66.

Daniels, E. W. (1959). *Ann. N.Y. Acad. Sci.* **78**, 662.

Darlington, C. D. (1932). "Chromosomes and Plant-Breeding." Macmillan, London.

Darlington, C. D. (1937). "Recent Advances in Cytology," 2nd ed. Blakiston, Philadelphia, Pennsylvania.

Darlington, C. D. (1939). "The Evolution of Genetic Systems." Cambridge Univ. Press, London and New York.

Darlington, C. D. (1956). "Chromosome Botany." Macmillan, New York.

Darlington, C. D. (1958). "The Evolution of Genetic Systems," 2nd ed. Cambridge Univ. Press, London and New York.

Darlington, J. D., and Upcott, M. B. (1939). *Chromosoma* **1**, 23.

Das, N. K., and Alfert, M. (1959). *Anat. Record* **134**, 548.

Das, N. K., and Alfert, M. (1961). *Proc. Natl. Acad. Sci. U.S.* **47**, 1.

Das, N. K., Patau, K., and Skoog, F. (1956). *Physiol. Plantarum* **9**, 640.

Davidson, D., and Anderson, N. G. (1960). *Exptl. Cell Research* **20**, 610.

Davies, H. G. (1952). *Exptl. Cell Research* **3**, 453.

Davis, M., and Smith, C. L. (1957). *Exptl. Cell Research* **12**, 15.

de Duve, C. (1959). *In* "Subcellular Particles" (T. Hayashi, ed.), pp. 128-159. Ronald Press, New York.

Deeley, E. M., Davies, H. G., and Chayen, J. (1957). *Exptl. Cell Research* **12**, 582.

de Harven, E., and Bernhard, W. (1956). *Z. Zellforsch. u. mikroskop. Anat.* **45**, 378.

de Harven, E., and Dustin, P., Jr. (1960). *In* "Les actions antimitotiques et caryoclastiques des substances chimiques" (J. Turchini and P. Sentein, eds.), pp. 189-198. Colloque No. 88. C.N.R.S., Paris.

Delamater, E. D. (1953). *Intern. Rev. Cytol.* **2**, 158.

Delamater, E. D. (1959). *Exptl. Cell Research* **16**, 636.

Delbrück, M., and Stent, G. S. (1957). *In* "The Chemical Basis of Heredity" (W. D. McElroy and B. Glass, eds.), p. 699. Johns Hopkins Press, Baltimore, Maryland.

De Robertis, E., and Franco Ruffo, H. (1957). *Exptl. Cell Research* **12**, 66.

de Terra, N. (1960). *Exptl. Cell Research* **21**, 34.

Devillers, G., and Rosenberg, J. (1953). *Compt. rend. acad. sci.* **237**, 1561.

Deysson, G. (1956). *In* "Les facteurs de la croissance cellulaire" (J. A. Thomas, ed.), p. 241. Masson, Paris.

Dirksen, E. R. (1961). Ph.D. Thesis, Univ. of California, Berkeley, California.

Dornfeld, E. J., and Owczarzak, A. (1958). *J. Biophys. Biochem. Cytol.* **4**, 243.

Ducoff, H. S., and Ehret, C. F. (1959). "Mitogenesis." Univ. of Chicago Press, Chicago, Illinois.

Duncan, R. E., and Persidsky, M. D. (1958). *Am. J. Botany* **45**, 719.

Duryee, W. R., and Doherty, J. K. (1954). *Ann. N.Y. Acad. Sci.* **58**, 1210.

Dustin, P., Jr. (1956). *In* "Les facteurs de la croissance cellulaire" (J. A. Thomas, ed.), p. 189. Masson, Paris.

Edwards, J. L., Koch, A. L., Youcis, P., Freese, H. L., Laite, M. B., and Donalson, J. T. (1960). *J. Biophys. Biochem. Cytol.* **7**, 243.

Eigsti, D. H., and Dustin, P., Jr. (1955). "Colchicine in Agriculture, Medicine, Biology, and Chemistry." Iowa State College Press, Ames, Iowa.

Emanuelsson, H. (1958). *Arkiv. Zool.* **11**, 110.

Ephrussi, B. (1927). *Protoplasma* **1**, 107.

Ephrussi, B. (1953). "Nucleo-cytoplasmic Relations in Micro-organisms." Clarendon Press, Oxford.

Ephrussi, B. (1958). *J. Cellular Comp. Physiol.* **52**, Suppl. **1**, 35.

Erickson, R. O. (1947). *Nature* **159**, 275.

Errera, M. (1957). *In* "Protoplasmatologia" (L. V. Heilbrunn and F. Weber, eds.), Vol. X/3. Springer, Vienna.

Esau, K. (1953). "Plant Anatomy." Wiley, New York.

Estable, C., and Sotelo, J. R. (1955). "Symposium on the Fine Structure of Cells," p. 170. Interscience, New York.

Evans, H. J., and Savage, J. R. K. (1959). *Exptl. Cell Research* **18**, 51.

Faed, M. J. W. (1959). Ph.D. Thesis. Division and Growth Relationships in Single Cells. Univ. of Edinburgh, Scotland.

Falk, G. (1956). *Science* **123**, 632.

Fawcett, D. W., Ito, S., and Slautterback, D. B. (1959). *J. Biophys. Biochem. Cytol.* **5**, 453.

Fell, H. B., and Hughes, A. F. W. (1949). *Quart. J. Microscop. Sci.* **90**, 355.

Firket, H., Chèvremont-Comhaire, S., and Chèvremont, M. (1955). *Nature* **176**, 1075.

Fischer, A. (1899). "Fixierung, Färbung und Bau des Protoplasmas." Fischer, Jena.

Fischer, H., Hug, O., and Lippert, W. (1952). *Chromosoma* **5**, 69.

Flemming, W. (1882). "Zellsubstanz, Kern und Zelltheilung." Vogel, Leipzig.

Fritsch, F. E. (1935). "The Structure and Reproduction of the Algae," p. 609. Cambridge Univ. Press, London and New York.

Fol, H. (1891). *Anat. Anz.* **6**, 266.

Ford, C. E., Hamerton, J. L., and Mole, R. H. (1958). *J. Cellular Comp. Physiol.* **52**, Suppl. **1**, 235.

Frederic, J. (1954). *Ann. N.Y. Acad. Sci.* **58**, 1246.

Friedenwald, J. S., and Sigelman, S. (1953). *Exptl. Cell Research* **4**, 1.

Fuerst, C. R., and Stent, G. S. (1956). *J. Gen. Physiol.* **40**, 73.

Fujii, T. (1954). *Nature* **174**, 1108.

Fujii, T. (1955a). *J. Fac. Sci. Univ. Tokyo, Sect. III* **7**, 313.

Fujii, T. (1955b). *J. Fac. Sci. Univ. Tokyo, Sect. III* **7**, 327.

Galinsky, I. (1949). *J. Heredity* **40**, 289.

Gates, R. R. (1942). *Botan. Rev.* **8**, 337.

Gaulden, M. E. (1957). *Proc. 1st Pan Am. Cancer Cytol. Congr., Miami, Florida.*

Gaulden, M. E., and Carlson, J. G. (1947). *Genetics* **32**, 87.

Gaulden, M. E., and Carlson, J. G. (1951). *Exptl. Cell Research* **2**, 416.

Gaulden, M. E., and Perry, R. P. (1958). *Proc. Natl. Acad. Sci. U.S.* **44**, 553.

Gaulden, M. E., Carlson, J. G., and Tipton, S. R. (1949). *Anat. Record* **105**, 16.

Gavaudan, P. (1956). *In* "Les facteurs de la croissance cellulaire" (J. A. Thomas, ed.), p. 275. Masson, Paris.

Gay, H. (1956). *Cold Spring Harbor Symposia Quant. Biol.* **21**, 257.

Gay, H. (1960). *Sci. American* **202**, 126.

Geilenkirchen, W. L. M., and Zeuthen, E. (19⁻8). *Compt. rend. trav. lab. Carlsberg* **31**, 7.

Geitler, L. (1938). "Chromosomenbau"—Protoplasma Monographien, No. 14. Bornträger, Berlin.

Geitler, L. (1941). *Ergeb. Biol.* **18**, 1.

Geitler, L. (1953). *In* "Protoplasmatologia" (L. V. Heilbrunn and F. Weber, eds.), Vol. VI/c. Springer, Vienna.

Gelfant, S. (1958). *Exptl. Cell Research* **15**, 423.

Gelfant, S. (1959). *Exptl. Cell Research* **16**, 527.

Gerassimov, J. J. (1905). *Flora (Jena)* **94**, 79.

Goldschmidt, R. B. (1955). "Theoretical Genetics." Univ. of Calif. Press, Berkeley, California.

Goldstein, L., and Micou, J. (1959). *J. Biophys. Biochem. Cytol.* **6**, 301.

Gray, J. (1924). *Proc. Cambridge Phil. Soc., Biol. Sci.* **1**, 164.

Gray, J. (1931). "A Textbook of Experimental Cytology." Cambridge Univ. Press, London and New York.

Gray, L. H. (1951). *Brit. J. Radiol.* **24**, 1.

Grell, K. G. (1956). "Protozoologie." Springer, Berlin.

Gross, P. R. (1957). *Trans. N.Y. Acad. Sci.* **20**, 154.

Gross, P. R., and Spindel, W. (1960). *Ann. N.Y. Acad. Sci.* **90**, 500.

Gross, P. R., Philpott, D. E., and Nass, S. (1958). *J. Ultrastruct. Research* **2**, 55.

Guttman, R. (1952). *Am. J. Botany* **39**, 528.

Guttman, R. (1957). *J. Biophys. Biochem. Cytol.* **3**, 129.

Guyot, M., Poussel, H., and Gavaudan, P. (1960). *In* "Les actions antimitotiques et caryoclasiques de substances chimiques" (J. Turchini and P. Sentein, eds.), p. 51. Colloque No. 88. C.N.R.S., Paris.

Haberlandt, G. (1921). *Beitr. allgem. Botan.* **2**, 1.

Hamburger, K., and Zeuthen, E. (1957). *Exptl. Cell Research* **13**, 443.

Hamburger, K., and Zeuthen, E. (1960). *Compt. rend. trav. lab. Carlsberg* **32**, 1.

Hanson, E. D. (1958). *Systematic Zool.* **7**, 16.

Hanson, J., and Huxley, H. E. (1955). *Symposia Soc. Exptl. Biol.* **9**, 228.

Haque, A. (1953). *Heredity* **7**, 429.

Harris, H. (1956). *Brit. J. Exptl. Pathol.* **37**, 512.

Harris, H. (1959). *Biochem. J.* **72**, 54.

Hartmann, M. (1928). *Zool. Jahrb. Abt. Allgem. Zool. Physiol. Tiere* **45**, 973.

Harvey, E. B. (1934). *Biol. Bull.* **66**, 228.

Harvey, E. B. (1936). *Biol. Bull.* **71**, 101.

Harvey, E. B. (1951). *Ann. N.Y. Acad. Sci.* **51**, 1336.

Harvey, E. B. (1960). *Biol. Bull.* **119**, 87.

Hase, E., Morimura, Y., and Tamiya, H. (1957). *Arch. Biochem. Biophys.* **69**, 149.

Hase, E., Morimura, Y., Mihara, S., and Tamiya, H. (1958). *Arch. Mikrobiol.* **31**, 87.

Hase, E., Mihara, S., Otsuka, H., and Tamiya, H. (1959). *Arch Biochem. Biophys.* **83**, 170.

Heath, J. E. (1954). *Exptl. Cell Research* **6**, 311.

Heidenhain, M. (1895). *Arch. Entwicklungsmech. Organ.* **1**, 473.

Heidenhain, M. (1907). "Plasma und Zelle," Pt. 1. Fischer, Jena.

Heilbrunn, L. V. (1920). *J. Exptl. Zool.* **30**, 211.

Heilbrunn, L. V. (1921). *J. Exptl. Zool.* **34**, 417.

Heilbrunn, L. V. (1952). *In* "Modern Trends in Physiology and Biochemistry" (E. S. G. Barron, ed.), pp. 123-134. Academic Press, New York.

Heilbrunn, L. V. (1956). "The Dynamics of Living Protoplasm." Academic Press, New York.

Heilbrunn, L. V., and Wilson, W. L. (1948). *Biol. Bull.* **95**, 57.

Heitz, E. (1956). "Conference on Chromosomes" (at Waggeningen, Netherlands), pp. 1-21, W. E. J. Tjeenk Willink, Zwolle, Netherlands.

Henneguy, L. F. (1896). "Leçons sur la cellule," p. 350. Georges Carré, Paris.

Henneguy, L. F. (1898). *Arch. anat. microscop.* **1**, 481.

Hertwig, O. (1909). "The Cell" 2nd English ed. Macmillan, New York.

Hertwig, R. (1908). *Arch. Zellforsch.* **1**, 1.

Hill, A. V. (1928). *Proc. Roy. Soc.* **B104**, 41.

Hiramoto, Y. (1956). *Exptl. Cell Research* **11**, 630.

Hiramoto, Y. (1958). *J. Exptl. Biol.* **35**, 407.

Hirshfield, H. I., and Pecora, P. (1956). *J. Protozool.* **3**, 14.

Hoffman, J. G. (1949). *Bull. Math. Biophys.* **11**, 139.

Hoffman, J. G. (1953). "The Size and Growth of Tissue Cells." C. C Thomas, Springfield, Illinois.

Hoffmann-Berling, H. (1954a). *Biochim. et Biophys. Acta* **15**, 226.

Hoffmann-Berling, H. (1954b). *Biochim. et Biophys. Acta* **15**, 332.

Hoffmann-Berling, H. (1959). *In* "Cell, Organism and Milieu" (D. Rudnick, ed.), p. 45. Ronald Press, New York.

Holden, J. W., and Mota, M. (1956). *Heredity* **10**, 109.

Holter, H., and Zeuthen, E. (1957). *Pubbl. staz. zool. Napoli* **29**, 285.

Hotchkiss, R. D. (1954). *Proc. Natl. Acad. Sci. U.S.* **41**, 49.

Hotchkiss, R. D. (1955). *J. Cellular Comp. Physiol.* **45**, Suppl. 2, 1.

Holtzer, H., Abbott, J., and Cavanaugh, M. W. (1959). *Exptl. Cell Research* **16**, 595.

Howard, A., and Pelc, S. R. (1951). *Exptl. Cell Research* **2**, 178.

Howard, A., and Pelc, S. R. (1953). *Heredity* **6**, 261.

Hsu, T. C. (1955). *J. Natl. Cancer Inst.* **16**, 691.

Hsu, T. C. (1959). *In* "Developmental Cytology" (D. Rudnick, ed.), p. 47. Ronald Press, New York.

Huettner, A. F. (1933). *Z. Zellforsch. u. mikroskop. Anat.* **19**, 119.

Huggins, C., Tapley, D. F., and Jensen, E. V. (1951). *Nature* **167**, 592.

Hughes, A. F. W. (1949). *J. Roy. Microscop. Soc.* **69**, 215.

Hughes, A. F. W. (1950). *Quart. J. Microscop. Sci.* **91**, 251.

Hughes, A. F. W. (1952a). *Symposia Soc. Exptl. Biol.* **4**, 256.

Hughes, A. F. W. (1952b). "The Mitotic Cycle." Academic Press, New York.

Hughes, A. F. W. (1959). "A History of Cytology." Abelard-Schuman, New York.

Hughes, A. F. W., and Preston, M. M. E. (1949). *J. Roy. Microscop. Soc.* **69**, 121.

Hughes, A. F. W., and Swawn, M. M. (1948). *J. Exptl. Biol.* **25**, 45.

Hughes-Schrader, S. (1931). *Z. Zellforsch. u. mickroskop. Anat.* **13**, 742.

Hughes-Schrader, S. (1943). *Biol. Bull.* **85**, 265.

Hughes-Schrader, S. (1947). *Chromosoma* **3**, 1.

Hughes-Schrader, S. (1948a). *Advances in Genet.* **2**, 127.

Hughes-Schrader, S. (1948b). *Chromosoma* **3**, 257.

Hughes-Schrader, S. (1955). *Chromosoma* **7**, 420.

Hughes-Schrader, S., and Ris, H. (1941). *J. Exptl. Zool.* **87**, 429.

Hunter-Szybalska, M. E., Szybalski, W., and Delamater, E. D. (1956). *J. Bacteriol.* **71**, 117.

Huxley, H. E. (1958). *Sci. American* **199**, 66.

Huxley, H. E. (1960). *In* "The Cell" (Brachet, J., and Mirsky, A. E., eds.), Vol. 4. Academic Press, New York.

Hyppio, P. A., Tsou, T. M., and J. B. Wilson (1955). *Cytologia* (*Tokyo*) **20**, 166.

Iida, T. T. (1942). *Zool. Mag.* (*Tokyo*) **54**, 364.

Immers, J. (1957). *Exptl. Cell Research* **12**, 145.

Inoué, S. (1952a). *Exptl. Cell Research* **2**, Suppl. **2**, 305.

Inoué, S. (1952b). *Biol. Bull.* **103**, 316.

Inoué, S. (1953). *Chromosoma* **5**, 487.

Inoué, S. (1959). *In* "Biophysical Science—A Study Program" (J. L. Oncley, ed.), p. 402. Wiley, New York.

Inoué, S. (1960). *Ann. N.Y. Acad. Sci.* **90**, 529.

Inoué, S., and Bajer, A. (1961). *Chromosoma.* In press.

Inoué, S., and Dan, K. (1951). *J. Morphol.* **89**, 423.

Inoué, S., and Hyde, W. L. (1957). *J. Biophys. Biochem. Cytol.* **3**, 831.

Ishizaka, S. (1958). *J. Exptl. Biol.* **35**, 396.

Ito, S. (1960). *J. Biophys. Biochem. Cytol.* **6**, 433.

Iverson, R. M., and Giese, A. C. (1957). *Exptl. Cell Research* **13**, 213.

Iwamura, T. (1955). *J. Biochem.* (*Tokyo*) **42**, 575.

Izutsu, K. (1959a). *Mie Med. J.* **9**, 1.

Izutsu, K. (1959b). *Mie Med. J.* **9**, 15.

Jacob, F., and Wollman, F. L. (1958). *Symposia Soc. Exptl. Biol.* **12**, 75.

Jacob, F., Schaeffer, P., and Wollman, E. L. (1960). *Symposium Soc. Gen. Microbiol.* **10**, 67.

Jacobson, W. (1954). *In* "Chemistry and Biology of the Pteridines," (G. E. W. Wolstenholme and M. P. Cameron, eds.), p. 329. Churchill, London.

Jacobson, W., and Webb, M. (1952). *Exptl. Cell Research* **3**, 163.

Jacquez, J. A., and Biesele, J. (1954). *Exptl. Cell Research* **6**, 17.

Jeener, H., and Jeener, R. (1952). *Exptl. Cell Research* **3**, 675.

Jensen, E. V. (1959). *Science* **130**, 1319.

Jensen, W. A., and Kavaljian, L. G. (1958). *Am. J. Botany* **45**, 365.

Johnson, F., Eyring, H., and Polissar, M. J. (1954). "The Kinetic Basis of Molecular Biology." Wiley, New York.

Jones, R. F., and Lewin, R. A. (1960). *Exptl. Cell Research* **19**, 408.

Jungers, V. (1931). *La Cellule* **40**, 298.

Kaufmann, B. P. (1948). *Botan. Rev.* **14**, 57.

Kaufmann, B. P. (1960). *In* "The Cell Nucleus" (J. S. Mitchell, ed.), p. 251, Academic Press, New York.

Kaufmann, B. P., and Das, N. K. (1954). *Proc. Natl. Acad. Sci. U.S.* **40**, 1052.

Kaufmann, B. P., and McDonald, M. (1956). *Cold Spring Harbor Symposia Quant. Biol.* **21**, 233.

Kaufmann, B. P., McDonald, M., and Gay, H. (1948). *Nature* **162**, 814.

Kawamura, K. (1954). *Jap. J. Genetics* **29**, 131.

Kawamura, K. (1955). *Cytologia* (*Tokyo*) **20**, 47.

Kawamura, K. (1957). *Cytologia* (*Tokyo*) **22**, 337.

Kawamura, K. (1960a). *Exptl. Cell Research* **21**, 1.

Kawamura, K. (1960b). *Exptl. Cell Research* **21**, 9.

Kawamura, N. (1960). *Exptl. Cell Research* **20**, 127.

Kawamura, N., and Dan, K. (1958). *J. Biophys. Biochem. Cytol.* **4**, 615.

Katznelson, Z. S. (1959). *Tsitologia* (*U.S.S.R.*) **1**, 238.

Kelly, L. S. (1957). *Progr. Biophys. and Biophys. Chem.* **8**, 145.

Kimball, R. F., and Barka, R. (1959). *Exptl. Cell Research* **17**, 173.

Kimball, R. F., Caspersson, T., Svenson, G., and Carlson, L. (1959). *Exptl. Cell Research* **17**, 160.

Klein, G., and Klein, E. (1957). *Symposia Soc. Exptl. Biol.* **11**, 305.

Klein, G., and Klein, E. (1958). *J. Cellular Comp. Physiol.* **52**, Suppl. **1**, 125.

Kleinfeld, R. G. (1953). Ph.D. Thesis. Univ. of Chicago, Chicago, Illinois.

Kleinfeld, R. G., and von Haam, E. (1959). *J. Biophys. Biochem. Cytol.* **6**, 393.

Kojima, M. K. (1959a). *Embryologia* **4**, 191.

Kojima, M. K. (1959b). *Embryologia* **4**, 211.

Koller, P. C. (1947). *Symposia Soc. Exptl. Biol.* **1**, 270.

Kornberg, A. (1959a). *Harvey Lectures Ser.* **53**, p. 83.

Kornberg, A. (1959b). *In* "Biophysical Science—A Study Program" (J. L. Oncley, ed.), p. 200. Wiley, New York.

Krahl, M. E. (1950). *Biol. Bull.* **98**, 175.

Kriszat, G. (1954). "Die Wirkung von Adenosintriphosphat auf die Teilung und Entwicklung des Seeigeleies bein Anwendung von Hemmungsfactoren." Akademisk Avhandling, Stockholm.

Kriszat, G., and Runnström, J. (1951). *Trans. N.Y. Acad. Sci.* **13**, 162.

Kupka, E., and Seelich, F. (1948). *Chromosoma* **3**, 302.

Kurosumi, K. (1958). *Protoplasma* **49**, 116.

Kuwada, Y. (1929). *Mem. Coll. Sci., Kyoto Imp. Univ.* **4**, 199.

Kuwada, Y., Shinke, N., and Oura, G. (1938). *Z. wiss. Mikroskop.* **55**, 8.

LaCour, L. F., and Chayen, J. (1958). *Exptl. Cell Research* **14**, 462.

LaCour, L. F., and Pelc, S. R. (1958). *Nature*, **182**, 506.

LaCour, L. F., and Pelc, S. R. (1959). *Nature* **183**, 1455.

LaCour, L. F., Chayen, J., and Gahan, P. S. (1958). *Exptl. Cell Research* **14**, 469.

Lafontaine, J. G. (1958). *J. Biophys. Biochem. Cytol.* **4**, 777.

Lamb, A. B. (1907). *J. Exptl. Zool.* **5**, 27.

Landau, J. V., Marsland, D., and Zimmerman, A. M. (1955). *J. Cellular Comp. Physiol.* **45**, 309.

Lansing, A. I. (1952). *In* "Problems of Aging" (A. I. Lansing, ed.), p. 3. Williams and Wilkins, Baltimore, Maryland.

Laser, H. (1933). *Biochem. Z.* **264**, 72.

Laughlin, H. H. (1919). *Carnegie Inst. Wash. Publ.* **265**, 488.

Lederberg, J. (1959). *Harvey Lectures Ser.* **53**, p. 69.

Lepper, R. (1956). *Botan. Rev.* **22**, 375.

Lettré, H. (1952a). *Cancer Research* **12**, 847.

Lettré, H. (1952b). *Z. Krebsforsch.* **58**, 621.

Lettré, H. (1954). *Ann. N.Y. Acad. Sci.* **58**, 1264.

Lettré, H., and Lettré, R. (1957). *Naturwiss.* **44**, 406.

Lettré, H., and Lettré, R. (1958). *Rev. hématol.* **13**, 337.

Lettré, H., and Lettré, R. (1959). *The Nucleus* **2**, 23.

Lettré, H., and Lettré, R. (1960). *In* "L'action antimitotique et caryoclasique de substances chimiques" (J. Turchini and P. Sentein, eds.), p. 25. Colloque No. 88. C.N.R.S., Paris.

Lettré, H., and Schleich, A. (1955). *Protoplasma* **44**, 314.

Lettré, H., and Siebs, W. (1956). *Protoplasma* **46**, 523.

Lettré, R. (1955). *In* "Symposium on the Fine Structure of Cells," pp. 141-150. Interscience, New York.

Levinthal, C., and Crane, H. R. (1956). *Proc. Natl. Acad. Sci. U.S.* **42**, 436.

Lewis, W. H. (1939). *Science* **89**, 400.

Lewis, W. H. (1942). "The Structure of Protoplasm," p. 163. Iowa State College Press, Ames, Iowa.

Lewis, W. H. (1947). *Anat. Record* **97**, 433.

Lillie, R. S. (1911). *J. Morphol.* **22**, 695.

Lima-de-Faria, A. (1958). *Intern. Rev. Cytol.* **7**, 123.

Lindner, A. (1959). *Cancer Research* **19**, 189.

Lindsley, D. L., and Novitski, E. (1958). *Genetics* **43**, 790.

Longwell, A., and Mota, M. (1960). *Endeavour* **19**, 100.

Longwell, A., and Svihla, G. (1960). *Exptl. Cell Research* **20**, 294.

Lorch, I. J. (1952). *Quart. J. Microscop. Sci.* **93**, 475.

Lorch, I. J., Danielli, J. F., and Hörstadius, S. (1953). *Exptl. Cell Research* **4**, 253.

Love, R. (1957). *Nature* **180**, 1338.

Lushbaugh, C. C. (1956). *J. Histochem. and Cytochem.* **4**, 499.

Lwoff, A. (1950). "Problems of Morphogenesis in Ciliates." Wiley, New York.

Maaløe, O., and Hanawalt, P. C. (1961). *J. Mol. Biol.* **3**, 144.

Maaløe, O., and Lark, K. G. (1954). *In* "Recent Developments in Cell Physiology" (J. A. Kitching, ed.), p. 159. Academic Press, New York.

Maas, W. K., and Gorini, L. (1958). *In* "Physiological Adaptation" (C. L. Prosser, ed.), p. 151. Am. Physiol. Soc., Washington, D. C.

McClung, C. E. (1940). *Tabul. Biol., Hague* **18**, 1.

McDonald, B. (1958). *Biol. Bull.* **114**, 71.

McFall, E., and Stent, G. (1959). *Biochim. et Biophys. Acta* **34**, 580.

McGrath, R. (1959). *Exptl. Cell Research* **16**, 459.

McLeish, J. (1954). *Heredity* **8**, 385.

McMahon, R. M. (1956). *Caryologia* **8**, 250.

McMaster-Kaye, R., and Taylor, J. H. (1958). *J. Biophys. Biochem. Cytol.* **4**, 5.

Makino, S., and Nakahara, H. (1953a). *Z. Krebsforsch.* **59**, 298.

Makino, S., and Nakahara, H. (1953b). *Cytologia (Tokyo)* **18**, 128.

Makino, S., and Nakahara, H. (1955). *Chromosoma* **7**, 14.

Makino, S., and Nakanishi, H. (1955). *Chromosoma* **7**, 439.

Maltaux, M., and Massart, J. (1906). *Rec. Inst. bot. Léo Errera, Brux.* **6**, 369.

Manton, I. (1945). *Am. J. Botany* **32**, 342.

Manton, I. (1950). *Biol. Revs. Cambridge Phil. Soc.* **25**, 486.

Mark, E. L. (1881). *Bull. Museum Comp. Zool. Harvard* **6**, 173.

Marquardt, H. (1938). *Z. Botan.* **32**, 401.

Marshak, A. (1955). *Intern. Rev. Cytol.* **4**, 103.

Marsland, D. (1951). *Ann. N.Y. Acad. Sci.* **51**, 1327.

Marsland, D. (1956). *Intern. Rev. Cytol.* **5**, 199.

Marsland, D. (1957). *In* "Influence of Temperature on Biological Systems" (F. H. Johnson, ed.), p. 111. Am. Physiol. Soc., Washington, D. C.

Marsland, D. (1958). *Sci. American* **199**, 36.

Marsland, D., Zimmerman, A. M., and Auclair, W. (1960). *Exptl. Cell Research.* In press.

Marty, M. (1954). *Rev. cytol. et biol. végétale* **15**, 107.

Maruyama, Y. (1956). *J. Bacteriol.* **72**, 21.

Maruyama, Y., and Lark, K. G. (1959). *Exptl. Cell Research* **18**, 389.

Maruyama, Y., and Yanagita, T. (1956). *J. Bacteriol.* **71**, 542.

Mazia, D. (1952). *In* "Modern Trends in Physiology and Biochemistry" (E. S. G. Barrón, ed.), p. 77. Academic Press, New York.

Mazia, D. (1954). *In* "Glutathione" (S. Colowick *et al.*, eds.), p. 209. Academic Press, New York.

Mazia, D. (1955). *Symposia Soc. Exptl. Biol.* **9**, 335.

Mazia, D. (1956a). *Am. Scientist* **44**, 1.

Mazia, D. (1956b). *Advances in Biol. and Med. Phys.* **4**, 70.

Mazia, D. (1957). *In* "The Chemical Basis of Heredity" (W. D. McElroy and B. Glass, eds.), p. 169. Johns Hopkins Press, Baltimore, Maryland.

Mazia, D. (1958a). *Exptl. Cell Research* **14**, 486.

Mazia, D. (1958b). *J. Cell. Comp. Physiol.* **52**, Suppl. 1, 315.

Mazia, D. (1959a). *Harvey Lectures Ser.* **53**, p. 130.

Mazia, D. (1959b). *In* "Sulfur in Proteins," (R. Benesch *et al.*, eds.), p. 367. Academic Press, New York.

Mazia, D. (1960). *In* "L'action antimitotique et caryoclasique de substances chimiques," (J. Turchini and P. Sentein, eds.), p. 167. Colloque No. 88. C.N.R.S., Paris.

Mazia, D. (1961). *In* "Biological Structure and Function" (T. W. Goddwin, and O. Lindberg, eds.). Academic Press, New York.

Mazia, D., and Dan, K. (1952). *Proc. Natl. Acad. Sci. U.S.* **38**, 826.

Mazia, D., and Hirshfield, H. I. (1950). *Science* **112**, 297.

Mazia, D., and Prescott, D. M. (1954). *Science* **120**, 120.

Mazia, D., and Roslansky, J. D. (1956). *Protoplasma* **46**, 528.

Mazia, D., and Zimmerman, A. M. (1958). *Exptl. Cell Research* **15**, 138.

Mazia, D., Harris, P. J., and Bibring, T. (1960). *J. Biophys. Biochem. Cytol.* **7**, 1.

Mazia, D., Chaffee, R. R., and Iverson, R. M. (1961a). *Proc. Natl. Acad. Sci. U.S.* **47**, 788.

Mazia, D., Mitchison, J. M., Medina, H., and Harris, P. (1961b). *J. Biophys. Biochem. Cytol.* **10**, in press.

Mercer, E. H., and Wolpert, L. (1958). *Exptl. Cell Research* **14**, 629.

Meselson, M., and Stahl, F. W. (1958). *Proc. Natl. Acad. Sci. U.S.* **44**, 671.

Metcalf, M. M. (1923). *U.S. Natl. Mus. Bull. No.* **120**, 248.

Metz, C. W. (1933). *Biol. Bull.* **64**, 333.

Metz, C. W. (1936). *Cytologia* **7**, 219.

Miescher, F. (1897). "Histochemische und Physiologische Arbeiten." Vogel, Leipzig.

Miles, A. A., and Pirie, N. W. (1956). *Symposia Soc. Gen. Microbiol.* **6**.

Milovidov, P. (1949). "Physik und Chemie des Zellkernes." Protoplasma Monographien, Vol. 20, Pt. 1. Bornträger, Berlin-Nikolassee.

Milovidov, P. (1954). "Physik und Chemie des Zellkernes." Protoplasma Monographien, Vol. 20, Pt. 2. Bornträger, Berlin-Nikolassee.

Mirsky, A. E., and Ris, H. (1951). *J. Gen. Physiol.* **34**, 451.

Mitchison, J. M. (1952). *Symposia Soc. Exptl. Biol.* **6**, 105.

Mitchison, J. M. (1953). *J. Exptl. Biol.* **30**, 515.

Mitchison, J. M. (1957). *Exptl. Cell Research* **13**, 244.

Mitchison, J. M., and Swann, M. M. (1952). *J. Exptl. Biol.* **29**, 357.

Mitchison, J. M., and Swann, M. M. (1953). *Quart. J. Microscop. Sci.* **94**, 381.

Mitchison, J. M., and Swann, M. M. (1954). *J. Exptl. Biol.* **31**, 461.

Mitchison, J. M., and Swann, M. M. (1955). *J. Exptl. Biol.* **32**, 734.

Mitchison, J. M., and Walker, P. M. B. (1959). *Exptl. Cell Research* **16**, 49.

Mole-Bajer, J. (1958). *Chromosoma* **9**, 332.

Monné, L. (1944). *Arkiv. Zool.* **35A**, 1.

Monroy, A., and Montalenti, G. (1947). *Biol. Bull.* **92**, 151.

Montgomery, P. O'B., and Bonner, W. A. (1959). *Exptl. Cell Research* **17**, 378.

Moore, A. R. (1933). *J. Exptl. Biol.* **10**, 230.

Moore, A. R. (1938). *Proc. Soc. Exptl. Biol. Med.* **38**, 162.

Morgan, T. H. (1896). *Arch. Entwicklungsmech. Organ.* **3**, 339.

Moses, M. J., and Taylor, J. H. (1955). *Exptl. Cell Research* **9**, 474.

Mota, M. (1952). *Arch. Pat.* (*Lisbon*) **24**, 336.

Mota, M. (1957). *Proc. Intern. Genet. Symposia Tokyo & Kyoto, 1956* p. 113.

Mota, M. (1959). *Exptl. Cell Research* **17**, 76.

Mulnard, J. (1958). *Arch. biol.* (*Liége*) **69**, 645.

Murray, R. G. E. (1960). *In* "The Bacteria." (I. C. Gunsalus and R. Y. Stanier, eds.), Vol. 1, p. 35. Academic Press, New York.

Nakahara, H. (1952). *Cytologia* (*Tokyo*) **17**, 168.

Nanney, D. L. (1957). *In* "The Chemical Basis of Heredity" (W. D. McElroy and B. Glass, eds.), p. 134. Johns Hopkins Press, Baltimore, Maryland.

Nanney, D. L., and Rudzinska, M. A. (1960). *In* "The Cell" (J. Brachet and A. E. Mirsky, eds.), Vol. 4, p. 109. Academic Press, New York.

Nasatir, M., and Stern, H. (1959). *J. Biophys. Biochem. Cytol.* **6**, 189.

Neifakh, A. A., and Rott, N. N. (1958). *Doklady Akad. Nauk. S. S. S. R.* **125**, 256.

Němec, B. (1929). *Protoplasma* **7**, 99.

Neufeld, E., and Mazia, D. (1957). *Exptl. Cell Research* **13**, 622.

Newton, A. A., and Wildy, P. (1959). *Exptl. Cell Research* **16**, 624.

Nickerson, W., and Falcone, G. (1959). *In* "Sulfur in Proteins" (R. Benesch *et al.*, eds.), p. 409. Academic Press, New York.

Novitski, E. (1955). *J. Cell. Comp. Physiol.* **45**, Suppl. 2, 151.

Oestergren, G. (1945a). *Hereditas* **31**, 498.

Oestergren, G. (1945b). *Botan. Notiser* **1945**, 157.

Oestergren, G. (1949). *Hereditas* **35**, 445.

Oestergren, G. (1950). *Hereditas* **36**, 1.

Oestergren, G. (1951). *Hereditas* **37**, 6.

Oestergren, G. (1954). *Congr. intern. botan., 8e Congr., Paris, 1954* **9**, 15.

Oestergren, G., and Bajer, A. (1960). *In* "L'action antimitotique et caryoclasique de substances chimiques" (J. Turchini and P. Sentein, eds.), p. 199. Colloque No. 88. C.N.R.S., Paris.

Oestergren, G., Koopmans, A., and Reitalu, R. (1953). *Botan. Notiser* **1953**, 417.

Oestergren, G., and Wakonig, T. (1954). *Botan. Notiser* **1954**, 357.

Padilla, G. M., and James, T. W. (1960). *Exptl. Cell Research.* In press.

Painter, R. B., Forro, F., and Hughes, W. L. (1958). *Nature* **181**, 328.

Palmade, C., Chevallier, M. R., Knobloch, A., and Vendrely, R. (1958). *Compt. rend. acad. sci.* **246**, 2534.

Pardee, A. B., Jacob, F., and Monod, J. (1959). *J. Mol. Biol.* **2**, 165.

Pasteels, J. (1955). *Bull. classe sci. Acad. roy. Belg.* [5] **41**, 761.

Pasteels, J., and Lison, L. (1950). *Arch. biol.* (*Liége*) **61**, 445.

Pätau, K., and Swift, H. (1953). *Chromosoma* **6**, 149.

Pätau, K., Das, N. K., and Skoog, F. (1957). *Physiol. Plantarum* **10**, 949.

Pauling, L., and Corey, R. B. (1953). *Proc. Natl. Acad. Sci. U.S.* **39**, 84.

Pease, D. C. (1941). *J. Morphol.* **69**, 405.

Pease, D. C. (1946). *Biol. Bull.* **91**, 145.

Pelling, G. (1959). *Nature* **184**, 656.

Perakis, N. (1947). *Acta Anat.* **4**, 225.

Perry, R. P. (1957). *Exptl. Cell Research* **12**, 546.

Pfeiffer, H. H. (1938). *Biodynamica* **2**, 1.

Pfeiffer, H. H. (1952). *Pubbl. staz. zool. Napoli* **23**, 147.

Pfeiffer, H. H. (1954). *La Cellule* **56**, 241.

Pfeiffer, H. H. (1956). *Protoplasma* **46**, 585.

Philpot, J. St. L., and Stanier, J. E. (1957). *Nature* **179**, 102.

Piza, S. (1943). *Am. Naturalist* **77**, 442.

Plaut, W., and Mazia, D. (1956). *J. Biophys. Biochem. Cytol.* **2**, 573.

Plesner, P. E. (1958). *Biochim. et Biophys. Acta* **29**, 462.

Policard, A., and Bessis, M. (1953). *Exptl. Cell Research* **8**, 583.

Politzer, G. (1934). "Pathologie der Mitose," Protoplasma Monographien No. 7. Bornträger, Berlin.

Pollister, A. W. (1933). *Biol. Bull.* **65**, 529.

Pollister, A. W. (1939). *Proc. Natl. Acad. Sci. U.S.* **25**, 189.

Pollister, A. W. (1941). *Physiol. Zoöl.* **14**, 268.

Pollister, A. W., and Pollister, P. F. (1943). *Ann. N.Y. Acad. Sci.* **45**, 1.

Pollister, A. W., and Ris, H. (1947). *Cold Spring Harbor Symposia Quant. Biol.* **12**, 147.

Pontecorvo, G. (1958). *Symposia Soc. Exptl. Biol.* **12**, 1.

Popoff, M. (1908). *Arch. Zellforsch.* **1**, 245.

Porter, H. K. (1957). *Symposia Soc. Exptl. Biol.* **11**.

Porter, K. R. (1955). In "Symposium on the Fine Structure of Cells," p. 236. Interscience, New York.

Porter, K. R. (1957). *Harvey Lectures Ser.* **51**, p. 175.

Porter, K. R. (1961). In "The Cell" (J. Brachet and A. E. Mirsky), Vol. 2, p. 621. Academic Press, New York.

Porter, K. R., and Machado, R. D. (1960). *J. Biophys. Biochem. Cytol.* **7**, 167.

Potter, V. R. (1958). *Federation Proc.* **17**, 691.

Powers, E. L., and Ehret, C. F. (1955). *Proc. 1st Intern. Conf. Peaceful Uses Atomic Energy, Geneva, 1955* **8**, 239.

Prescott, D. M. (1955). *Exptl. Cell Research* **9**, 328.

Prescott, D. M. (1956a). *Expt. Cell Research* **11**, 86.

Prescott, D. M. (1956b). *Exptl. Cell Research* **11**, 94.

Prescott, D. M. (1959). *Ann. N.Y. Acad. Sci.* **78**, 655.

Prescott, D. M. (1960). *Exptl. Cell Research* **19**, 228.

Price, J. M., and Laird, A. K. (1950). *Cancer Research* **10**, 650.

Puck, T., and Marcus, P. I. (1956). *J. Exptl. Med.* **103**, 653.

Quastler, H. (1960). *Ann. N.Y. Acad. Sci.* **90**, 580.

Quastler, H., and Sherman, F. G. (1959). *Exptl. Cell Research* **17**, 420.

Rabinovitch, M., and Plaut, W. (1956). *Exptl. Cell Research* **10**, 120.

Rabinowitz, M. (1941). *J. Morphol.* **69**, 1.

Raikov, I. B. (1958). *Arch. Protistenk.* **103**, 129.

Rapkine, L. (1931). *Ann. physiol. physiochim. biol.* **7**, 382.

Rasch, E., Swift, H., and Klein, R. M. (1959). *J. Biophys. Biochem. Cytol.* **6**, 11.

Rashevsky, N. (1940). "Advanced Applications of Mathematical Biology." Univ. of Chicago Press, Chicago, Illinois.

Rattenbury, J. A., and Serra, J. A. (1952). *Portugaliae Acta Biol. Ser. A.* **3**, 239.

Rauther, M. (1930). "W. Kukenthal Handbuch der Zoologie," Vol. 2, p. 249. Gruyter, Berlin and Leipzig.

Rebhun, L. I. (1959). *Biol. Bull.* **117**, 518.

Rebhun, L. I. (1960). *Ann. N.Y. Acad. Sci.* **90**, 357.

Rhoades, M. M. (1952). "Heterosis," p. 66. Iowa State College Press, Ames, Iowa.

Richards, B. M. (1960). In "The Cell Nucleus." (J. S. Mitchell, ed.), p. 138. Academic Press, New York.

Richards, B. M., and Bajer A. (1961). *Exptl. Cell Research* **22**, 503.

Richards, B. M., Walker, B. M. B., and Deeley, E. M. (1956). *Ann. N.Y. Acad. Sci.* **63**, 831.

Ris, H. (1943). *Biol. Bull.* **85**, 164.

Ris, H. (1949). *Biol. Bull.* **96**, 90.

Ris, H. (1956). *J. Biophys. Biochem. Cytol.* **2**, 385.

Ris, H., and Kleinfeld, R. (1952). *Chromosoma* **5**, 363.

Roberts, H. S., and Johnson, N. S. (1956). *Biol. Bull.* **110**, 334.

Robinow, C. F. (1957). *Bacteriol. Rev.* **20**, 207.

Robinow, C. F. (1960). In "The Cell" (J. Brachet and A. E. Mirsky, eds.), Vol. 4, p. 46. Academic Press, New York.

Rosenbaum, R. M., and Wittner, M. (1960). *Exptl. Cell Research* **20**, 416.

Roslansky, J. D. (1957). Ph.D. Thesis. Univ. of Calif., Berkeley, California.

Ross, K. F. A. (1954). *Quart. J. Microscop. Sci.* **85**, 425.

Rosza, G., and Wyckoff, R. (1951). *Exptl. Cell Research* **2**, 630.

Roth, L. E., Obetz, S. W., and Daniels, E. W. (1960). *J. Biophys. Biochem. Cytol.* **8**, 207.

Rothstein, A. (1954). In "Protoplasmatologia" (L. V. Heilbrunn and F. Weber, eds.), Vol. 2. Springer, Vienna.

Rouiller, C., and Fauré-Fremiet, E. (1958). *J. Ultrastruct. Research* **1**, 289.

Ruby, A. (1961). Ph.D. Thesis, Univ. of Calif., Berkeley, California.

Rustad, R. (1956). M.A. Thesis. Univ. of Calif., Berkeley, California.

Rustad, R. (1959). *Exptl. Cell Research* **16**, 575.

Rustad, R. (1960). *Exptl. Cell Research* **21**, 596.

Ruthmann, A. (1958). *J. Biophys. Biochem. Cytol.* **5**, 177.

Ryter, A., and Kellenberger, E. (1958). *Z. Naturforsch.* **136**, 597.

Sakai, H., and Dan, K. (1959). *Exptl. Cell Research* **16**, 24.

Sandritter, W., and Krygier, A. (1959). *Z. Krebsforsch.* **62**, 596.

Sato, S. (1958). *Chromosoma* **23**, 383.

Schaechter, M., Benzon, M. W., and Maaløe, O. (1959). *Nature* **183**, 1207.

Schaede, R. (1929). *Planta* **8**, 383.

Schaede, R. (1930). *Planta* **11**, 243.

Scherbaum, O. (1957a). *Exptl. Cell Research* **13**, 11.

Scherbaum, O. (1957b). *Exptl. Cell Research* **13**, 24.

Scherbaum, O. H. (1960). *Ann. Rev. Microbiol.* **14**, 283.

Scherbaum, O., and Rasch, G. (1957). *Acta Pathol. Microbiol. Scand.* **41**, 161.

Scherbaum, O., and Zeuthen, E. (1954). *Exptl. Cell Research* **6**, 221.

Scherbaum, O., and Zeuthen, E. (1955). *Exptl. Cell Research* Suppl. 3, p. 312.

Scherbaum, O. H., Louderback, A. L., and Jahn, T. L. (1958). *Biol. Bull.* **115**, 269.

Scherbaum, O. H., Louderback, A. L., and Jahn, T. L. (1959). *Exptl. Cell Research* **18**, 150.

Schmidt, W. J. (1939). *Chromosoma* **1**, 253.

Schmitt, F. O. (1956). *Nature* **177**, 503.

Schneider, A. (1873). *Ber. oberhess. Ges. Natur- u. Heilk.* **40**, 69.

Schneider, B. (1933). *Z. Zellforsch. u. mikroskop. Anat.* **17**, 255.

Scholander, P. F., Claff, C. L., Sveinsson, S. L., and Scholander, S. I. (1952). *Biol. Bull.* **102**, 185.

Scholander, P. F., Leivestad, H., and Sundnes, G. (1958). *Exptl. Cell Research* **15**, 505.

Schrader, F. (1939). *Chromosoma* **1**, 230.

Schrader, F. (1946). *Biol. Bull.* **90**, 625.

Schrader, F. (1947). *Chromosoma* **3**, 22.

Schrader, F. (1953). "Mitosis," 2nd ed. Columbia Univ. Press, New York.

Schultz-Larsen, J. (1953). *Acta Pathol. Microbiol. Scand.* **32**, 567.

Schwann, M. J., and Schleiden, T. (1839). *In* "Schwann and Schleiden's Researches." Sydenham Society, London, 1847 (Engl. trans., H. Smith).

Schwann, T. (1839). "Ostwald's Klassiker der Exakten Wissenschaften," No. 176. Engelmann, Leipzig, 1910 (facsimile reprint).

Schwartz, D. (1955). *J. Cellular Comp. Physiol.* **45**, Suppl. **2**, 171.

Schwartz, V. (1956). *Biol. Zentr.* **75**, 1.

Scott, D. B. M., and Chu, E. (1958). *Exptl. Cell Research* **14**, 166.

Scott, D. B. M., and Chu, E. (1959). *Exptl. Cell Research* **18**, 392.

Selby, C. C. (1953). *Texas Repts. Biol. and Med.* **11**, 728.

Selman, G. G., and Waddington, C. H. (1955). *J. Exptl. Biol.* **32**, 700.

Serra, J. A. (1947). *Portugaliae Acta Biol.* **2**, 25.

Sharp, L. W. (1934). "Introduction to Cytology." McGraw-Hill, New York.

Shimamura, T. (1940). *Cytologia (Tokyo)* **11**, 186.

Shimamura, T., and Ôta, T. (1956). *Exptl. Cell Research* **11**, 346.

Shimamura, T., Ôta, T., and Hishida, T. (1957). *Symposium Soc. Cell. Chem. (Tokyo)* **6**, 21.

Short, R. B. (1946). *Biol. Bull.* **90**, 8.

Siebs, W. (1960). *Z. Zellforsch. u. mikroskop. Anat.* **51**, 535.

Sigenaga, M. (1940). *Japan. J. Botany* **10**, 383.

Singer, M. (1952). *Quart. Rev. Biol.* **27**, 169.

Sinnott, E. W., and Bloch, R. (1941). *Am. J. Botany* **28**, 225.

Sisken, J. E., and Kinosita, B. (1961). *J. Biophys. Biochem. Cytol.* **9**, 509.

Skoog, F., and Miller, C. O. (1957). *Symposia Soc. Exptl. Biol.* **11**, 118.

Smith, C. L. (1959). *Proc. Roy. Soc.* **B150**, 372.

Sonneborn, T. M. (1947). *Advances in Genet.* **1**, 263.

Sotelo, J. R., and Trujillo-Cenoz, O. (1958). *Z. Zellforsch.* **49**, 1.

Sparrow, A. H., Moses, M. J., and Steele, R. (1952). *Brit. J. Radiol.* **25**, 182.

Spiegelman, S., Aronson, A. I., and Fitz-James, P. C. (1958). *J. Bacteriol.* **75**, 102.

Staiger, H. (1950). *Experientia* **6**, 140.

Stebbins, G. L., and Shah, S. S. (1960). *Developmental Biol.* **2**, 477.

Steffenson, D. (1959). *Brookhaven Symposia in Biol.* **12**, 103.

Steinberg, M. S. (1958). *Am. Naturalist* **92**, 65.

Stern, C. (1938). *Am. Naturalist* **72**, 350.

Stern, C. (1960). *Nature* **186**, 179.

Stern, H. (1956). *Ann. Rev. Plant Physiol.* **7**, 91.

Stern, H. (1958). *J. Biophys. Biochem. Cytol.* **4**, 157.

Stern, H. (1959a). *Botan. Rev.* **25**, 351.

Stern, H. (1959b). *In* "Sulfur in Proteins" (R. Benesch *et al.*, eds.), p. 391. Academic Press, New York.

Stern, H., and Kirk, P. (1948). *J. Gen. Physiol.* **31**, 243.

Stern, H., and Timonen, S. (1954). *J. Gen. Physiol.* **38**, 41.

Stern, H., Johnston, F. B., and Setterfield, G. (1959). *J. Biophys. Biochem. Cytol.* **6**, 57.

Stich, H. (1951). *Chromosoma* **4**, 429.

Stich, H. (1954). *Chromosoma* **6**, 199.

Stich, H., and McIntyre, J. (1958). *Exptl. Cell Research* **14**, 635.

Strangeways, T. S. P. (1923). *Proc. Roy. Soc.* **94**, 137.

Strasburger, E. (1880). "Zellbildung und Zelltheilung." Fischer, Jena.

Strasburger, E. (1893). "Histologische Beiträge," Vol. 5. Fischer, Jena.

Strasburger, E. (1900). "Histologische Beiträge," Vol. 6. Fischer, Jena.

Strehler, B. L. (1959). *Quart. Rev. Biol.* **34**, 117.

Sueoka, S. (1960). *Proc. Natl. Acad. Sci. U.S.* **46**, 183.
Swann, M. M. (1951a). *J. Exptl. Biol.* **28**, 417.
Swann, M. M. (1951b). *J. Exptl. Biol.* **28**, 434.
Swann, M. M. (1952). *Symposia Soc. Exptl. Biol.* **6**, 89.
Swann, M. M. (1953). *Quart. J. Microscop. Sci.* **94**, 369.
Swann, M. M. (1954a). In "Recent Developments in Cell Physiology" (J. A. Kitching, ed.), p. 185. Academic Press, New York.
Swann, M. M. (1954b). *Exptl. Cell Research* **7**, 505.
Swann, M. M. (1957). *Cancer Research* **17**, 727.
Swann, M. M. (1958). *Cancer Research* **18**, 1118.
Swann, M. M., and Mitchison, J. M. (1950). *J. Exptl. Biol.* **27**, 226.
Swann, M. M., and Mitchison, J. M. (1953). *J. Exptl. Biol.* **30**, 506.
Swann, M. M., and Mitchison, J. M. (1958). *Biol. Revs. Cambridge Phil. Soc.* **33**, 103.
Swanson, C. P. (1943). *Papers Mich. Acad. Sci.* **28**, 133.
Swanson, C. P. (1957). "Cytology and Cytogenetics." Prentice-Hall, New York.
Sweeney, B., and Hastings, J. W. (1958). *J. Protozool.* **5**, 217.
Swift, H. (1950a). *Physiol. Zoöl.* **26**, 301.
Swift, H. (1950b). *Proc. Natl. Acad. Sci. U.S.* **36**, 643.
Swift, H. (1953). *Intern. Rev. Cytol.* **2**, 1.
Swift, H., and Kleinfeld, R. (1953). *Physiol. Zoöl.* **26**, 301.
Sylvén, B., Tobias, C. A., Malmgren, H., Ottoson, R., and Thorell, B. (1959). *Exptl. Cell Research* **16**, 75.
Symposium on Chromosome Breakage. (1952). *Heredity* **6**, Suppl.
Szent-Györgyi, A. (1951). "Chemistry of Muscle Contraction," 2nd ed. Academic Press, New York.
Takeda, S., and Izutsu, K. (1960). *Symposia Cell Chem.* (*Japan*) **10**, 245.
Tamiya, H., Iwamura, T., Shibata, K., Hase, E., and Nihei, T. (1953). *Biochim. et Biophys. Acta* **12**, 23.
Tandler, C. J. (1955). *J. Histochem. and Cytochem.* **3**, 196.
Tandler, C. J. (1959). *Exptl. Cell Research* **17**, 560.
Tartar, V. (1957). *J. Exptl. Zool.* **135**, 387.
Taylor, E. W. (1959). *J. Biophys. Biochem. Cytol.* **6**, 193.
Taylor, J. H. (1957). *Am. Naturalist* **91**, 209.
Taylor, J. H. (1958). *Genetics* **43**, 515.
Taylor, J. H. (1959). *Am. J. Botany* **46**, 477.
Taylor, J. H., and Taylor, S. H. (1953). *J. Heredity* **44**, 129.
Taylor, J. H., Woods, P., and Hughes, W. (1957). *Proc. Natl. Acad. Sci. U.S.* **43**, 122.
Theile, H. (1948). *Z. Naturforsch.* b,**3**, 7.
Thomar, H. (1959). *Compt. rend. trav. lab. Carlsberg, Sér. physiol.* **31**, 207.
Tischler, G. (1922, 1951). "Allgemeine Pflanzenkaryogie." Bornträger, Berlin.
Tolmach, L. J., and Marcus, P. I. (1960). *Exptl. Cell Research* **20**, 350.
Torrey, J. G. (1958). *Science* **128**, 10.
Torrey, J. G. (1959). In "Cell, Organism, and Milieu" (D. Rudnick, ed.), p. 189. Ronald Press, New York.
Tsumita, T., and Chargaff, E. (1958). *Biochim. et Biophys. Acta* **29**, 568.
Upcott, M. (1939). *Chromosoma* **1**, 178.
Uretz, R. B., Bloom, W., and Zirkle, R. E. (1954). *Science* **120**, 197.
Van Beneden, E. (1876). *Bull. acad. roy. méd. Belg.* **42**, Ser. II, 35.

van Wisselingh, C. (1909). *Beih. botan. Zent.* **24**, 133.
Vendrely, R. (1955a). *Intern. Rev. Cytol.* **4**, 115.
Vendrely, R. (1955b). *In* "The Nucleic Acids" (E. Chargaff and J. N. Davidson, eds.), Vol. 2, p. 155. Academic Press, New York.
Vincent, W. S. (1955). *Intern. Rev. Cytol.* **4**, 269.
Vogel, H. J. (1957). *In* "The Chemical Basis of Heredity" (W. D. McElroy and B. Glass, eds.), p. 276. Johns Hopkins Press, Baltimore, Maryland.
von Borstel, R. C., and Rekemeyer, M. L. (1958). *Nature* **181**, 1597.
von Lenhossék, M. (1898). *Verhandl. anat. Ges. Kiel* **12**, 106.
von Möllendorf, W. (1939). *Z. Zellforsch. u. mikroskop. Anat.* **29**, 706.
Voutilainen, A. (1953). *Acta Pathol. Microbiol. Scand.* **99**, Suppl., p. 1.
Wada, B. (1932). *Cytologia (Tokyo)* **4**, 114.
Wada, B. (1935). *Cytologia (Tokyo)* **6**, 381.
Wada, B. (1950). *Cytologia (Tokyo)* **16**, 1.
Wada, B. (1955). *Caryologia (Tokyo)* **7**, 389.
Wada, B. (1957). *Cytologia (Tokyo)* **22**, 442.
Walker, P. M. B., and Mitchison, J. M. (1957). *Exptl. Cell Research* **13**, 167.
Walker, P. M. B., and Richards, B. M. (1959). *In* "The Cell" (J. Brachet, and A. E. Mirsky, eds.) Vol. 1, p. 91. Academic Press, New York.
Walters, M. S. (1958). *Am. J. Botany* **45**, 271.
Waris, H. (1950). *Physiol. Plantarum* **3**, 1.
Wassermann, F. (1929). *In* "Handbuch der mikroskopischen Anatomie des Menschen" (W. von Möllendorff, ed.), Vol. 1, part 2, p. 1. Springer, Berlin.
Wassermann, F. (1939). *Arch. Exptl. Zellforsch. Gewebezücht.* **22**, 238.
Watson, J. D., and Crick, F. H. C. (1953). *Nature* **171**, 737.
Waugh, D. F. (1954). *Advances in Protein Chem.* **9**, 326.
Waugh, D. F. (1959). *In* "Biophysics—A Study Program" (J. L. Oncley, ed.), p. 84. Wiley, New York.
Weber, H. H. (1955). *Symposia Soc. Exptl. Biol.* **9**, 271.
Weber, H. H. (1958). "The Motility of Muscle and Cells." Harvard Univ. Press, Cambridge, Massachusetts.
Weiss, P. (1955). *In* "Biological Specificity and Growth" (E. G. Butler, ed.) Princeton Univ. Press, Princeton, New Jersey.
Weisz, P. B. (1956). *J. Exptl. Zool.* **131**, 137.
Wenneker, A. S., and Sussman, N. (1951). *Proc. Soc. Exptl. Biol. Med.* **76**, 683.
Went, F. W. (1957). "The Experimental Control of Plant Growth." Chronica Botanica Co., Waltham, Massachusetts.
Went, H. A. (1959a). *J. Biophys. Biochem. Cytol.* **5**, 353.
Went, H. A. (1959b). *J. Biophys. Biochem. Cytol.* **6**, 447.
Went, H. A., and Mazia, D. (1959). *Exptl. Cell Research Suppl.* **7**, 200.
Wessenberg, H. S. (1958). Studies on the Life Cycle and Morphogenesis of *Opalina*. Ph.D. Thesis. Univ. of Calif., Berkeley, California.
Whaley, W. G., Mollenhauer, H. H., and Leech, J. H. (1960). *J. Biophys. Biochem. Cytol.* **8**, 223.
Whitmore, G. F., Till, J. E., Gwatkin, R. B. L., Simonovitch, L., and Graham, A. F. (1958). *Biochim. et Biophys. Acta* **30**, 583.
Wichterman, R., and Figge, F. H. J. (1954). *Biol. Bull.* **106**, 253.
Widner, W. R., Storer, J. B., and Lushbaugh, C. C. (1951). *Cancer Research* **11**, 877.
Wilkins, M. H. F., and Zubay, G. (1959). *J. Biophys. Biochem. Cytol.* **5**, 55.
Wilson, E. B. (1901). *Arch. Entwicklungsmech. Organ.* **12**, 531.

Wilson, E. B. (1902). "The Cell in Development and Inheritance," p. 112. Macmillan, London.

Wilson, E. B. (1916). *Proc. Natl. Acad. Sci. U.S.* **2**, 321.

Wilson, E. B. (1925). "The Cell in Development and Heredity," 3rd ed. Macmillan, New York.

Wolpert, L. (1960). *Intern. Rev. Cytol.* **10**, 164.

Woodard, J. W., and Swift, H. (1958). *J. Biophys. Biochem. Cytol.* **4**, 383.

Woods, P. S., and Schairer, M. U. (1959). *Nature* **183**, 303.

Woods, P. S., and Taylor, J. H. (1959). *Lab. Invest.* **8**, 309.

Yasuzumi, G., Pappas, G. I., Yamamoto, G. O., and Tsubo, I. (1961). *Z. Zellforsch. u. mikroskop. Anat.* **53**, 141.

Young, I. E., and Fitz-James, P. C. (1959). *Nature* **183**, 372.

Zalokar, M. (1960). *Exptl. Cell Research* **19**, 559.

Zamecnik, P. C., and Keller, E. B. (1954). *J. Biol. Chem.* **209**, 337.

Zamenhof, S. (1957). *In* "The Chemical Basis of Heredity" (W. D. McElroy and B. Glass, eds.), p. 351. Johns Hopkins Press, Baltimore, Maryland.

Zeuthen, E. (1946). *Compt. rend. trav. lab. Carlsberg. Sér. chim.* **25**, 191.

Zeuthen, E. (1949). *Am. Naturalist* **83**, 303.

Zeuthen, E. (1951). *Pubbl. staz. zool. Napoli* **23**, 47.

Zeuthen, E. (1953a). *Arch. néer. zool.* **10**, Suppl. 1, p. 31.

Zeuthen, E. (1953b). *J. Embryol. Exptl. Morphol.* **1**, 239.

Zeuthen, E. (1955). *Biol. Bull.* **108**, 366.

Zeuthen, E. (1958). *Advances in Biol. and Med. Phys.* **6**, 37.

Zeuthen, E. (1960). *Exptl. Cell Research* **19**, 1.

Zimmerman, A. M. (1958). *Federation Proc.* **17**, 692.

Zimmerman, A. M. (1960). *Exptl. Cell Research* **20**, 529.

Zirkle, R. E. (1956). "Cellular Aspects of Basic Mechanisms in Radiobiology," Nuclear Science Series Report No. 8, Publication No. 450, p. 1. Research Council, Washington, D.C.

Zirkle, R. E. (1957). *Advances in Biol. and Med. Phys.* **5**, 104.

Zirkle, R. E., and Bloom, W. (1953). *Science* **117**, 487.

Zubay, G., and Watson, M. R. (1959). *J. Biophys. Biochem. Cytol.* **5**, 51.

AUTHOR INDEX

Numbers in italic indicate the pages on which the references are listed.

413

SUBJECT INDEX

A

Acanthamoeba, mitotic time of, 155
Acrydium, 269
Actin, mitotic apparatus and, 246, 287
Actinosphaerium eichhornii, division of, 312, 390
Actomyosin,
　hydration and, 284
　mitotic apparatus and, 287
Adenosine diphosphate, mitotic apparatus and, 249
Adenosine triphosphatase, mitotic apparatus and, 249-250, 287
Adenosine triphosphate,
　anaphase model and, 285-286, 352
　cell division and, 143-144, 146
　cytokinesis and, 335-337
　mitotic apparatus and, 243, 287, 352-354
Adenylic acid, mitosis and, 353
Adenylic nucleotides, mitotic apparatus and, 248, 355
Agapanthus, prophase II in, 30
Agaricaceae, synapsis in, 40
Agglutination, synapsis and, 38
Aging, cell division and, 83
Agmatoploidy, origin of, 70
Agriotis mancus, pachytene bouquet of, 16
Agrobacterium rubi, polyploid cells and, 115
Alcaligenes fecalis, ribonucleic acid synthesis in, 371
Alchemilla, meiosis in, 7-8
Alcohol, *see also* Ethanol
　mitotic centers and, 119
Aldolase, mitotic cycle and, 352
Algae, coenocytic, 84
Algae, cytokinesis in, 314
Allium, see also Onion
　meiosis in, 8
　root tip, mitosis in, 303, 304
Allium fistulosum, chiasmata in, 24
Amebae,
　giant, division of, 88
　mitosis, cell surface and, 359

Amino acids, mitotic apparatus and, 246, 287
Aminopterin, metaphase plate and, 230
Aminopyrin, asters and, 119
Amitosis,
　description of, 90-91
　occurrence of, 91
Ammonia, chromosomes and, 168
Amoeba,
　movement, rate of, 278
Amoeba proteus,
　anucleate, biosynthesis in, 362
　division,
　　biosynthesis and, 360, 361
　　nuclear membrane and, 194-195
　　nuclear volume and, 149
　generation time of, 103-104
　growth curve of, 368
　locomotion, cytokinesis and, 332
　natural synchrony of, 375
　regeneration of, 83
　size, cell division and, 99-100
Anaphase,
　chromosome paths in, 280-285
　contractile mechanisms and, 285-294
　duration of, 156-157, 159
　interzonal region and, 298-299
　mitotic apparatus in, 294-300
　mitotic blocks and, 161, 299-300
　model of, 285-287, 352
　movement,
　　individual chromosomes and, 270-272
　　quantitative data on, 269-270
　　types of, 272-280
　　velocity of, 270
　sister chromosomes in, 267-269
　spindle elongation in, 298-299
Anaphase I, events of, 28-29
Anaphase II, events of, 30
Androgens, cell division and, 392
Angela guianensis, premetaphase stretch in, 205
Anisolabis, chromosome movement in, 25, 203
Anoxia, mitosis and, 351, 353
Antephase, antimitotic action and, 386

Histone,
  bacteria and, 93
  chromosomes and, 168
  deoxyribonucleic acid synthesis and, 110
  leptonema and, 14
  meiosis and, 9-10
Holomastigotoides,
  chromosomes of, 165, 169-172
  mitosis in, 348
  prophase in, 148
  telophase in, 305
Homarus, see Lobster
Homoptera, centromeres of, 56
Hormones, cell division and, 392, 393
Humbertiella, metaphase plate in, 231
Hybrids, meiosis in, 9
Hydra, synchronous divisions in, 389
Hydrogen bonds, mitotic apparatus and, 256
Hydrogen peroxide, mitotic apparatus and, 243, 249, 250
Hydrostatic pressure,
  anaphase and, 299
  cytokinesis and, 328, 334-336, 341, 344
  metaphase plate and, 230
  mitotic apparatus and, 236, 307
Hypomyces, synapsis in, 40

I

Icerya purchasi, meiosis in, 61
Ilyanassa,
  mitosis, inhibition of, 353
Inosine triphosphate, mitotic apparatus and, 249
Insects, meiosis in, 11, 31
Intermitotic time, measurement of, 151-152
Interphase, meiosis and, 29
Iodoacetamide, nuclear membrane and, 311
Iodoacetate, mitotic inhibition by, 386
Ions, chromosomes and, 168
Iris,
  endosperm, 274
  mitosis in, 156
  spindles in, 319, 320

K

Karyomeres,
  formation of, 306-307, 309, 348, 387
  nucleoli and, 309
Kinetin, 392, *see also* Kinins
  meiosis and, 8
  polyploid cells and, 115
Kinetochore(s), 265, *see also* Centromeres
  centrioles and, 126-128, 129
  chromosomal multiplicity and, 173
  chromosome movement and, 285, 288-294
  diffuse, chromosome movement and, 289-291
  fiber formation by, 266-267
  gliding of, 291-292
  irradiation of, 209, 216-218, 229
  jet propulsion of, 292, 303
  metakinesis and, 208, 209
  metaphase and, 212-221
  metaphase plate and, 225, 230, 231
  mitosis and, 86, 116
  monopolar figures and, 227-229
  multiplicity of, 213-214
  mutations and, 213
  polarization of, 223-225
  reproduction of, 147, 214, 224
  strength of, 293
Kinetosomes, *see* Basal granules
Kinins, *see also* Kinetin
  cell division and, 388
  cytokinesis and, 319
"Kinoplasm," mitotic apparatus and, 140

L

Lactobacillus acidophilus, synchronous division of, 381
Laplatacris dispar,
  spermatid, centrioles of, 118
Leptonema,
  chromosome arrangement in, 12
  chromosomes in, 14-17
  deoxyribonucleic acid in, 43
Leptotene, deoxyribonucleic acid synthesis in, 107
Leucocytes, 393
  mitosis of, 284
Lilium,
  chiasmata in, 49